# Naked in the Stream

## Isle Royale Stories

# Naked in the Stream

---

## Isle Royale Stories

## Vic Foerster

Arbutus Press
Traverse City, Michigan

Arbutus Press
Publishers since 1998
2364 Pinehurst Trail
Traverse City, Michigan 49686

Cover art:  Oil on linen, Boat and Stars, Joyce Koskenmaki
Illustrations: Joyce Koskenmaki
Maps: hand drawn and lettered, Michael Moore

Library of Congress Cataloging-in-Publication Data

Foerster, Vic.
Naked in the stream : Isle Royale stories / Vic Foerster.
p. cm.
ISBN 978-1-933926-22-3
1.  Hiking--Michigan--Isle Royale National Park. 2. Camping--
Michigan--Isle Royale National Park--Guidebooks. 3.  Isle Royale
National Park (MIch.)--Description and travel.  I. Title.
GV199.42.M512I845 2010
917.74'9970444--dc22
2009054420

Printed in the United States of America

In Memory of Our Dads
who led us down the trail and then wisely, stepped aside.


Charles E. Foerster Jr.

&

Robert Glupker

# CONTENTS

PROLOGUE                                    12

AN EXPEDITION                               15

CAPTAIN DON                                 31

LITTLE BROTHERS & SISTERS                   42

OF MOOSE AND WOLVES                         50

THE LITTLE STUFF                            60

PANCAKES                                    67

FROM THE WATER                              70

TOP OF THE FOOD CHAIN                       84

AN OFF-SHORE BREEZE                         88

INTO THE WIND                               122

THE WAVES OF MINONG                         133

THE CROSSING                                141

THE HOWELLS                                 159

SPRINKLED IN STARLIGHT                      169

MEN, WOMEN, CANOES AND KAYAKS               184

FISHING FOR WORDS                           204

FISH TALES                                  210

NAKED IN THE STREAM                         226

ACKNOWLEDGMENTS                             283

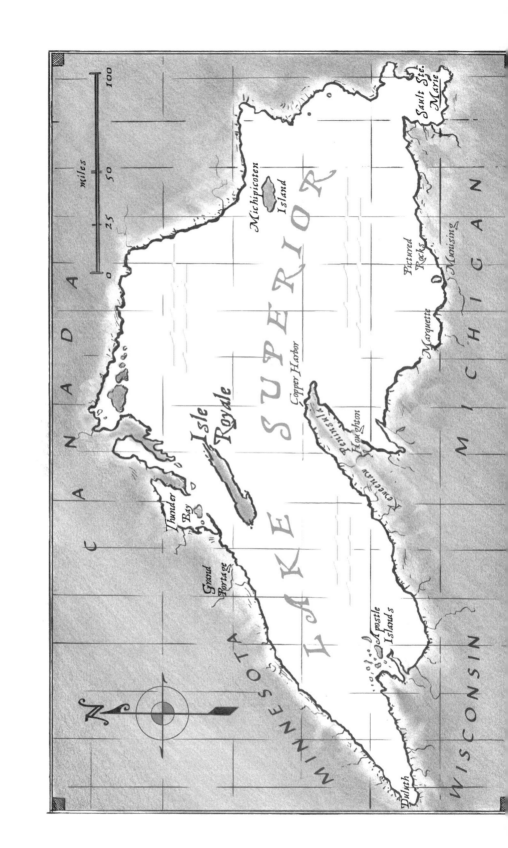

miles

0    25    50    100

C A N A D A

MINNESOTA

Grand
Portage

Thunder
Bay

Isle
Royale

Michipicoten
Island

LAKE SUPERIOR

Copper Harbor

Keweenaw
Peninsula

Houghton

Apostle
Islands

WISCONSIN

Duluth

Marquette

Pictured
Rocks

Munising

M I C H I G A N

Sault Ste.
Marie

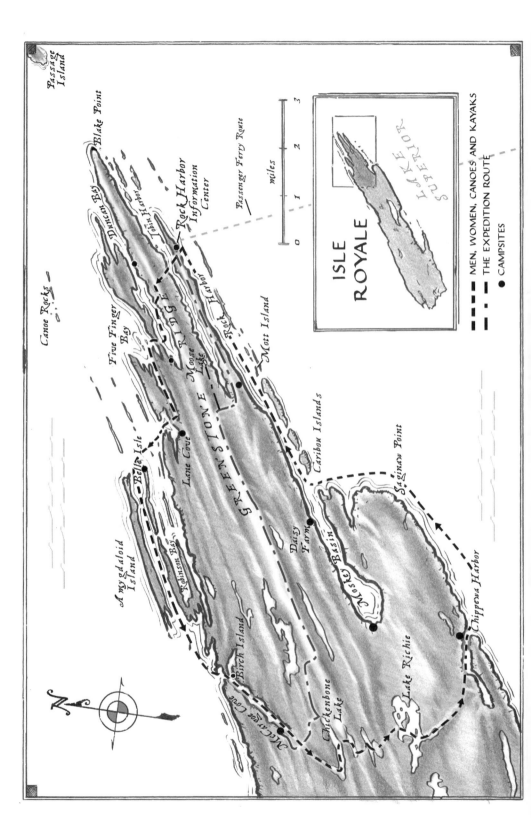

*Passage Island*

*Blake Point*

*Canoe Rocks*

*Duncan Bay*

*Tobin Harbor*

Rock Harbor
Information
Center

*Five Finger Bay*

G R E E N S T O N E   R I D G E

*Moose Lake*

*Rock Harbor*

*Matt Island*

*Belle Isle*

*Lane Cove*

*Caribou Islands*

*Amygdaloid Island*

*Robinson Bay*

*Daisy Farm*

*Saginaw Point*

*Birch Island*

*Moskey Basin*

*McCargoe Cove*

*Chickenbone Lake*

*Lake Richie*

*Chippewa Harbor*

N

ISLE
ROYALE

LAKE SUPERIOR

miles

0    1    2    3

*Passenger Ferry Route*

▬ ▬ ▬  MEN, WOMEN, CANOES AND KAYAKS

▬ · ▬ · ▬  THE EXPEDITION ROUTE

●  CAMPSITES

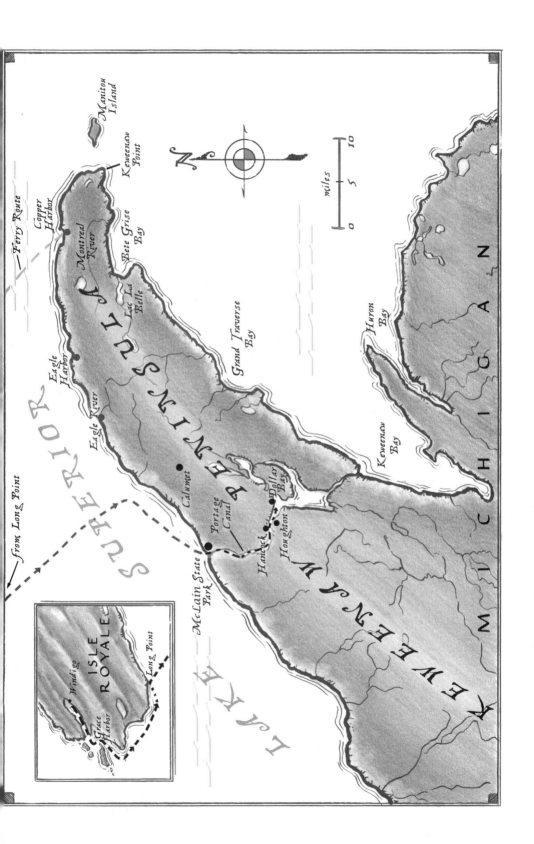

# PROLOGUE

STANDING AT THE PROW, I FACED FORWARD INTO THE WIND AND BREATHED. The steel hull of the passenger ferry sliced through the lake, curling the gentle seas into two bow waves breaking on either side of the ship. At twelve knots, my eyes watered. Accustomed to pulling my way through the water with a paddle, the speed seemed reckless.

It was a relief to feel Lake Superior air on my face again. After spending a week outdoors, camping, I needed to get out of the pilothouse where I'd been catching up with Captain Don. Canoeing the past seven days and sleeping outside every night made me conscious of the slightest indoor sensation. Although Don had the doors wide open, the cabin still felt stuffy.

Only three other passengers were on the forward deck at the prow. It offered no protection from the cold breeze. People came and went quickly. We were two hours into the four-and-one-half hour boat ride from Isle Royale to Copper Harbor, and by now, the campers had scattered across the ship, each of them settled into a seat to their liking. Returning to the Michigan mainland, their vacations now over, everyone had that look on their face they get when they're reliving the past. There were only one-to-two footers on the lake. It was going to be a smooth ride today. Several passengers were sleeping. I walked over and stood alongside a young man leaning against the outside rail. With his elbows propped on the railing, he was staring out at the lake. He glanced over, smiled, and nodded. When I was in the pilothouse, I noticed him because he remained on the front deck, not leaving his vigilant study of the lake to find a cozier spot inside.

"How are you doing?" I asked, leaning forward against the rail next to him.

He didn't say anything for so long that I wondered if he heard. But then he said without turning to look at me, "You know … I feel … absolutely … wonderful. This was my first trip to Isle Royale … and … I can't begin to say how great it was … to get so far away. It's so … quiet." His voice trailed away with the word "quiet" as if he was reluctant to speak too loudly. He then slowly turned, looked squarely into my face and asked, "How many times have you been to Isle Royale?"

His question surprised me, and it shouldn't have. It's a common question among passengers on the *Isle Royale Queen*. It's one of those icebreakers campers use when they meet someone they've never met before. But I hadn't thought about it for a long while. At my hesitation, he looked at me even more intently.

"I'm not sure," I said.

"Really?"

"Well, I've been coming almost every year for thirty years and sometimes more than once a year. I suppose it depends on how you count."

He seemed to have a hard time digesting that, so I added, "That's not a lot. Ken, my fishing partner, has been coming ten years longer than I, and of course, some people actually live and work out there."

He turned back to look at the lake again and said, "I can't imagine."

People get like that on Isle Royale. Separated from cars and traffic, TV and computers, their cell phones and all of the other accoutrements of civilization, returning to a more natural rhythm of living—it slows a person down. The wilderness island creates a more relaxed pace, makes me think about how I really feel about a matter before I jump into a conversation and squeeze my opinion into the frenetic discussions I so often have at home.

I found myself staring at him. He gazed back out at the water with a composed, relaxed expression, as if several years of hard living had recently melted away from such a young face. It struck me that he looked like me, only a me from thirty years ago.

Always eager to talk about Isle Royale, I proceeded to tell him about some of what I'd experienced over the years—close encounters with wolves and moose, the great fishing, sunrises over Lake Superior, and paddling across water so smooth the wake from the canoe was the largest ripple. But, after a few moments, I too became quiet. Maybe I sounded shallow. It felt like I was trying to impress him instead of sharing the experience, which he was so clearly reliving at that moment. It was as if I was showing him around my trophy room or talking about my trips to the island like each one was another notch on my adventure belt. Shutting up, I wished him well, walked around the ship to the stern and rejoined Ken.

He was sitting outdoors on the stern deck where we normally stake ourselves for the voyage home, reading a book he'd started on the island. I sat down next to him and watched the ship's wake and prop wash, which stretched behind us for a couple of hundred feet before dissolving into the lake. I couldn't get the brief conversation or the passenger's demeanor out of my mind. He made me realize my attitude about Isle Royale had changed over the years. Actually, it was more than that. He made me see I will never again look at the island as he does right now. But there was a time …

# AN EXPEDITION

"THIS WILL NEVER WORK," KEN SAID. "BY THE TIME WE GET DOWN TO THE lake, if we can even get near it, it'll be dark. I was planning on topping off our water bottle, but I think we better hike toward this hilltop and see if we can find a decent place to set up our tent."

"Good idea. That doesn't look promising at all." I said, pointing toward the wetland below. "We're going to get thirsty."

"Yeah, well, you need to toughen up."

I shifted my backpack on my shoulders, looked up the slope, and we set out. The trees and ferns thinned as we got higher. Prospects for finding a camp location improved as we climbed. At the top of the rise, we found an old moose trail where the ground was beat down from their heavy feet. The small opening in the woods at the crest looked ideal. We stopped, walked around the clearing, and glanced at each other.

Ken took off his pack. "We better find some firewood while there's enough daylight."

Everything had gone as planned until we left the trail. It was early September, and my first day of my first trip to Isle Royale. Moving east through the thick woods late that afternoon along the small rise of land we needed to follow to reach Moose Lake, we quickly found ourselves tripping over unseen rocks and fallen tree limbs. We couldn't see these obstacles because we were wading through dense ferns growing chest high. They formed a green blanket four feet off the ground preventing us from seeing anything below them. We were also on our out-bound journey, which meant we were hiking with fully loaded backpacks over land where flat, smooth ground is nonexistent. For most of those three miles through the backcountry, it was like trying to walk across a cluttered, unfamiliar room with our eyes closed and dressers on our backs.

When we finally glimpsed "the lake" through the trees, daylight was fading. The blue spot on our map we'd been attempting to reach called Moose Lake—the lake below— turned out to be no more than a glorified swamp. At its center, there was only a small patch of open water the size of a large puddle. A thick tangle of bog plants—witchhazel, swamp willow, cedar, alders and brambles surrounded the swamp. It hadn't taken us long to decide to camp elsewhere.

Lots of deadwood lay close by. I quickly acquired a nice stack of bark, twigs, and sticks. Spruce cones and birch bark, even wet, will ignite from the feeblest match. I soon had a small flame going and fed the fire while Ken broke out the tent and rain tarp. He cleaned rocks and sticks off the ground, laid out the ground-tarp and set up the small tent we'd brought with us. This was the only night we planned to use the tent. We hoped to sleep inside the park's lean-to shelters the rest of our stay.

The air was damp and it felt like rain. The sky was overcast and our fire reflected the moist conditions. Its flames licked weakly at the tinder. The night was going to get very dark. In the growing dusk, the fire threw light only a few feet into the surrounding trees. Soon I couldn't see a thing beyond its light.

The last chore we did before making ourselves comfortable for the evening was to find some cooking sticks. We'd packed in steaks for our first night's meal and had cut them into cubes to roast over a fire. Finding a green aspen shoot, I broke it off and ran the stick through the meat. As it cooked, the aroma made my stomach growl. We'd worked up an appetite, and I was barely able to allow the meat to completely cook, now wishing I'd carried in two steaks. For the next twenty minutes, Ken and I said little. We bit into chunks of blackened beef, red in the middle, oozing grease that worked down our chins. There was little wind to stir the surrounding trees. The loudest sounds in the forest were our groans of satisfaction and the sizzle of the fire when juice from the roasting meat dripped into the embers.

Last thing we did before turning in was pop some corn, which would become a nightly ritual. We then hoisted our backpacks into the trees. There are no bear on Isle Royale, but it's still necessary to hang the packs to prevent fox and mice from ripping into them. We crawled into the pup tent, our sleeping bags already spread out inside. Ken was sound asleep before I could count backwards from ten.

I lay there wide awake. No matter which way I turned in my sleeping bag, I couldn't get comfortable. Ken was right, too much easy living. The musty smell of the old tent and years spent in a real bed made it difficult to relax. My thoughts swirled, overloaded by all of the new sensations from the past two days.

I tried to recall our trip up to the point where we reached our campsite. Working backward, I thought about the afternoon hike and morning's ride across Lake Superior. Enroute, the Captain had explained, over the ship's intercom, how the rangers would meet us at the docks to get our travel itineraries and go over park rules. Last night, we'd stayed at the Pines Motel in Copper Harbor. It had taken twelve hours yesterday to drive north from southern Michigan, and now—two whole days later—here I lie.

I'd been wanting to do a wilderness expedition for as long as I could remember. Growing up in a post-World War II, grid-like development in the suburbs of Detroit, the few scattered woodlots that remained undeveloped seemed like vast frontiers. We played for hours in the "woods," as my friends and I called them. We would pretend we were wilderness scouts or soldiers out on patrol, imagining ourselves tramping through distant virgin forests.

I must have fallen asleep. "Vic, there's a moose outside," Ken whispered.

I sat up with a jerk, the top of my head pressed against the roof of our small tent.

"What?"

"Ssshh, there's a moose—just outside. Sounds like a bull. Listen."

I heard a deep, primal grunt and then the thud of heavy footfalls. I could have sworn the ground shook.

"What's that?"

Tree limbs snapped and I heard leaves ripped from their branches. An animal that sounded the size of a mastodon stood outside with nothing but a sheet of nylon between us.

Ken said, as if it was my fault, "I thought this site looked suspicious. We're probably on his path to the lake."

Sitting upright in our sleeping bags, we listened harder. It was pitch black inside the tent. The moose tramped a step or two and stripped another branch.

"Let's see where he is," Ken said.

I heard Ken grope on the floor for the flashlight. When he clicked it on, it was like a flood lamp. He slid out of his sleeping bag, unzipped the tent fly, and crawled outside.

Unsure of what to do, but knowing I didn't want to stay inside alone, I shoved my head outside, not risking stepping completely out of the tent.

"Where is he?"

Ken scanned the woods with the flashlight and when we heard movement to our left, he shone the light toward the sound. There, partially screened by trees and shadows, was our moose.

He was the size of a horse; a horse with antlers. Two huge eyes flickered in the light. The bull was feeding. A sprig of aspen leaves stuck out of his mouth. He had this bemused expression on his face, as if puzzled by this new obstruction in the middle of his road. He stood there staring at us, munching the branch.

We stared back.

We watched each other for at least ten minutes, though it felt much longer. The moose flinched first. He lowered his head to grab another mouthful of leaves, and stripped a whole branch as easily as I rip a sheet of paper. The swing of his massive head was like watching heavy furniture move through the air.

The bull didn't come any closer, thankfully, just continued to feed at the edge of the clearing. I glanced up at Ken, who was scratching his chin. "I'm going back to bed," he said.

"You've got to be kidding," I said, shocked at his unconcern.

"He's all right. He just doesn't like us being in the way, and he's too stupid to figure out what to do."

"Well, what happens if he does?"

Ken didn't reply. He crawled past me into the tent. Within a few seconds, he was snoring again.

I grabbed the flashlight and zipped up the tent, leaving it partially open so I could keep an eye on the moose. After Ken disappeared from the moose's field of vision, the animal began to feed in earnest, appearing to forget about us, or maybe just lulling us to sleep.

I knelt inside the door peeking out of the small opening. Dressed only in my underwear, I started to shiver. You're being an idiot, I thought. Get a grip. If we were in any real danger, would Ken be sleeping? Taking one last look at the moose, I zipped up the tent and got back into my sleeping bag. I turned off the flashlight and lay down.

If I had found it hard to fall asleep before, it paled next to how wide-awake I felt now. I lay there, trying not to move and cause my sleeping bag to rustle, listening intently to our new campmate. There would be long moments of complete silence, and I'd wonder, is he sneaking up on us? Do moose sneak? Every little squeak of a tent pole, rustle of nylon from the light breeze, or creaking branch brought me to full alert. Leaves stirred, is that him? I wasn't sure what was worse, the silence or his movement.

This is awful. Even if nothing happens tonight, what if he's still there in the morning?

We must have been blocking traffic because, just when I thought matters couldn't get any worse, some of his friends joined him. It sounded like a whole herd coming up their path from the swamp. Branches snapped, footfalls thudded, and the ground rumbled like a passing train. I listened to more deep moose grunts and the half bleat/half moan of cow moose. Sleep was definitely out of the question.

Even Ken woke up, rolled over in his sleeping bag and with a sleepy yawn said, "More of them, huh." With those words of enlightenment, he fell asleep again.

I was convinced one of them would trample us. It was only a matter of time. How could they miss? We were right in the middle of their path. Lying in my sleeping bag in the dark, I imagined several terrible ends to my short and uneventful life. The worst scenario, and the one I couldn't shake, was the news of our untimely and foolish deaths being told to our families. I could see the chaplains walking up the front walk to my house. I could picture Park Rangers in their forest-green uniforms holding my wife's hand, telling her of our last fateful moments.

I could also see how pissed-off she'd be. "Husband trampled to death by irate moose." That would be a great epitaph. She would find it difficult to understand what I was thinking to steal three miles into the backcountry, only to pick a tent site in the middle of a moose freeway. To get here we'd passed several perfectly good campgrounds, many of which her dad helped build when he worked here in the 1960s.

I had met Ken in college where we had become best friends. We both enjoyed the outdoors and the North Country. It was now ten years later. We had studied maps of Isle Royale for months. We'd agreed, right from the start, that neither of us cared much for covering lots of ground. We weren't interested in vying for the most miles hiked in a single day or walking the entire length of the island. Living downstate in large, crowded cities, we wanted to get as far away from civilization and people as possible—no busy campgrounds for us.

The year I turned thirty, Ken had asked me to go with him for a week of backpacking on Isle Royale. I jumped at the opportunity, believing my chance had finally arrived to go on a real wilderness trek. I somehow pulled myself away from my duties as a Garden Center manager and all the time constraints that had come with being a young father. My wife doesn't share my attitude for pushing boundaries, but is wise enough to pick her moments to let go. I was dialing Ken before she could finish saying, "I suppose so ..."

Laying awake in the tent, I thought of my childhood friends who never left Detroit. What would they say if they could see me dropped off on a wilderness island in Lake Superior? As kids, we'd never heard of Isle Royale. The island is 650 miles away from Detroit, and although still being within the State, it's the equivalent of driving from Detroit to Georgia. I felt like I'd stepped into Jack London's *Call of the Wild*.

Starting at the sound of another loud crack of timber, I thought, "How sad is this? In trying to avoid other campers all we'd achieved was to die on our very first night under a moose hoof."

Daylight barely seeped through the tent walls. The light was so faint I wondered if it was real. I hadn't slept.

Ken stirred and then got up. I could still hear moose outside. He unzipped the tent and crawled through the flap. "Get out of here," he yelled. I could hear him clapping his hands and kicking at the ground. The moose herd crashed down the hill. The noise faded away until I could hear nothing except a few songbirds singing as if this was just any other morning and not the day I was allowed to continue living.

"Come on," Ken said. "We have to get moving. I'll restart the fire to make oatmeal."

I didn't say anything in return, too tired to argue. The woods must be browsed to the ground as far as the eye can see, I thought, and then asked from inside the tent, "What's left of our camp site?"

I grabbed my pants and boots and slipped out of the tent. Holding them in my hands, I wearily stood up and gazed around. Everything looked the same. No hoof prints next to the tent, no torn or rutted earth, the forest still green—nothing was changed.

Ken was stacking wood for the fire and turned to see what I was doing. "What are you looking at?"

I didn't know what to say.

"This is going to be a big day," Ken said. "It's fifteen miles from here to McCargoee Cove. I'm giving us one extra packet of oatmeal each. The way you look this morning, you'll need it."

We hurried through breakfast, packed, and got underway.

Every part of my body felt stiff. Retracing our way through the tangled woods and chest-high ferns back to the park trailway, I tripped and stumbled behind Ken, who didn't appear to feel any effects from last night. Four painful hours later and with only three miles covered, we broke through the trees and onto the trail where we left it yesterday. I looked up the path to the right, the direction we'd be taking. The trail snaked up a long, steep slope that crested at the top of the Greenstone Ridge.

"Let's have a swig of water before that climb," I said.

"We should wait. There's only about half a canteen left, and nowhere to refill it, not until we reach McCargoee Cove. Maybe if you just take one sip. But go easy."

He passed me the canteen and under his watchful eye, I took a small swig of water. He did too.

"Okay, that's a little better," I said. "At least we can see where we're going now."

The trail that climbs to the top of the Greenstone Ridge wouldn't feel far if it were a level sidewalk. Unfortunately, the path is rocky, steep, uneven, and laced with tree roots. The trail up the slope makes countless switchbacks. In spite of my disdain for all of the traffic on the streets back home, I was beginning to appreciate my ancestors' zeal for building roads.

With each belabored step up the hill, the straps from my backpack cut deeper into my shoulders. My mother had bought the pack for my thirtieth birthday. She was as excited as I was when she heard about this trip and wanted to help. Having never owned a backpack before and having never hiked as far as I knew, she'd found a sale at the local discount sporting goods outlet. "Walked out with a steal of a deal," she told me. I didn't have the heart not to use it.

Had I known what was in store for me, I wouldn't have been so considerate of her feelings. In that climb to the top of the Greenstone Ridge, I learned more about why good outdoor gear is expensive than if I'd been to a week-long conference on outdoor survival. The backpack was a hard-framed, bright orange Tri-Pack. I have no idea why it's called a Tri-Pack, other than it had three ways to cause pain.

The nylon straps had no padding so the pack felt like it was tied on with rope. Since I was wearing only a tee shirt to keep from overheating, my shoulders were getting raw.

Supplies rattled and bounced around inside of it. The pack would shift or lurch unexpectedly no matter how I balanced the load. I almost toppled over several times.

The third pain was psychological. When Ken first saw it, I thought he might actually hit me. I'd been fortunate to have him walk me through picking out the rest of my clothing and gear. He'd learned a lot of hard lessons from his three previous stays at Isle Royale. We had wanted to blend in with the terrain. We were supposed to be old-time explorers. We were trying to look like we had traveled thousands of miles in the wilderness, no worse for wear. Whenever Ken looked back down the trail to see how I was doing, he shielded his eyes in mock protest at the blaze-orange cheap, Tri-Pack mounted like a beacon atop my shoulders.

When we reached the top of the Greenstone Ridge, Ken finally stopped to rest.

"Let's have a drink, but not too much," he said.

Through gasps for air, I asked. "How much farther?"

"To McCargoe Cove? Ten miles, I'd say."

"Ten miles? Are you sure? It's got to be almost noon."

"It'll get a little easier now. It's mostly downhill from here."

We unbuckled our packs and helped each other out of them. Released, I felt eighty pounds lighter.

"Did I ever tell you how my first day on Isle Royale went?" Ken asked.

"No."

"I drove up here with a couple of friends straight from high school graduation. We were trying to reach McCargoe Cove just like we are. Got so thirsty on the trail that when we came to the fire tower, which is, or at least used to be, a mile down the trail from here, we broke into the fire tower to look for water. The door was locked, so we smashed it open. It was terrible. We found a few rations; but there was no water."

"You stole supplies from the rangers?"

"Yeah, not one of our better moments. Mike was a mess. His feet were as bad as I've seen. He didn't own any boots and wore old gym shoes. There was a first-aid kit in the tower, so we wrapped his feet, grabbed some old candy bars, and he was able to continue."

"I can't imagine wearing only gym shoes on this rock."

"By the time we reached McCargoe Cove, we couldn't travel any farther. They hardly left the campground for two weeks. We ended up taking the water-taxi back to Rock Harbor."

I was beginning to feel a little better. Maybe I wasn't doing so bad after all. Slow start to the day or not, our view had greatly improved. From the ridge top, I could see Lake Superior stretch to the horizon. We were on an island in the largest lake in the world. Big vistas and cool lake breezes—this was more like it. We stood there resting, snacking on Kit Kat bars, gathering our strength for the next leg.

From our vantage point, we could see up and down the length of the forty-eight-mile island. Tall hard ridges with lakes and swamps between them; all running parallel to each other. The ridge tops and valleys look like waves of land. Several of the hiking trails are named after the ridges they follow, such as the Minong Ridge Trail, Feldtmann Ridge Trail, and Greenstone Trail. We'd followed one of the smaller rolls of land yesterday to get through the backcountry to reach Moose Lake. It showed up on the topo maps we'd studied prior to coming.

Isle Royale is only nine miles wide at its widest point. But unless you're a long-legged moose, it's impossible to travel straight across the width of the island, against the grain. The only way to get past the boggy lowlands is to follow the designated trails laid out by the park service. Where paths couldn't be created to get around the wetlands, the trail crews built raised boardwalks through the swamps.

In Ken's and my debates back home as to what parts of the island we wanted to see during the seven days we had for our vacations, we finally agreed to cross over the island and use the McCargoe Cove campground as base camp. McCargoe Cove is on the north side of Isle Royale. Ken had stayed there before and knew where to fish. The cove is a two-mile long, slender body of water that empties into Lake Superior. Steep, wooded hillsides run the length of both sides of the cove. On the map, the narrow inlet looks like someone took an axe to the land, making a deep wedge across the grain of the island.

The McCargoe Cove campground lies at the very end of an inlet, fourteen trail miles from Rock Harbor. Backpackers staying for three days or less can't hike that far and return to Rock Harbor in time to catch the passenger ferries. The secluded, distant location thins the crowds—one of our priorities.

I instantly liked the sound of McCargoe Cove. I couldn't believe we were really going to drive to the farthest northern tip of Michigan's Upper Peninsula, catch a boat, and travel north across Lake Superior to the state's northernmost island, and then hike to its north shore.

This was the real Northwoods.

Ken shoved the canteen into his pack, and we set out again. He'd been right. Our hike did get easier. Although it should have been obvious, I was surprised to find it so much less difficult backpacking across level ground versus climbing uphill. The breeze on top of the ridge kept me cool. The view was spectacular. Things were definitely looking up.

A little water plus some food and rest can energize a person. We now hiked along at a brisk pace. I'd gotten my second wind, and for the next half hour we made good time. But we were still hiking on top of the ridge after a half an hour turned into an hour, which turned into two, and eventually became three hours. Having studied the map, I knew our campsite was several miles north of the Greenstone Ridge.

Today's hike would be no leisurely stroll. When we decided to stay at Moose Lake the first night to avoid the campgrounds, we made today's journey three difficult miles farther. It forced us to backtrack through the same thick, tangled brush. Sitting back home in the living room, studying maps, and writing our itinerary from the comfort of an easy chair, it made sense. We had wanted to experience the genuine Isle Royale. We wanted to break trail—no campgrounds or pathways for us. Unfortunately, it was already mid-afternoon, and we were barely past where we'd left off the day before. If we wanted to reach McCargoe Cove before dark, we would have to do more of a forced march than a gentle hike through a park.

The Greenstone Trail is smooth, as trails go on Isle Royale, but hard as stone. It should be. Isle Royale is made of some of the oldest rock found on the planet. The literature about the island, which I'd also studied before coming, talks about the pre-Cambrian stratum that makes up most of Isle Royale and how it survived a series of ice-ages. Millions of tons of ice had compressed and scraped the island several times. The Greenstone Ridge is the island's high point, and it suffered the worst of those glacial poundings. Little soil dusts its top. What plants do survive spring right from bedrock. The roots cling to hairline cracks and fissures in the stone, like woody fingernails strained to their limit.

The bottoms of my feet were getting hot, and I was pretty sure blisters were forming on my heels, not to mention my shoulders. By the time we found the path that led down to Chickenbone Lake toward McCargoe Cove, my feet hurt every time I set a foot down. We started down the steep path.

There I learned another lesson. Going downhill is as tough as climbing uphill. I didn't understand why. I'd looked forward to coasting downhill. If it had been so much easier traveling across level ground, I thought descending should be easier still.

With each and every step, and with God knows how much weight atop my back, (our packs were so heavy, we decided not to weigh them) I dropped an extra few inches and with extra force right onto the ball of each foot. All that weight and pressure hammered down on a space no bigger than a couple of square inches. The downhill hike and the Tri-Pak did this one-two punch to my feet. They were already tender. I grimaced and sometimes groaned aloud. Ken was starting to wince too.

"Keep going," Ken said. "This is where we find out what we're made of."

"Where are we?"

"After we climb down this slope, the trail should bend northwest. It will take a couple of hours to reach the East Chickenbone Lake Campground. Then it's another couple of hours to McCargoe Cove. If we push it, we should make it."

"This isn't pushing?"

Ken didn't answer, and I didn't say anymore.

The trail down the north slope of the Greenstone takes several sharp, switchback-turns on its descent across the steep hillside. Toward the bottom, the path eventually feathers into uplands of poplar and birch. The scent of the air changed from baked rock to the sweet odor of fermenting leaves found only in aspen groves. Another half-mile and the path dropped onto broad, soggy lowlands packed with conifer trees. The trail turned into mud, and the ground was soft and wet, which actually felt good on my burning feet. I was grateful for the change.

We hiked for an hour through woods of spruce, fir, and cedar. The evergreen trees were so close together that only a green tuft at each tree's crown, well above our heads, showed any life. All else was bare. We were fenced on either side by dry, brittle branches. The limbs were draped with a mossy lichen—the only thing able to survive in so little sunlight. Our feet made no sound on the needle-covered soft trail. But for an occasional clank from my pack, our passing would have been perfectly quiet.

The air was still and damp. The trees enclosed us and the silence was oppressive. Breathing became more difficult. At last, through the trees, we saw a lake peeking between the dark trunks.

"East Chickenbone Lake," Ken said. "There's the camp-ground sign."

"Why don't we stay here?"

"There are no shelters at this end of the lake. It's a terrible place to pitch a tent. The ground is cold and wet, and overrun with mosquitoes." For proof, a few mosquitoes caught up to us as we slowed to check out the site.

"We camped here—once." Ken said.

I could tell by his expression he was reminiscing.

He said through a frown, "That was a bad night."

We reached the water's edge and stopped to gaze at the lake, which appeared shallow and weedy at this end. "Looks like good pike fishing," I said.

"Probably, but it'd be hard to pull a lure through all those weeds."

As we stood together at the east end of Chickenbone Lake, the west wind ran the entire length of the lake before reaching our faces. The breeze over the water felt like taking a shot of oxygen after walking under the conifers. The sun was getting low to the horizon, and we still had a ways to go. Even so, we paused a moment longer, gazing up at the Greenstone Ridge that marched away into the distance. The rippled lake also stretched away before us, reflecting the northern flank of the green-sided hill. Nothing man-made was in sight—no buildings, no power lines, no towers—and no sound of a motor.

"I should warn you about something," Ken said.

"What?"

"McCargoe Cove. When we get there—you need to be careful."

"Why's that?" I couldn't imagine what this new threat could be.

"You'll want to jump into the lake."

"Yeah?"

"Don't. I almost drowned. I was so happy to finally reach camp, so hot and thirsty, I stripped and launched off the far end of the dock."

"Was it too shallow?"

"No, it was Memorial Day Weekend. The ice had melted only six weeks earlier. When I hit the water, the cold knocked the wind out of me."

"Oh my God. You're lucky you made it back to shore."

"Maybe it's warmer in September. All the same, I've never jumped into the lake again."

We slowly walked away from Chickenbone Lake, and those last three miles to McCargoe Cove were some of the longest miles I've ever traveled. Never did I foresee something as simple as walking becoming such an excruciating task. The path wouldn't end and no more conversation passed between us except for abbreviated warnings. "Thorns" … or … "Watch your head" … or … "Pack," all the rest of the information implied.

Ken was slowing down. He kept leading the way, still determined to reach camp by nightfall. But he looked exhausted, and if he looked bad, then I must have looked like death warmed over.

I felt only pain. My feet were past caring about. My shoulders needed First Aid. How or why I kept moving, I couldn't say. The northern woods I'd dreamed about exploring spread all around me, and the expedition I'd always dreamed about lay at my feet.

I no longer cared.

My mind wandered between a clinical examination of my physical and mental condition to wanting to break down into an emotional heap. I noticed none of the scenery or terrain. All of my attention was riveted on placing one foot in front of the other. I focused only on the trail at my feet. Head down, I hiked in a fog. To merely walk, to breathe, and to stay upright was all that mattered.

We came to a small creek. Ken slowed, and I almost walked into him. He hesitated, and then crossed over the water on a wooden plank set there by the trail crews. How they managed to lug lumber and saws this far into the bush, I couldn't imagine.

"One more mile," Ken said, as if he had a mouth full of cotton. Our canteen emptied three hours earlier. "This is the trail from West Chickenbone to McCargoe." He turned right and I followed. We dared not slow our momentum.

The sun had just set behind the hills. Shafts of light slanted through the treetops. The woods were taking on that late evening stillness, and there was a mile to go yet.

I remember little of that last half-hour's hike. We moved at a snail's pace, feeling like snails with our houses on our backs. Numbed by fatigue during that last stretch, I only have a recollection of the trail's end. I can still hear the hollow thump of our boots on the heavy planks that crossed the marsh into McCargoe Cove. We trudged down the boardwalk and through the last few tag alders. Breaking free of the swamp, we labored up the short slope to the nearest open park shelter. We stepped through the screen door. It squeaked and slammed shut behind us.

We peeled our backpacks off and dropped them on the floor. Standing in the middle of the hut, I had my first look at the wooden plank walls that would become our home for the next few days. I turned and gazed out the front screened wall onto the quiet cove with its solitary dock. The water mirrored the tall hill across the bay.

"We made it … I made it. I can't believe we made it," I whispered.

Ken said in a hoarse voice, "I'm going for water. Why don't you unpack."

He stepped through the screen door and limped down the path to the lake. He walked to the end of the dock, wearily stooped over, and dunked the empty canteen into the lake, causing the reflection of the other shore to dimple. Ken then stood up, raised the canteen to his lips, and drank it down.

The fallen sun lit only the crests on the far ridges. Not a single leaf stirred, no birdsong sounded nor rustle of grass. McCargoe Cove was so smooth I thought I could skate on it. My heart pounded in my chest and then slowly quieted to its normal rhythm. I stood there weak and thirsty, scanning the quiet little cove, too tired to move.

When he finished drinking, Ken wiped his mouth with his sleeve and paused for a long moment. I was a full two hundred feet away from him. But even from that distance, I could see him take in a deep breath and sigh. Bending down, he leaned over again to refill the canteen. With one last glance at the still water, he turned and walked back to our shelter.

I stood right where I'd dropped my Tri-Pack. When he walked in, he gave me a nod, smiled, and handed me the canteen. The ice-cold water made me gag at first. I took slower sips. When I finished we started to take everything out of our packs to set up camp.

I felt like I'd been in a fight. I was beat up, stiff, sore, dirty, and a kind of tired I'd never known.

I couldn't have been happier.

Like the night at Moose Lake, I survived.

We spent the entire next day recovering. I didn't do much more than limp around the campground and gawk at everything.

The following day we were up to hiking one mile to an inland lake to fish. I had no success casting from shore, and quickly lost what little tackle I had brought to snags. I returned to camp early.

Wanting to explore anyway, I started back to our shelter and left Ken to fish. I spent my time examining some of the little rills that flowed into McCargoe Cove and studied trees, interesting plants, and a host of flora unique to the island.

While I ate a box of raisins, sitting on the dock toward the end of the day, Ken finally returned. He was carrying a twelve-pound northern pike. He'd run a stick through the gills and lugged it back to camp for over a mile so I could get a picture of it. He said he'd thrown a Mepp's spinner out at least a thousand times until the pike finally struck.

When we got back home, he sent that picture to the tackle company that makes the lure. They put the photo in the Hall of Fame section in their magazine. Ken framed it. The caption beneath it reads, "Master Angler, Ken Glupker with his twelve-pound Northern, caught somewhere on Isle Royale." The picture hangs on a wall in his family room to this day.

Our expedition into the north was as tough as I'd envisioned. The island looked as pristine as I'd hoped. Sharing the experience with Ken, a friend of many years, made it more poignant. In spite of the pain, maybe even because of the pain, we would be back.

# CAPTAIN DON

I CAUGHT MYSELF WONDERING ABOUT CAPTAIN DON. SNOW WAS FALLING, drifting down leisurely as snow does on windless days. Everything looked as it should for the heart of winter. Well below freezing, the snow-covered ground squeaked as I walked and there were few signs of movement in the silent whiteness. An occasional chicka-dee flitted from one snow-covered branch to another, the only re-minder that life still ticked on outdoors.

I walked into the house, made some coffee, and soon felt warm and comfortable, looking out my window at the quiet winter. The view was a long way from summer and from Lake Superior, where Captain Don lives and works. The scene outside the frosty pane of glass is so completely different from the fluid, ever changing seascape where he works. I have my books, an easy chair, and finally some time to reflect on last summer's blur of activities.

The *Isle Royale Queen* is probably dry-docked somewhere along the Great Lakes. No doubt Captain Don is docked somewhere in the Caribbean or South America, maybe Florida or Mexico. Wherever he is, I knew he'd earned his long winter's hiatus. On this quiet day, in the dead of winter, I thought it strange to have my wandering thoughts settle on Captain Don Kilpela and his passenger ship.

For a long time, I didn't know him at all. I only knew his boat.

When I first saw her, the *Isle Royale Queen* was an all-steel, forty-five footer with a strong hull riding high out of the water. The walls, decks, roof and rails were all made of hardened steel and built tough enough to withstand the storms that sweep across Lake Superior. Boarding her, you immediately felt like you could plow through ice floes.

It was, and still is, short on passenger comforts. There is a utilitarian feel about the ship. No decorations dress the walls nor does music play from the speakers. No curtains hang over the windows nor is there any carpeting. Instead, information and maps about the island-park are tacked to the forward walls. Signs direct you to life vests and fire extinguishers. The twin Cummings diesel engines drone loudly in the background and exhaust hangs in the air. The cabin doors stick from long exposure to moisture and the tiny snack bar is manned for only a few minutes shortly after leaving the harbor.

The passenger compartments have cushioned vinyl seats. The Formica tables have worn spots and are covered with old magazines. You can sit there in relative warmth and look out at the lake through the Plexiglas windows. But it's a dull and boring four and one-half-hour ride when viewed through a window frame that continually rises and falls with the waves.

Once seated, people tend to stay put. It's difficult to move about due to the ship's constant pitching. Restlessness and boredom may finally urge someone to investigate some other area accessible to them. As they work their way across the deck, they move in jerks and fits, holding onto support poles, the backs of seats, or any other solid object to keep from falling over. The simple act of trying to walk in a straight line can be a struggle.

Outside and running along both sides of the ship are two narrow, outer walkways ringed with chest-high railings. At the bow, the two walkways merge into an open-air deck that curves upward at the bow and forms a point at the prow. There are no seats, just the sloping steel floor to stand on. In fair weather, the bow is a pleasant place to watch the lake. It offers the best view with the freshest air. However, if the wind kicks up at all, the cold water of Superior splashes over the prow, making the bow uninhabitable.

The stern is another outdoor area for passengers to view the open lake, free from any window frame restraints. It's roofed overhead, but open on three sides. A small group of people will sit outside at the stern braving the cold, perhaps smoking. This is where Ken and I always sit.

The *Isle Royale Queen* ferries passengers between Isle Royale National Park and Copper Harbor, Michigan. I have always felt the *Queen's* trimmed-down riggings and spartan comforts are appropriate. The ship's bare bones, hard lines, and cold ride help you get into shape physically as well as mentally. The place it takes you to has even fewer amenities than the boat. There are no roads, no towns, and no utilities to speak of. There's mostly nothing but the wilderness it's slowly being turned into by the Park Service. The island was once home to miners, loggers, and fishermen, but those days are remembered only by a few.

The trip is often uncomfortable. At times it can literally be a sickening journey.

On my first lake crossing, Ken, who had been to the island before, warned me ahead of time about the rigors of the boat trip. He showed me where to sit to have the smoothest ride. The stern, he said, is the most stable part of a ship.

For close to thirty years, we have tried to get to the island for a week's vacation. We take my beat-up old canoe and spend most of our time fishing the Island's many coves and bays. But when weather permits, we prefer to fish the open lake, albeit close to shore, to hunt for dinner. We love the big water. Only from a canoe, without the benumbing noise of a boat motor and with only a sheet of aluminum between us and the water, can we feel Superior's slightest movements or get any real sense of her more intimate thoughts.

I've read that the middle of Lake Superior is practically void of life. The lake currents, which contain most of the nutrients and aquatic life, move primarily along the shoreline. The rivers that empty into Superior at the perimeter don't mix with the colder and slightly denser water at the center of the lake. Their waters get turned where they meet this large body of cold water and stay within a few miles of the shoreline as does the plankton and other microorganisms. The center of the lake is basically a vast area of sterile cold water.

With time I learned to enjoy the four and one-half hour ferry ride. I came to look forward to it and even yearned for the trip over the rest of the year. The journey feels like an absolution. I enter the lake at Copper Harbor bearing the cares and responsibilities of my normal urban life and emerge from the lake at Rock Harbor freed of such concerns. As we travel over that water, watching the mainland slowly dwindle and then disappear beyond the horizon, I can feel the lake purify me. It removes the last stubborn traces of city life, leaving them behind with the submerged mainland.

Because of the way I feel about the lake crossings, I wondered about Captain Don, who spends his workdays on it. What must it be like to travel over this water every day each summer? I suppose it becomes mundane at times, but if it is, he never acts like it.

On every trip, much like an airline pilot does, Don gives a brief message to the passengers. He gives a marine weather forecast, goes over safety procedures, and provides updates on recent world and local news if we are returning to Copper Harbor. Interspersed in his routine announcements are a few interesting tidbits about Lake Superior. Within these remarks, and noticeable even through the scratchy intercom, I could detect a touch of awe in his voice. I got to know him a little better with each vacation. The dinners, drinks, and conversations we eventually shared (only after I had been coming to the island for several years) confirmed my suspicions.

Reaching a remote island comes with a price. And it is no more apparent than on the *Isle Royale Queen*. In spite of all of my lofty thoughts about Don, his ship, and the lake, the locals call the *Isle Royale Queen* the "Barf Barge." It's a very appropriate moniker. Like myself, most of the passengers are tourists and wan-a-be wilderness trekkers. Our destination is the park and very little thought is given ahead of time to the boat ride to get there. It's considered just another leg in the journey to start what we consider our real vacation.

Lake Superior ought never to be taken lightly. The waves and rollers are noted for being close together and steep. The wind frequently changes direction and waves often become disorganized. The result is tall, steep, random waves coming from several directions. If you get caught on the lake at the wrong time, you feel like a bug on the surface of the water in a tub where the bather won't sit still.

Due to the lake's tendency for sudden changes of disposition, one of the first items of business covered in Captain Don's messages is the protocol for dealing with seasickness. This procedure—if need arises—is to get to the edge of the boat as quickly and as safely as possible (not always an easy task) and relieve yourself over the railing without falling overboard. I have had the dubious benefit of witnessing this technique first-hand from my outdoor vantage point on the stern deck. My position affords me a full view of many a green-faced participant. One of the first things Ken taught me was, if you don't want to get sick, stay outside and stay at the stern. In rough seas, this is the calmest part of a tossing ship. If you stay indoors where it's warm and cloistered, where the window frames constantly rise and fall, the horizon pitches to and fro, waves are tossing and turning and where you are constantly off-balance, well … the consequences are inevitable.

A few years ago, just after getting back to Copper Harbor from a particularly smooth crossing, I met Captain Don with some other island visitors at Mariner North Restaurant. After eating camp food for a week, I look forward to eating and drinking as if I had been shipwrecked for months.

I sat down with Captain Don, Bob Guiliani and his wife Linda, who are photographers and frequent visitors. Joining us were Captain Don's sister, Jojo and her husband-to-be at that time, Mark. As we settled in to make an evening of it, the conversation turned to infamous boat rides across the lake. We each had our own tale to tell of woeful lake crossings, but Captain Don, in the tradition of many a boat Captain, is a great storyteller. He was by far the authority on the subject at our table and whenever he spoke, we listened closely. The talk quickly became lively and loud. The drinks were starting to go to our heads and the glow among us warmed considerably.

When it came around for my turn to share a story, I started my adventure as most everyone else's … "The winds rose unexpectedly …" for within minutes of leaving the island that day, the rollers, which had been significant already, doubled in size and began to heave the *Queen* around as if we were on a lifeboat.

I remember this storm because of what happened to a passenger sitting across from me. The guy caught my eye because he looked so miserable for someone dressed so stylishly. He could have stepped out of an outdoor magazine—North Face jacket, Merrell boots that cost more than my canoe, and designer sunglasses. It seemed like someone dressed this sharp should wear a model's frozen smile.

I sat in my usual spot on the stern deck facing aft. He was ten feet away, sitting on a bench seat in the very back corner of the ship. There, he clung to the pole next to him, his eyes closed tightly to the now fearsome panorama of the aroused lake. Although he appeared to be sleeping, whenever a larger wave pitched the boat, his face twitched. He sat huddled in his corner, holding that same tense pose.

Well into the trip, and without any warning, the entire ship lurched. A rogue wave swept across us and submerged most of the stern deck, dropping it into the lake. The water level rose sharply before anyone could shout out, engulfing him up to his chin and me to my knees. I had a bizarre split-second glimpse of only his head sticking above of the surface of the water. The expression on his face is what I'll always remember. It was something far beyond surprise and shock. His eyes, now on this disembodied head, were as wide-open as they had been squeezed shut the instant before. A cold mixture of terror, pain, and bewilderment flashed across his face. The wave raced away, falling from the stern as fast as it had overcome us. Freed from the lake's choke-hold, he sprang out of his seat. For a moment, he stood there in disbelief at what just happened.

To his credit, he slowly pulled himself together, shook himself like a dog when it shakes water from its fur, and settled back into his seat. A shy smile of embarrassment touched the corners of his mouth as he noticed the rest of us were staring at him. He never closed his eyes the rest of the way to Copper Harbor.

I glanced at Captain Don as I finished my tale. He looked annoyed. Thinking back on it now, it's no wonder Don was perturbed. I'm sure he doesn't consider having one of his passengers almost swept overboard funny or exciting.

After we each shared our roughest boat ride stories, the talk took an odd turn and we started discussing our sickest and messiest trips. Here Captain Don and Mark (who had worked on the island for a couple of summers) held center stage. Mark took over and gave a full and vivid account—as we ate—of how it's usually the biggest and boldest passengers who get hit the worst with seasickness.

He began his account by pantomiming those first faint symptoms. You aren't quite sure whether those pangs you feel are from becoming sick or just indigestion. He portrayed, with astounding accuracy, that unsettled rumbling that slowly builds in your stomach. Mark fidgeted uncomfortably in his chair, acting nervous, glancing around the restaurant, trying to hide his growing queasiness. Satisfied with this part of his rendition, he explained to us how the discomfort eventually reaches a critical point. It's that moment where you cross a line of realization and know what's coming but won't admit it ... can't admit it. An alarmed expression grew in Mark's eyes. He did a few audible dry burps and swallowed hard several times attempting to keep food down, demonstrating for us this dawning grim knowledge.

He continued his act, oblivious to the sidelong glances he was beginning to gather from the diners at the nearby tables. Mark then went from a verbal description to a live re-enactment of how the big guys' tough demeanor dissolves into a sallow-faced ugliness. The inevitable conclusion is approaching. The lugs try, with all of their considerable might, to quell the build up of wretched lava boiling within, but with a sickening certainty, know the battle is lost!

Mark suddenly stood up, his chair falling backwards, and raced across the restaurant with his hands over his mouth to the bar. He dodged tables as if being pitched back and forth across a storm-tossed deck, bolting for an imaginary boat railing. With all semblance of dignity vanished, he gave a perfect performance of the once proud passenger erupting over the rail. Bending over the far side of the bar, his face hidden from our view, Mark's body retched time and time again until his heaving torso calmed. Slowly straightening up, with a weak and relieved expression, another gathering storm formed in his eyes. He quickly bent over the bar again and re-enacted hurling more cargo. His life-like performance sent the patrons and the bartenders scurrying, several to the nearest exits.

Mark, now all alone at the deserted bar, stood and turned to face us, mockingly wiping his mouth with his sleeve, beaming with pride. We rose and applauded, laughing our heads off. Anywhere else, we'd have found the whole episode disgusting at best. Here it seemed fitting. He bowed to the greatly diminished audience and returned to our table.

There was one lake journey that I did not tell that night, nor did Captain Don. Up until that crossing, I had looked upon his Captain's job with a little envy. After all, I remember thinking, how difficult can it be to steer a boat to the same destination every day over some of the most beautiful water on earth.

Prior to our setting out from Rock Harbor for the return voyage home, the marine forecast had predicted four-to-eight footers with diminishing westerly winds. But shortly after we set out, they steadily increased instead, reaching gale force strength only one hour after leaving Rock Harbor. The west wind never changed direction, which gave the waves an opportunity to gain momentum and build upon themselves. They grew until eventually ten-to-eighteen footers were bearing down on us, with some waves even larger.

Most of the people on board had used the *Queen* before. It was late September, and the passengers were more seasoned and accustomed to rough trips. With the onset of fall, the weather begins to deteriorate. Winds pick up, it's colder, and the days are shorter. Fewer people use the park at that time of year. Typically, only those who don't mind trading a little discomfort for a more isolated and uninhabited island experience go to Isle Royale.

At first, we made light of the growing seas, almost reveling in the wilder lake conditions. But before long, we were exchanging nervous glances. The rollers had become massive and the wave tops were being blown apart, spraying sheets of water horizontally across the crests. Until then, I had never experienced the full power of a storm on the lake. The waves are not only tall, but also broad. Their size lends them volume, as if whole city blocks are rolling and flowing along. Every second street represents the distance to the next wave top. The ship, which had felt so strong before, now seemed small and frail compared to the size and power of the rolling hills of water.

Our course to Copper Harbor caused us to travel at a diagonal to the waves. Climbing up and down each one, the ship would lean far to one side as we traversed up the face of a wave and then lean hard the other way steaming down it. We would tilt so far we needed to brace ourselves in our seats to keep from falling off them. A few passengers actually did tumble out of their chairs and across the deck. The prospect of enduring four hours of such a ride showed on the faces of those I could see from my seat. Soon our concerns were reduced to hoping to just make it over the top of each roller. Within one short hour, the journey had turned into a wave-climbing expedition that repeated itself over and over again.

Despite the discomfort, I caught myself feeling excited, indeed, even exhilarated. For, despite the stormy looking water, it was a bright sunny day and Lake Superior felt more like it was playing than angry. It made me feel like I was a child caught dangerously between two big brothers wrestling in the living room and paying me no heed. I could almost hear lake and wind saying, "If you get hurt, it's not our fault. You should have stayed out of the way."

The sky held no threat of rain and the air had no trace of haze or mist to it. Sunlight beamed unimpeded through the clean northern air. From the top of each wave, we could see to the distant horizon with an amazing clarity, and for one brief instant, we were afforded a view that exposed one blue ridge after another, capped with a streaming white froth. The vista's resolution was too sharp, too bold, too raw, making it hard to look at for any length of time. It was both dreadful and beautiful, all at once. You felt relieved when the ship fell into the trough of the next swell.

The sun penetrated Superior's clear water with visible rays of sunshine. They streamed into the depths, where its powerful light quickly faded and then went out. As we climbed a wave and approached its peak, the sun shone straight through the peaks causing wave tops to glow. The liquid walls thinned as we approached their peaks, the tops lit from behind as with a bright blue lamp. Cresting the roller, the full power of the sun would then break free from behind the wave and once again glare down upon a sea running wild.

Some waves curled and crashed with a heavy boom that hurt our ears. The wind shrieked across the boat and we cowered in our seats trying to stay warm as best we could. My thoughts bounced from misery to excitement—from a pragmatic evaluation of my plight to an artistic or religious contemplation. I felt like I was in a movie. I had this disconnect from reality. I didn't feel scared or that we were in any real danger, and I don't know if I was just naïve, confident of my eternal destiny, or incapable of fully grasping our real life predicament after spending too much time watching disaster flicks. If we had gone down, I'm fairly certain that I would have been surprised and puzzled at how this sort of thing could possibly happen to me.

Ken, however, had a stillness about him that made me re-evaluate our situation. We were in fifty-five degree water and far from any help. No one issued life jackets and no message came from the Captain or crew. I asked Ken about it and he said, "There's no point. No lifeboats and you wouldn't last more than twenty minutes in that cold water anyway."

Ken had spent a lot of time on the Great Lakes and the concern on his face was real. Once, when he caught me looking over at him, he said, without letting anyone else hear, "I don't know if we're going to make it."

I was startled and got a little shook. I'd never seen him this way before. We had experienced some tight moments before—narrow escapes in our canoe, hanging from a cliff by our finger tips, and car rides that should never have taken place. He turned away and then looked back at me again. Our eyes met and nothing more was said.

We continued to suffer through the ride. Tremendous rollers swept under us. Twice, Don changed course in order to run with waves so large he wouldn't risk quartering them. I thought we were going to have to change course permanently and run before the seas, hoping the wind gave out before the lake did. But he'd return to his original course after a few anxious minutes. Several times, we leaned so far over to one side that I thought we were going to roll. The boat would hang onto its tenuous balance as if it was a sailboat on a hard tack, hesitate, and then swing upright.

There was little conversation. Passengers became introspective and quiet. Meaningful looks were exchanged between friends and family—and that was about all. I remember thinking, this must be what they mean when they say the sea puts the fear of God into you.

About half an hour out from Copper Harbor, the waves began to subside ever so slightly. They were still large but seemed to lack the same intensity they had shown earlier. Another fifteen minutes and we knew all was well. The lake was rough but unmistakably diminishing. Talk across the boat slowly returned.

Just as we were beginning to relax enough to venture talking about it, Captain Don suddenly appeared on the back deck. We were surprised to see him. I have rarely seen him on the stern deck during a voyage. He just stood there for a long moment, looking back over the lake we had just crossed. He was smoking a cigarette and I thought it kind of strange until I noticed that his hand holding the cigarette was trembling. It was at that moment, and not until that moment, I fully realized, it had been close.

He seemed lost in thought and oblivious to us, showing no sign of what he was thinking. Out of an emotionally steeled face, he mumbled a few words I couldn't catch, turned, flicked his cigarette into the lake, and went back up to the pilot house.

In retrospect, I perhaps understand a little better what people with jobs like his go through from time to time. I once heard an airline pilot recite the old adage about how a pilot's work is hours and hours of dull and boring routine, interspersed with a few brief seconds of terror and barely controlled panic. Policemen, firemen, soldiers, and pilots all share a certain kind of work experience few of us will ever fully appreciate. I have never looked at their jobs quite the same since.

Back home … I took another sip of coffee, breathed out a comfortable sigh, and gazed upon the peaceful white landscape outside my window. Yes, it is peculiar, and yet somehow appropriate, to think of Captain Don just now. I hope he's having a good time in the Caribbean or wherever he's relaxing this winter.

He earned it.

# LITTLE BROTHERS AND SISTERS

AN ISLAND IS A FRAGILE ENVIRONMENT WHERE THE RESIDENT WILDLIFE reaches a tenuous balance. That balance includes cohabitation with the human fauna. Only after spending more than one week at Isle Royale did I begin to feel like I was getting a handle on the wildlife. Native Americans call them little brothers and sisters. Toward the end of a month-long stay, I began to see why.

It took at least two weeks before my dulled urbanized hearing, sight, and smell quickened to the point where I could sort one natural sound from another. I needed to remove myself from the incessant background noise of running motors and the visual overload that normally surrounds me at home. I needed to allow my senses to grow more acute, sensitized enough to catch that quiet movement or soft rustle.

After staying on the island for a whole month, I also noticed for the first time, that most vacationers to the island—myself included—have an agenda not too different from their normal task-lists back home. Many park visitors are intent upon squeezing as much kayaking, traveling, fishing, hiking, or whatever spins our recreation-propellers into our time-off as we can. Much is missed in the process.

I have come to think Europeans have it right when it comes to taking a 'Holiday.' If you can't get away for at least a month, you haven't really begun to unwind.

At McCargoe Cove, the sun rises over the ridge across the bay from the campground. I stood on shore with another hiker one summer morning absorbing the heat from the sun after it had crested the hill. Nights are cool, even in August, and the sun felt good. He was quietly talking about his trip, and what he had seen and the places he hoped to get to before returning home, mildly complaining about the brief time he had to do all that he wished. We were keeping our voices low because many of the other campers were still asleep.

While he was talking, I could hear the sounds of a heavy animal approaching through the shallows at the end of the cove. He wasn't in sight yet. The thick vegetation growing along the water's edge hid him from our view. The sound of steps sloshing through the lake could easily be mistaken for waves lapping on shore. But I'd been on the island for a couple of weeks by this time, long enough to distinguish between the two sounds. For me, it was obvious that a moose was about to clear the tag alders to our right.

"There's a moose coming," I said, interrupting him. He paused in mid-sentence. He looked over at me, opened his mouth to ask, "What moose?" when the bull came around the corner. He splashed up the bank and ambled, in a moose's deceptively awk-ward-looking walk, right toward us to get to the aspen thickets behind the campground.

The situation was dangerous. The bull's course would take him no more than ten feet away. Moose have terrible eyesight. If we startled him, he might feel surrounded and bolt. They may look clumsy, but when the need demands it, moose can out pace wolves. If we happened to be in his way, he'd easily trample us like the small trees he's accustomed to plowing over.

"Don't move," I said. Fortunately, the guy froze, and the moose lumbered by us only a canoe paddle length away. He smelled like he lived in a swamp, which I imagine he did. It was a musky sort of odor. His scent hung in the damp morning air for a long time after he disappeared into the woods.

People become a part of the community of wildlife at Isle Royale. We play a role mid-May through mid-October. The rest of the year, we desert the island, which seems like a very good idea. Leave the poor beasts alone for a while; give them a little time to themselves.

The park has several campgrounds scattered across the main island and on select outer islands in strategic places. People are encouraged by the rangers to use the designated trails and to stay in the campgrounds and refrain from using the backcountry. You may get a backcountry "use permit" if you request one, but the number of permits are limited. As a result, park visitors congregate into packs of their own at campgrounds and along trailways.

The campgrounds attract scavengers. The most notorious is the fox where one and sometimes two hang out at the Belle Isle campground, located on an isolated outer island on the more remote north shore. Ken and I often stay at Belle Isle because of its remoteness. The foxes have been hanging around our campground, as we like to think of it, for as long as I can remember. They'll steal food, clothes, or anything light enough to carry off when left unattended and sometimes even while attended. They seem inquisitive by nature and very bold. People can almost hand-feed them and I confess to trying it a few times. I've had one of them inches from my exposed fingers, but was never quite successful at coaxing him to actually take the candy bar from my hand. One fox got within a couple of inches. But it occurred to me at the last second that dangling fingers in front of a wild animal's teeth, who may or may not distinguish fingers from food, was not altogether wise.

In the past, I worried—a little—about the camp foxes. What do they do the rest of the year when they can't feed on people's discards? The rangers warn you not to feed the animals, particularly the foxes, because it only encourages them further. They're right, of course, and I don't feed them anymore. My concerns were eased when I was fortunate to witness a couple of incidents.

One windy afternoon while Ken was casting from Fish Rock, a place where we fish from shore when the weather is too rough for getting out in the canoe, a fox trotted into our campsite carrying a squirrel in its mouth. He acted exactly like a domestic cat does after capturing a mouse. There was a proud demeanor about him, as if he was showing off his trophy for me. He tossed it in the air, pawed at it on the ground, and glanced my way, as if to see if I noticed his prowess. I had been reading at our picnic table and said aloud, "good catch." He visibly puffed up, stood more erect, and trotted jauntily a few feet farther away. Then, in more fox like fashion, he stood guard over his prey, snatched it and bolted the whole squirrel down in one gulp. He stood there digesting his food with that uncomfortable, yet satisfied expression that crosses your face when eating your favorite food too fast.

There must be a million fox squirrels on Isle Royale. They're everywhere. I can hear them chatter and scurry through the trees or on the forest floor wherever I go and at any time of the day. At dawn, they make a chatter-like call that sounds exactly like an old wind-up alarm clock going off. Ken and I often mention it. Our best guess is they're either letting all of the other squirrels know their whereabouts at first light or they're just happy to make it through the night. Either way, they'd be a steady and dependable diet for a fox. It wasn't until this escapade at the picnic table that it occurred to me that fox squirrels were named for a reason.

Another scavenger frequents the lakeside campgrounds. They too affect what we leave unattended outside lakeside shelters. Otters bring a campground alive with their seemingly boundless energy. Even when they lie down, you sense their barely contained urge to leap to their next activity. It's as if their natural state of being is motion and not rest. Otters' famous curiosity almost caused us an otter-emergency during one trip.

We had just pulled into West Caribou Island, paddling the five miles along the south shore of the main island from Chippewa Harbor. The two shelters on West Caribou Island lay on the leeward side, facing inward toward the long sheltered bay of Rock Harbor. Just off shore in front of the campground, fish were rising and almost before we unpacked the canoe, Ken was casting from the dock. He was using a heavier spoon that's easier to cast than the lighter tackle we normally put on for trolling. He threw out the silver/red bait. It made a graceful arc and landed with a heavy plop when it hit the water. At that same instant, an otter surfaced nearby. We hadn't noticed him when we came into camp. The otter swiftly peered around and then submerged.

Before he could react, Ken felt a heavy jerk on his pole. He had the wherewithal to release his bail to let the line go slack, hoping he hadn't set hooks into the otter. We waited a few tense seconds to see if his now limp fishing line would start moving through the water with a catch neither of us wanted to unhook. After what seemed like an extremely long time, the otter resurfaced thirty feet from the bait. Ken quickly reeled in. I couldn't be sure, but the otter appeared to sulk and glower at us from out in the lake. He voiced a quiet otter-rumble from his throat that sounded like disgust. He scowled at us for a few seconds and then seemed to shake off his bad mood, perk up, and go back to his explorations.

Later that day he came ashore and cozied up to us. He actually lay down at our feet, as comfortable with our presence as an old family pet.

Incidents like these can make it easy to forget that the scavengers who frequent the campgrounds are not tame animals. It becomes most apparent when different species confront each other.

When I turned fifty, I decided to spend a month on the island in way of celebration. When other campers found out I was staying that long, I'd get asked, "What do you eat?" The implication in their question was, "how do you carry a month's supply of food on your back?"

My reply was, "I eat fish." I never tired of eating the same thing every night, and to this day, I have yet to have fish in a restaurant that compares to the lake trout we prepare.

Ken loves to fish even more than I do, and when he and I go together to Isle Royale, we spend most of each day fishing from the canoe. As a result, we need to clean fish daily. He has raised dressing trout to an art form and his patience with amateurs, such as myself, who waste meat with bad cuts, is minimal. He certainly has a difficult time watching me clean fish. I can feel his impatience as I work, his feet shuffling, peering over my shoulder, not resisting the urge to critique each cut I make. I don't think I'm actually that bad, but he is good. I'd rather just let him clean the fish than have him watch me, feeling his irritation grow.

When you clean fish, the heads and guts have to go somewhere, and the park has a policy requiring all fish heads, skins, and entrails be either dropped into the deeper water of the nearby lake or left on shore cut into four-inch chunks. This is explained to all park visitors during orientation. When we stay at the Belle Isle campground, there's a deep cove where we normally take the remains.

On our first trip where we took a canoe, we either weren't paying close enough attention to the ranger's instructions or decided to ignore them. After cleaning our catch, we left the fish carcasses—whole—on the beach for the gulls and other scavengers, thinking what could be more natural?

Isle Royale was fished commercially in the past and several families worked it from ice-out in April until late November. Many of the small isles and lakes are named after these fishermen, their wives, or their children. There's a long-standing agreement between fishermen and seagulls concerning fish guts that likely dates back to prehistoric times. The birds hover over harvesters in anticipation because they seem to have been genetically imprinted to understand that the chum is pitched to the sea. Although no one has commercially fished Isle Royale for several years, a few gulls will briefly circle our canoe when we fish.

We found out the hard way that this long-term agreement doesn't work as well on Lake Superior. The gulls dragged our whole-fish remains off the beach into the water where they are safer. Unfortunately for them, they don't seem to realize that when they let go of their prize, it sinks. If the water is deeper than two feet, when the gull drops the fish in order to feed, the remains fall to the bottom of the lake. Seagulls are incapable of diving.

There, in the clear deeper water, just a few feet from shore, and where all can see them, rest our fish remains. It frustrates and tantalizes the seagulls, who eventually fly away in frustration. The carcasses will lie in the shallows for months, slowly decomposing in the ice-cold waters of Superior, and not too pretty for campers who happen upon the scene and are seeking a more pristine lake-front experience.

While getting water for camp down at the beach during a later fishing trip at Belle Isle, I noticed an otter hauling one of our fish remains up out of the forty-foot-deep hole where we dump them. He was carrying it toward shore, about two hundred feet from where I stood. What the otter didn't notice, and I could from my vantage point inside of the natural amphitheater-shaped cove, was the camp fox also watching the otter. The fox was carefully making his way through the trees toward the spot where the otter was swimming, fish carcass in tow.

I felt like a spectator anticipating the clash of two foes. I waved to Ken, over by the shelter tying up leaders, to come and watch.

The otter pulled his catch onto a small, six-foot wide gravel shelf on shore between two large boulders and was getting settled in to dine on lake trout. As he did, the fox confronted him from atop a rock. Both of them tensed and crouched as if to pounce upon each other. The fox jumped down onto the beach and like two fighters in the ring, they circled, as if testing the will of their opponent. The otter with the fish in its mouth snarled and hissed, skittering side to side, always facing the fox. Silent but more confident, the fox slowly edged in closer.

I wanted to shout to the otter to back into the lake where he'd easily escape, but he didn't. The fox lunged and grabbed an end of the carcass that trailed closest to him. They commenced to play tug of war with the remains of one of our fish.

They never tried to bite or scratch each other, as if that was against the rules. Like two boys wrestling on a playground at recess, they seemed to do as much as they dared without coming to actual blows and getting into real trouble. After a full minute of snarling, growling, and pulling each other across the stones, the otter finally relented and the fox yanked the fish away. He quickly scampered up the hillside and disappeared.

The otter whimpered aloud and looked visibly humiliated. He slinked back into the lake, where he floated dead-still in the cove. Very un-otter like, he appeared unsure of himself.

He must have made a decision because he abruptly swam straight back to the area of our fish-dump, dove, and came back up with another carcass from the bottom of the lake. He proceeded to carry it back to the same spot on shore between the two boulders. The fox, who had already eaten the first fish, noticed the otter returning. He swiftly jogged back to intercept another trout for himself.

Like a replay, the otter came ashore and the fox, now bolder than ever, quickly wrenched the fish away from him and fled. The otter, devastated once again, stood alone on his shelf, head hanging to the ground. This time, however, he wasted no time feeling sorry for himself. He did a swift turnabout with what appeared to me pronounced determination. He went straight back into the lake for more.

The third time, the fox was waiting for the otter atop the rock before the otter could even return to the shelf. Despite clearly seeing the fox waiting for him, the otter waded ashore with another fish. The fox looked visibly bloated from his two previous meals. During their third match, I wasn't sure if the portly fox would be agile enough for another battle or interested in more fish. He was.

If the otter had just carried his food to one of the isolated island rocks in the deep cove, all very safe from foxes, he could have eaten in peace. The otter never did connect his problem with his choice of shoreline feeding location. We've never seen an otter take another fish carcass from the cove.

# OF MOOSE AND WOLVES

W<small>HUMP-WHUMP-WHUMP-WHUMP-WHUMP.</small>

"Vic…" Ken said quietly, trying to wake me out of that co-matose condition I'm in those first two hours after I fall asleep for the night.

Whump-whump-whump-whummp-whump-hmp.

"Pssst … Vic! …" The thumps reverberated just outside our back shelter wall, my head no more than a foot from the wall.
"Is .. is … that a fox … under the shelter?" I stammered.

I wasn't thinking straight yet, and at first the noise reminded me of a large dog's tail beating on a wooden floor when it's excited. The loud steady thumping sound boomed in the quiet of the middle of the night. I worked hard to pry my eyes open and when I did, couldn't see any better than when they were closed. It was an overcast night and no hint of starlight entered our shelter. The heavy pounding grew more urgent.

Ken tried to muffle a snicker, and said in a hushed tone from his sleeping bag, "It's the moose. They're screwing right behind our shelter."

I was awake now. And, as I lay there on our bare wood floor, in my mummy sleeping bag, on a remote outer island on the north shore of Isle Royale National Park, a pair of lusty moose were using our park shelter for a behind-the-shack rendezvous. I lay there in the dark listening.

Whump, whump, whump, whump hump, ….CRASH!!

I jumped two feet off the floor, even zipped up to my chin in my bag. The bull had dismounted the cow, falling hard against the two-by-six plank wall—the wall only inches away from my head. A very deep, human-sounding, satisfied sigh rumbled from the bull. I then heard the cow groan and trot a few paces away.

The bull was panting, catching his breath. I could almost feel the steam through the wall. Then there was a long silent pause like someone with apnea whose loud snores suddenly stop. I stopped breathing, too, listening. After a space of time that would have asphyxiated me, the bull coughed, breathed, stumbled forward, and slowly shuffled off into the woods. His footfalls faded until we heard only surf from the lake.

"Oh my God, can you believe that?" I said to Ken. "I thought he was going to fall right through the roof."

Ken let himself go and laughed aloud, making no effort now at staying quiet. "Fox … what were you thinking?"

We both tossed and turned in our sleeping bags. I'd hear Ken chuckle to himself every once in awhile from his bedroll a few feet away. We were both trying to come to grips with what had just occurred. I lay awake, straining to listen for other "night noises" well into the night. It was at least three in the morning before I fell asleep again.

Most everyone hopes to see moose when they come to Isle Royale, perhaps not so intimately, but a visit to the park feels incomplete if you don't see at least one. You usually aren't disappointed. Moose are widely dispersed across Isle Royale. The moose population is four times the normal mainland moose-per-square-mile rate and they are not a quiet animal. They also tend to live near water, making them easier to spot. Campers evidently don't bother them much, so chances for seeing one are good.

There are no deer or bear on Isle Royale. It's too far for them to swim—twelve miles minimum from Canada to the north. Deer won't venture that far over the winter ice and bear hibernate. There once were woodland caribou. They were hunted out a hundred years ago. The moose were hunted out as well, but reestablished themselves. It's anybody's guess as to whether they returned to Isle Royale by swimming or came across on the ice. Moose swim extremely well and can move as fast through the water as two grown men can paddle a canoe. My guess is they swam. Pilots have reported seeing them swimming in Lake Superior halfway between Isle Royale and Minnesota.

They're bigger in real life than one might expect. They stand taller than a horse, and their goofy appearance gives them a sort of favorite uncle kind of appeal. When people visit the island, moose are the most frequently discussed animals.

I have never read anything to back up our thinking, but it's Ken's and my belief that the moose deliberately hang out near campgrounds. We postulate the moose are trying to keep away from the wolves, which are extremely shy of humans. No hunting is allowed in the park. Wolves are the moose's only natural enemy. I have never seen a wolf. They are so wary that even the people who work here all summer rarely see them. Wolves would certainly avoid campgrounds and as a result, create a safety-zone for moose.

When it comes to wildlife, Ken is a throwback to an earlier era. Back home he fishes year round, hunts only in season—he's very strict about this, and owns several skins and mounts. He once brain-tanned enough deer hides to create an entire buckskin outfit—head to toe. Brain tanning is a time consuming method for curing hides. He scooped out the brains, concocted this tanning-goop, and then smeared it on the hides. He bought a book explaining the correct process. He liked the idea of utilizing every part of the deer.

His freezer is always well stocked with wild game and fish. He has that utilitarian attitude toward wildlife that I've noticed in other people who partially subsist on fish and game.

I have seen Ken stalk moose and come within an arm's length to get a good picture—a strongly discouraged practice prohibited by the Park Service. I have a picture of him taking such a picture. I am safely shooting from twenty-five feet behind him, looking over his shoulder. He actually had to back up because the moose didn't fit in the frame of his viewfinder. He told me afterward all he could see was brown hair.

The bulls go into rut in September and their moods intensify as the month goes along. They get ornery, bolder, and increasingly territorial. We often go to Isle Royale in September to avoid the mosquitoes and crowds. Regardless of the bulls' touchy disposition, Ken has a habit of enticing them into camp if he hears one nearby.

When he has a mind to, Ken does a moose call. To my ears, his imitation bull-grunts sound authentic, but you'd think the moose would know the difference. It's sort of like me trying to mimic a southern accent for a Georgian. They spot me a mile away. Maybe the bulls' hormonal charged brains make them daft because Ken's calls do work. More often than not, we'll hear the bull work his way through the woods toward Ken's calls. The bull returns Ken's grunts, getting closer and closer until he finally breaks through the trees into camp. (Ken also does a loon call, which I'm positive sounds sick at best. They too respond for him, returning trills and whoops. One can only guess at what they make of his loonish yodels.)

Ken has several different methods for moose calling. Sometimes he will bellow and grunt. Sometimes he'll bang the canoe paddles together, imitating the sound of clashing bulls. Other times he'll thrash the bushes as if a moose is making a rub. On one such occasion, where a bull came within thirty feet, the bull became so irritated at finding no one to brawl, he turned his attention to a young tree. The moose splayed his legs wide for balance, neck muscles rippling, snorting in anger at an imaginary foe. He then commenced to thrash the poor tree, raking it with his antlers. When he finished his battle with the eight-foot-tall fir, he left it a crumpled heap.

Cows and calves are more timid than bulls, and they don't respond to Ken's mock battles or grunting. They make a very different sound than the males. It's more of a bleat. Sometimes, cows will blow loudly through their noses, giving an alarm call much like a deer does. Most of the time, however, the cows simply ignore people or slowly walk away when you get too close to them.

We have had a number of close encounters over the years and not always intentionally.

We were portaging into an inland lake to do some walleye fishing. Ken carried the canoe and I toted our gear. Lugging an aluminum canoe and fishing tackle is not quiet work. On our way to the lake, he set the nose of the canoe down with a clang into the crotch of a multi-stemmed birch tree along the trail in order to rest. He picked up this trick from watching wilderness guides in the Boundary Waters. It helps them keep from having to lift the canoe all the way off the ground to hoist it onto their shoulders. We gladly grab any advantage for lightening the work. With the right tree, the canoe can be set at shoulder height, allowing us to merely walk beneath it to get underway again.

I dropped my pack and straightened up to wipe the sweat from my face, stretching my back. The thud of the tackle hitting the ground and the bang of the canoe against the tree must have sounded to a charged-up bull like another bull moose making a scrape. (Bulls will rub or scrape their antlers against trees to either polish them or mark their territory). A mature bull, who had been feeding down in the creek bottom that the portage trail followed, charged us plowing through the tangle of growth with the stealth of a tank.

We heard him before we saw him. Turning in that direction, we saw the tops of small trees and brush separating beyond the foliage immediately next to us. He emerged only fifteen feet away and we flung ourselves behind the birch tree. The bull came to a stop on the other side of the tree and stood there breathing hard, trying to figure out who we were. He'd take a step one way and we'd shift the other. He'd step back, and we'd move again, like some sort of cartoon skirmish.

To my disbelief, Ken said, "Get the camera. It'll make a great shot for Olivia's kids." His daughter, Olivia, is a fifth-grade schoolteacher. Our camera was in the pack right at the moose's feet.

To this request, I made some rather heated personal remarks.

I gathered my shattered wits and said to the moose in as steady a voice as I could muster, "I'm just a person, Mr. Moose. I'm not another moose, only another tourist. Don't be angry, we're just passing through." I thought, since they barely see, maybe if he heard me, he'd realize we were no threat.

Slowly, the fire in his eyes—and I'm sure I saw this—faded from his pupils. He shook his antlers and walked away as if annoyed.

The wolves set the tone for the wildlife on Isle Royale. They are the only large predator and if you took them off the island it certainly wouldn't turn into a petting zoo, but something vital would surely be missing. The moose, fox, beaver, rabbit, fox squirrels and anything else that can't fly are all fair game. Wolves keep everybody on their toes.

However, during the summertime, the people keep the wolves at bay. While we're here, the wolves seek the less inhabited portions of the island. But when we leave in the fall, I can't help but imagine them slinking out of the trees into the campgrounds to take advantage of the scavengers that grew soft over the summer.

A lot of popular research has recently been done about wolf behavior. These studies and Farley Mowat's book *Never Cry Wolf* coupled with its movie adaptation, have erased most people's fear of being eaten by the so-called ravenous wolf packs.

Isle Royale is the location for one of the most famous wolf research projects. For the past thirty years, Dr. Rolf O. Peterson headed an examination of the wolves on the island, a study that has been going on for fifty years. It is the longest running study of any wild mammal, according to his book *A Broken Balance*. Each year, Dr. Peterson has diligently observed and documented wolf health, populations, behavior, and interactions with the moose.

I had the opportunity to hear him speak at a fund-raiser dinner in Grand Rapids, Michigan. While he answered questions after his presentation, I noticed he tends to turn conversation away from discussing his remarkable career and prefers to focus on the wolves. Later, some of his students—some of whom took forestry classes with him at Michigan Tech and later worked with me at the tree service—confirmed his unassuming approach to his work.

He told the following story at the banquet.

Dr. Peterson said that within their own families and packs, wolves are very affectionate and protective. They are also extremely territorial. When a lone wolf strays into another pack's territory, they drive it off, many times to its death. He said as many wolves die from fights as from the elements or disease.

Dr. Peterson and his team of researchers do most of their on-site research during the winter. The wolves are more easily spotted from the air once the leaves fall and the ground is covered with snow. During one of their surveillance flights, the pilot and he noticed several wolves chasing a single wolf along a shoreline. A fight ensued, and to escape, despite a wolf's dislike for the water, the lone wolf swam into the bay that hadn't iced over yet.

The pack, after pacing up and down the shore for close to an hour, finally moved on. They apparently were satisfied they had either killed the interloper or successfully driven him away. The pilot circled overhead until he had to leave to refuel. The lone wolf was last seen floundering in the lake.

On their return trip, they noticed the wolf had managed to make it back to shore. Through their binoculars, he could be seen lying in the snow, barely moving. They feared he wouldn't survive.

The scientists observe a strict policy of non-intervention to retain the undisturbed status of the wolves. This insures that the research can remain true to its goal of evaluating wolves in the wild. They didn't try to help him. When they came back the following day, the wolf was still lying there but now appeared to be dead. They planned on landing the seaplane in the bay the next day to do a postmortem examination.

Dr. Peterson said he then witnessed something he'd never seen before. When they returned to perform the autopsy, a second wolf had appeared, evidently also unattached to a pack. She (as they discovered later) began to nurse the injured wolf back to health. She would lie alongside him, nosing and licking him, nudging him to move. She did this for several consecutive days.

The scientists returned every day to monitor the situation. Dr. Peterson told his audience that they were very concerned the pack might return. If they did, and found her, the pack would likely kill both of them. At that time, the wolves on the island had been declining for several years. Too much inbreeding is a serious concern in a closed ecosystem like Isle Royale. The loss of one or two more wolves would hurt.

Fortunately, the pack didn't come back and the male began to show signs of recovery. They continued to monitor the couple until, on one return flight, both wolves were gone.

Eventually, they became a third pack and helped turn the tide of a shrinking wolf population. It had dropped from a high of fifty animals in 1980 to an all-time low of sixteen in 1995. The wild-life researchers had been debating whether or not to break their long-standing policy and intervene to prevent the wolves from dying out completely. The debate is over for now. As of 2005, there are over thirty wolves in three, well-established packs.

I have been frustrated at least three times—that I know of— to miss seeing a wolf. Ken, on the other hand, has seen them twice while we were hiking together. Each time, they fled before I could react fast enough to see them. One of those times, Ken was even behind me on the trail as we were backpacking to Chippewa Harbor.

He whispered, loud enough for me to hear, "Vic, a wolf!" In the split second it took to lift my head from watching the ground at my feet, he was gone. He had been standing in the middle of the trail, only fifty feet away, straight ahead of us. The fresh tracks on the path proved he really had been there—something I doubted at first.

In the second encounter, Ken was ahead of me on the trail and suddenly froze. Without turning, he asked me to throw him our camera. I tossed it up the slope we were climbing. He caught the camera, swung around, and snapped a quick picture. Too late, the wolf was already gone. I ran up the trail to see if I could at least catch a glimpse. All I caught was the sound of a large animal running away through the trees.

My closest encounter was while sleeping. I was doing a solo trip and staying alone at Chippewa Harbor. No other hiking parties had come through for the past three days. I spent most of the daylight hours on the lake fishing, which left the campground deserted.

When I'd first hiked into Chippewa Harbor from Lake Richie—on the same trail where Ken saw a wolf eighteen years earlier—I saw some scat piles. I also heard wolves baying one night, a much quieter, low-key sound than the heart-rending howls I've heard in movies.

One wolf pack frequents the backcountry around Chippewa Harbor, and two days prior to my bedtime encounter, I felt like someone was watching me during a short day hike. I rarely feel uncomfortable in the wild, but my skin prickled for no apparent reason when I came down a path off the main hiking trail that leads to Mason Lake. It was a weird enough feeling that I turned around and retreated the way I'd come.

Other campers have related similar experiences just prior to seeing wolves. They report a certain electricity in the air. I believe some dormant sense in the human species comes alive when wolves and humans get within close proximity of each other.

I was out of fish and down to a couple of packets of freeze-dried meals. I'd been on the lake fishing all day. Fishing was slow and I only caught a small Lake Trout. I cleaned him at shore using the blade of a canoe paddle as a cutting board. But the wind kicked up after I came in, making it too rough to take the guts back out and dump them in the lake, so I carried the mess into the woods and tossed it in some brush. I washed off the paddle and leaned it against the shelter.

In the middle of the night, I woke unexpectedly from the sound of my canoe paddle rattling against the shelter's screen where I'd leaned it. I could hear a snuffling and panting noise just outside. My startled movement in my sleeping bag probably spooked the wolf, because the paddle fell to the ground with a loud bang. I then heard a sound like dog nails scampering away on rock. I looked for tracks in the morning, but didn't find any. The paddle lay on the ground.

I think the wolf must have smelled the fish remains I tossed away, ate them, and then caught the scent of fish that remained on the paddle. I hadn't seen any fox at Chippewa Harbor, nor did the scampering noise sound like the much lighter fox. Nothing else on the island could make the sound of a dog's nails on rock. I'll never know for sure, but I'm convinced I'd had a wolf two feet from me where I lay sleeping—only the shelter's screen wall between us.

Just before the park closed for the winter, on the last scheduled boat trip to the mainland for the *Isle Royale Queen*, I talked to a park ranger, who was also leaving the island, about my night visitor. He gave me a curious look. He then related a similar event he'd experienced. Hiking along the Greenstone Ridge, he got caught out on the trail after dark, his hike taking longer than expected.

He was still an hour from camp, all alone. The moon was full that night and the trail well lit. Walking at a brisk pace, he heard and then saw a single wolf lope by, glancing at him as it went past. A few minutes later, it came back, slowing, taking a longer look. A bit later, it came back a third time and walked past him again.

He happened to run into Dr. Peterson later that summer and mentioned the wolf's strange interest in him. Rolf, as he is more often called by those who know him, said it was likely their inquisitive nature overtook the wolf's normal caution. The ranger then said, as an after-thought, that this occurred at night. Rolf stopped short. He looked hard at the ranger and said, "Oh, that's completely different. At night, you're on their turf. If you read any history on the frontier days, there are several believable accounts of wolves becoming aggressive after dark."

"Aggressive?" I said to the ranger. "That's a gentle way to say it."

# THE LITTLE STUFF

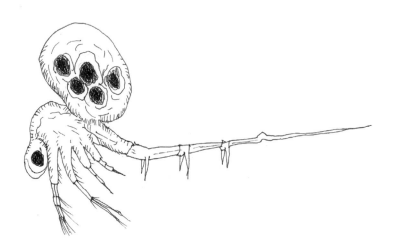

EVERYTHING MOVES A LITTLE SLOWER AT FIRST LIGHT. INSECTS ARE SLUGGISH, birds are less energetic, the winds are generally calmer, and life on the island wakes slowly. I move slower, too. It's a good time to study the little things. I might pick up a stone and examine it. I look more closely at a plant I hadn't noticed before. I focus intently on an individual sound and try to locate and identify it. There's a certain kind of joy in having time to slow down and indulge one's curiosity. Mornings on Isle Royale often lend themselves to that kind of satisfaction.

The shelters on Isle Royale, where my mornings begin, look like screened-in lean-tos. They have a ten-by-sixteen-foot wooden floor with three wooden walls. A roof slants at a steep angle toward the back. It falls so far that the rear wall is only four feet tall, and if a camper isn't careful, they can bang a head on the low ceiling. The front or fourth wall stands eight feet tall and is screened from top to bottom. A screen door opens onto a small campsite. A picnic table stands just outside, and the campsite may have a fire pit or grate, depending on whether the park service allows open wood fires in that particular campground.

At Isle Royale the shelters are home away from home.

My father-in-law worked on a trail crew on Isle Royale in the 1960s and his son, Brian, worked there for several years in the 1980s. Brian's dad helped build several of these shelters and they're kept in constant repair. The shelters are important for a more comfortable stay. Tents are all right, but the shelters are definitely a step up—literally two feet off the ground. Given the amount of rainfall and insects the island sees, they are as close to a cabin in the woods as you can find.

On mornings when I don't go fishing, I sit outside at the picnic table and read or write, and take time to just enjoy the view. I often pause while drinking my first cup of coffee to look for weather changes. In the dawn's quiet, I listen for wildlife or go for a short walk to see if there are any differences around camp from the night before. Are there any new moose rubs?

Camping for weeks at a time forces me to take very good care of my equipment. This is because if my fishing reel breaks down, I don't eat. If the flashlight batteries die, I can't see. If the camp stove doesn't work, if I lose my glasses, or break a paddle, if the canoe springs a leak, or if a great number of little things go wrong, I'm in big trouble. I spend a considerable amount of time paying attention to the details. The little stuff matters.

Several friends, when they found out I was planning to take a month-long trip to the island when I turned fifty, presumed I was taking a mini-sabbatical to do a mid-life checkup. My more spiritual friends asked if I was reassessing my relationship with God. My real reason was merely to go away. Although doing a mid-life checkup is a worthy purpose, and perhaps one I ought to do, thinking about my first fifty years on this planet wasn't what motivated me to spend a whole month on the island. I just wanted to finally have some time to look around, to actually have no agenda at all, and if lucky—and I didn't consider this essential—I also hoped to record some observations in a place where I could think more clearly.

These rather simple goals had the benefit of enabling me to feel free to examine the little stuff and give some attention to what lay at my feet each morning. After all, when I stand outside my camp at daybreak and look at a strange stone, or a new leaf, or a bird in the trees, what exactly am I looking at? I wasn't really looking for answers to the big questions; it was the little ones I hoped to resolve.

I love coming here, but if you forget even one little thing it takes to live on Isle Royale, the island has a nasty way to remind me to take care of business. With so many details to cover for a safe and comfortable stay, it's easy to forget something or in a moment of weakness decide to take an ill-advised shortcut. As a warning, every year this place extracts a piece of me in retaliation for some slip-up. One year, it wanted a big chunk.

Lake Superior is noted for being clear and cold. For several years, Ken and I would walk down to the shore, dip our jugs into the lake, and drink. We boiled the water, but only if making coffee. More often we would add kool-aid to give it flavor. Either way, the water always tastes great. But as I look down into the lake, before throwing the hose from my water purifier into a deep pool that looks so clean you want to touch it to see if its really there, I see them. When the angle of the light is just right, the *Bythotrephes* become visible. They're a Great Lakes bane. They were almost mine, too.

Any word that sounds like "bite" should be some sort of dreadful nemesis. *Bythotrephes* are a type of fresh water crustacean. They don't belong here. They're native to Northern Europe and the Black Sea. They are a recent newcomer to the Great Lakes and for such a miniature life form, they've created a mess of the aquatic food chain here. Introduced via the water from ballast tanks on international freighters, the spiny water flea, as they're more commonly called, have infiltrated all five of the Great Lakes. Normally Lake Superior feels the effects of these exotic pests the least. Its colder, deeper, more distant waters thwart these foreign invasions. Unfortunately, the spiny water fleas have thrived here and the shoals and reefs around Isle Royale have proved to be an ideal habitat. Some of the more protected shallows teem with them. They are distantly related to shrimp, lobster, and crayfish. But they are planktonic, meaning they must drift with the currents in order to relocate. They are also very prolific. A new wave of offspring emerges every two weeks. Their population is composed mostly of females. These females produce eggs without sexual reproduction. The eggs in the mother's brood pouch develop into more female offspring, which carry the next generation. This cycle of asexual reproduction requires no fertilization as long as water temperatures are neither too warm nor too cold and where food sources are abundant. Only during times of stress, such as low water temperatures, will normal reproduction require both males and females. Their eggs develop a thick coating, which allows the eggs to withstand extreme conditions such as the winters of Lake Superior. Adults die following reproduction.

The problem with the spiny water flea is they have a long spiked tail. I use the word long in micro-terms. They are no longer than a half inch from nose to tail. Ordinarily, baitfish like minnows, herring, perch, and smelt or young trout would feast upon these shrimp-like delicacies. But the spines on the tail prevent small baitfish from swallowing them. In fish tanks, biologists have watched minnows spit out one spiny water flea after another trying to eat them. Bait fish soon learn to avoid them altogether. With no major natural enemies, populations have exploded across the lakes.

I've see ducks dip their bills into the lake and swim through the water, feeding on the little fleas like sperm whales eat krill. Unfortunately, the ducks can't eat near enough to keep them in check. Marine biologists fear the spiny water flea will supplant the native crustaceans that the baitfish depends upon for food. As a result, baitfish populations might crash. This, of course, would have a devastating effect upon the game fish.

Two weeks after Ken and I returned home from one of our annual week-long September trips, I started to wake in the middle of the night unable to breathe. It wasn't that I was breathing hard or wheezing but that I-could-not-breathe-at-all! Awakened from my choking, I'd jump from bed. As I tried to inhale, the air would enter my stomach. The air passageways to my lungs were stopped. Instead of my diaphragm pumping air into my lungs, it directed air into my stomach. I could actually see my belly expand with each desperate gasp. My stomach looked exactly like a balloon filling with air with each puff.

I found the only remedy was to force myself to calm down and try to breathe very, very slowly. This apparently eased the strain on my airways enough for them to relax and revert to their normal function. When they did, air hissed from my stomach like from a relief valve. After an episode, I'd sit on the edge of the bed for a long while—gingerly breathing—hoping the crisis was over.

My wife awakened to find her husband fighting for his life, but could do nothing but watch as I did this desperate internal battle. It sounded terrible. I'd gasp loudly in my first attempts to suck in air. She'd watch me trying to calm myself, trying desperately to keep from gulping wind, stooped beside the bed attempting to slow my gasps.

"Are you all right?" she'd ask.

I was too scared to respond and didn't dare risk air for speaking.

"What's happening?" she'd plead.

Only after I was breathing normal again did I feel like I could risk explaining.

These midnight episodes occurred three times over the span of a week. There were no other symptoms, and other than these late-night bouts, I felt fine.

I rarely see doctors. I rarely need to. Now I begged to see my personal physician. I had to plead to get in because the appointment nurse said she couldn't schedule me right away.

"It'll be eight weeks before I can get you in," she said at first. "He has no openings before then."

After several attempts to convince her I really needed to see a doctor, I finally said with a voice that must have sounded desperate. "Check my records. How often have I seen the doctor in the past twenty years?"

I heard her keyboard click in the background. "It has been quite a while." The nurse responded. "Hit on the head with a falling limb, I see. That was four years ago. Hit on the head again nine years ago."

"Can it get more pressing than being unable to breathe?" I yelled into the phone.

She hesitated as if thinking this over and finally said, "How would tomorrow at ten be?"

My doctor is about my age, and I really like him. He has a good sense of humor and relates well with patients. He's allowed me some liberty when it comes to some of my riskier activities— nothing illegal, just climbing trees, playing hockey, that sort of thing. He encouraged the exercise.

I told him about my breathing problem.

He said after a short examination. "Mr. Foerster, you have asthma."

"What? I haven't had an asthma attack since I was a kid. I don't wheeze. How can it be asthma?"

He said, "People don't always wheeze after they become adults. Their air passageways are larger than little kids."

"Really? Well, now what?"

He scratched his chin a little. "You're in reasonably good shape for your age. I suggest you don't sleep on your back since it can constrict your airways and I'll give you some asthma medicine. You should be all right."

"Also, one other thing," he hesitated and then said, "You evidently picked up something that triggered these spasms. Considering you haven't had an attack in so long, it's likely you got into something you don't normally see at home. Do you filter your water when you go to Isle Royale?"

"No, it's Lake Superior. I've never needed to before."

"I've also been to Isle Royale, a beautiful place, love to get back there one day. If I remember correctly, I'm quite certain they warn you at the orientation about purifying the water."

"Yeah, they do," I hated to admit.

"See me if things don't improve quickly," he said with a look that implied you should know better.

I couldn't leave without asking, "How dangerous was this?"

"Pretty bad, you had a reaction to something you ingested. People have died from this sort of thing. In a few cases, stomachs burst."

Once again, the little things proved big. Taking a short cut on drinking water almost cost me dearly. I always thought if this place was going to get me, it would be something more exciting than a bug in the water, something like swamping in stormy seas or gored by a moose. Dying from an asthma attack doesn't sound very sexy.

I threw the water filter hose into the lake and started to pump. Cold, clear and now clean water slowly trickled into my water jug.

Yes, the little stuff matters.

At the start of a new day, with the cosmos obscured from view, I glanced around me as I pumped the water purifier. An interesting stone I hadn't noticed before glistened in the lake. Reaching down, I picked it up.

"I wonder what this is made of?"

# PANCAKES

IT WAS SIMPLY GORGEOUS. IT WAS THE MOST BEAUTIFUL PANCAKE I'D EVER seen. Early morning is my favorite part of the day, and breakfast has always been my favorite meal. This crowning culinary achievement only added to my joy.

We'd been trying to perfect our pancake cooking over the course of two previous trips to Isle Royale and our frustration level had reached a tipping point. After turning the batter into many a pile of crumbs and goo in the frying pan, and then attempting to eat the buttered, syrupy glob of partially cooked cake, it had finally occurred to us to relinquish our old-fashioned iron skillet and use a pan with a non-stick surface. The results turned out to be nothing less than stunning.

I'm sure this would have dawned on any ordinary cook long before we thought of it. However, when it came to our Isle Royale trips, we had been stubborn about avoiding the newer light-weight camping equipment available. We were bent on keeping a more traditional camp to see what it was like to be *voyageurs*. The voyageurs were noted for blending in with the natives, for their endurance and strength, and for portaging two hundred pound packs loaded with furs and trade goods. They crisscrossed the old Northwest, working the fringes of the Great Lakes, then making thousand mile journeys from the frontier to Montreal and back.

We carried a large frontier-ware coffeepot, ate venison jerky, used lead fishing weights, and insisted on eating bacon every morning. Portaging all of these supplies on our backs up and down the steep hills was supposed to make our fish camp feel authentic.

The extra work did create a few benefits. We ate steak and lake trout for dinner instead of macaroni and cheese or that other backpacker staple, trail-mix, which in my opinion closely resembles mixed birdseed. We looked forward to breakfasts and shore lunches and stopped for happy hour, a daily routine. Canoeing enabled us to carry more clothes and supplies than backpacking or kayaking. Lugging the heavy, more stable aluminum canoe, all of our fishing gear, food and all our supplies atop our shoulders was a strain. But once our base camp was set up, we slept and ate better than we sometimes did at home.

Be-that-as-it-may, after suffering through several ruined breakfasts, we had decided we could make an exception in our frying pan. The change in pans made all the difference.

As the new day warmed, the Belle Isle campground radiated a freshness that hinted of a great day to come. As we prepared breakfast, the morning sunshine streamed into our shelter. The new light flowed through the air as if you could reach out and feel the sunlight run through your fingers. The woods surrounding camp smelled of cedar and pine. The trees vibrated in the breeze. Lake Superior, which lay just a few feet away, pulsed with life and opportunity.

Ken gazed into his new frying pan and beamed at his achievement. His face shone as bright as the daylight that flowed around us. In the center of all of this streaming sunlight, as if under a heavenly spotlight, lay our humble pancake. He held the pan in amazement. The pancake was golden in the center with the edges browned and crisped just right. Steam rose from the pan, carrying an aroma of every comfort food I'd known. The rising cake really did look like it would melt in your mouth, if you could bring yourself to eat such beauty.

We both stared. When you come face-to-face with a newly created work of art, realizing you are witnessing firsthand the birth of a great masterpiece, the world stops revolving for a moment.

Slowly, it occurred to us that we now had the ability to create any number of these delicious marvels. Our growling stomachs brought us back to reality. The world began to revolve again, and with a startling suddenness, Ken slapped the pancake onto a plate. I poured some syrup over it, and we forked up a mouthful of hot, hunger-satisfying, delicious, make-your-eyes-close-to-only-sense the wonderful taste of early morning pancakes.

They did melt in our mouths. I could feel the heat flow through me as I swallowed. When we finished eating our first forkful, we opened our eyes at the same instant, stared wide-eyed at each other across the table and shouted in unison, "Let's make some more!"

And so we did. Pancake after pancake rolled from the pan to our plate to our stomachs. Every time we flipped a new one over, we would ooh and aah at the magical goodness of our newly found golden creations. Every mouthful was a celebration.

Over the past three decades, we have been back to the island many times and eaten many a breakfast. Each time we mix up a batch of pancake batter, it reminds me of that first time we created the perfect pancake. The simple pleasure is as warm and as real as that early morning when the sunlight poured over us.

Every once in a great while, during an ensuing trip, Ken will flip a pancake over in the pan and a smile will creep over his face. He'll look up, see my face reflecting his own expression, and know exactly what I am thinking. An understanding that comes from sharing adventures over many years passes between us. And, with that same suddenness, he will slap a pancake onto my plate and say,

"Need any butter?"

# FROM THE WATER

THERE IS A WHOLE WORLD ON ISLE ROYALE THAT BACKPACKERS RARELY GET TO see. The park is a fresh water archipelago. Hundreds of smaller islands surround the main island. They range in size from mere outcrops of rock to habitable islands several square miles in size. This is especially true at either end of the main island, where long coves and bays cut as deep as fifteen miles into Isle Royale proper.

Seeing the island from the water didn't occur to Ken and me until our second trip. We saw a couple pass by us in a canoe. They were carrying fishing poles. We were slogging along a well-used footpath with sixty-pound packs; hot, sweaty, and sore-footed. They waved at us as they glided by with a canoe full of gear and provisions we could never have carried in backpacks. We had our next trip all planned before we reached camp.

As much as I enjoy the woods, my view is restricted when I stand under the trees. Breaking free from the forest allowed me to see the sky and see, without obstruction, a horizon that stretches to the lake's rim. It also opened up an environment that consists of miles and miles of shoreline.

Paddling Lake Superior in a canoe gives us, by necessity, a very cautious attitude. We rarely venture far from shore. Winds can change direction suddenly and Ken and I have experienced firsthand the fear of paddling for all we're worth into a head wind and being pushed backwards. If an offshore wind becomes stronger than we can paddle against, it's only a matter of time before we're swept out into the lake.

Since we tend to hug the shoreline, we get to see a host of waterfowl, raptors, beavers, otters, muskrats, and songbirds. Wildlife is drawn to the water, and from our canoe, we have ringside seats to one of the finest wildlife refuges in the world.

WAACK! A stunned songbird fell from the sky. The falcon quickly circled around, snatched it off the water, and flew back into the trees at Belle Isle.

We were fishing along the north side of Johnson Island. I was focused on my rod tip, waiting for a strike of my own. My pole was set in a rod holder mounted to the deck at the prow of the canoe. Out of the corner of my left eye, I caught a flash of movement and had just enough time to turn and see the falcon streak by. A songbird had been trying to cross the bay. The collision was so close I could hear the smack when the falcon struck the wren. The little bird was dead on impact. It spiraled softly down. When it landed on the lake, it was so light it made no ripple.

Countless small birds inhabit Isle Royale and I have to believe the falcon rarely goes hungry for long. We'd seen this one earlier in the week sitting in a tree down in Robinson Bay. It will wait until some bird tries to take a shortcut over a cove or inland lake exposing themselves outside the protection of the trees. The falcons are so fast the slower songbirds don't stand a chance.

When he struck, he was no more than twenty feet away from us. The same event occurred one other time. Ken saw the falcon coming across the lake, and spoke out from the back of the canoe. When I spun around, he was no more than ten feet from my face.

Either my startled jump or Ken's shout saved that sparrow. The falcon pulled up short and the sparrow escaped.

Falcons are the only birds of prey I've seen hunt crows. We were fishing out by Cork Island one day when several crows began to raise a loud protest on the north side of Belle Isle Pointe. We were about a quarter of a mile from them. All we could see from that distance were black dots against the bright sky swarming in erratic patterns, diving, circling, and changing altitudes sharply. Their outcry carried over the water and seemed loud in a place where such noise draws unwanted attention from predators and scavengers.

We canoed closer, and as we approached them, one dot swelled into a faster bird, the falcon. He was diving on an entire mob of crows. The scene was like a World War I dogfight. Some of the crows were in flight and others roosting in the trees. Picking out one crow, the falcon dove, but the crow flipped upside down in the air to protect itself with its talons. It happened a few more times as we watched the falcon dart in after other crows. The strategy must work. We never saw any crows go down.

The falcon wheeled and swooped at will. A few crows would try to chase him, but it was a futile effort. None of them came close. He definitely had brass, because crows and ravens travel in groups and if you take one on, you take them all on. I can't imagine the falcon, even if he had managed to kill one, being left in peace to feed.

Maybe they were just playing some aerial game of tag. I've never seen any other event like it. Normally, crows and ravens harass owls, hawks, or other birds of prey—not the other way around.

As an arborist, I'm always looking up at trees and as a result I'm looking up at the sky. I often see birds of prey. Call it a "job-perk." It's amazing the number of hawks, owls, osprey, eagles, falcons, gulls, ravens, and crows that patrol the skies. Some people doubt me when I tell them I see eagles all the time. But I do. And when on Isle Royale, I see them almost every day. Eagles have a certain presence that demands attention. They never cease to make me stop whatever I'm doing when I spot one. When I see an eagle sitting atop an old snag on Isle Royale, peering with his binocular-like vision over a bay, it reminds me of one "eagle event" I witnessed back home.

I was called to examine a tree in the winter for a client who owns a home on Spring Lake in southern Michigan. The tree in question is in their front yard, which for people who live on the water means the lakeside of the property and not the streetside. This caused me some problems when I first started working until a client who was home and watching me circle their house in search of their tree finally enlightened me. This day, however, no one was around, which is often the case in the winter. I got out of my truck, walked around the corner of the house, and looked down at the lake. In the small space of open water created by a bubbler was a swan. Bubblers are pumps set in a lake to pump air and water, which prevents ice from forming. They're used to keep ice clear of docks and shore stations. The swan was swimming in tight, nervous circles in the opening.

I thought it was peculiar behavior. Despite their stately manner, swans are often pests for homeowners. They chase off ducks, geese, and even people if you get too close. They rule over the lakes they inhabit, so it was unusual for a swan to look so scared. I was sure I wasn't bothering him. When I looked up to find my tree, I found the reason for the swan's fear. Perched on a dead limb in the oak was a large bald eagle. He was obviously eyeing the swan. I backed up and hid around the side of the house, just enough to peek around the corner and watch.

They weren't fooled and I needed to keep moving. Another appointment time was catching up to me, so I stepped out and the eagle flew off at my approach. He cruised down the shoreline and disappeared around a point.

The oak was in need of some pruning. The dead limbs posed a threat to anyone using the yard below, which is what triggered the call from our client. I recommended some pruning, but didn't see anything warranting removing the eagle's tree, although he might miss his limb. I finished my inspection and glanced over at the swan who was beginning to settle down. I wondered aloud to him, "Do you think an eagle would dare take on a swan?" He didn't reply. They never do. He turned away and reverted to his normal snobbish demeanor.

My next stop was across the lake. I struck up a conversation with the homeowner who lived there year-round. We discussed her trees and during our conversation, I mentioned the eagle and swan to her.

She looked a little troubled and said, "Maybe that explains what happened to the other swan. There used to be two. I haven't seen the mate for several days."

A much more "Isle Royale eagle experience" occurred when I was starting a six-mile solo canoe trip from Chippewa Harbor to West Caribou Island. This was the same vacation when a wolf paid me a visit in the middle of the night. Owls sang to one another that evening. The owl's deep-throated calls reverberated on the cliff walls across Chippewa Lake as I fell asleep.

The next morning was cold. Damp air flowed through the channel from Lake Superior. The naturally formed channel creates a navigable waterway that leads into Chippewa Harbor from Lake Superior. The channel is divided in the middle by a large rock that protrudes out of the water. On the autumn equinox—the same day I was leaving Chippewa Harbor—the sun rises directly behind this sentinel rock. The rock could be used as a calendar, and I don't doubt it was used as such by the Ojibwa who camped here for centuries.

I was canoeing out the channel at dawn, the rock silhouetted against the sun, and could swear I saw the silhouette of an eagle perched on the cliffs alongside the channel. The fiery ball of the sun was so bright I could only take quick glimpses, the sun leaving black spots swimming in my eyes when I looked away. I thought it a trick of the eye, but the silhouette of the bird remained framed against the cliff, and in spite of the glare, I kept taking quick peeks.

As I paddled out the channel and the angle of light changed, the black silhouette slowly filled in. When I drew abreast of it, the bleary shape turned into the body of a bald eagle. He was sitting atop a small pinnacle of rock that stood out from the face of the cliff. When I came alongside of him, the sunlight had shifted from behind the eagle and beamed directly on him. His colors flamed in the intense light. His crown grew brilliant white, contrasting sharply against the flushed red rocks.

Then the head moved. He turned one way and then another, regally gazing up and down the shoreline.

The sun had fully crested Lake Superior, giving its full attention to the eagle. Every individual feather stood out. The gentle breeze ruffled their textured edges. I canoed past—no more than twenty feet away from him—not changing my pace. The eagle never flinched.

I paddled through the fresh water chasm with the new day gaining strength. The light stretched my horizon to the lake's edges, and Lake Superior spread before me like an invitation. I turned left and started the next leg of my journey. It wasn't until then that I stopped paddling, pausing to look back at the eagle from a more respectful distance. Floating offshore, rocking on the gentle rollers, I too scanned up and down the coast as Isle Royale warmed in the growing light. I lifted my paddle over my head, thanked him, and left Chippewa Harbor.

Ken was shaking his head as he walked back from the outhouse. He wound in and out of the trees as he followed the path back to camp. I could see him approaching from where I sat at the picnic table. He looked disgusted, mumbling to himself.

"What?" I said when he walked up.

He didn't respond.

"WHAT?" I said louder.

"Loons."

"Loons?"

"Yes, loons."

"Oh …" I knew what was bugging Ken.

Inside the outhouse door is a warning notice posted there by the park rangers. On the notice is a big picture of a loon and instructions on how to avoid annoying them. The warning is strategically placed so that campers can't help but read it while they "contemplate the eternal verities" as one of my uncles used to call it. I'll give Ken credit for this one. The inside of a latrine is a strange place to teach campers loon etiquette.

The intrusion on "his space" irritates Ken. In retaliation he often goes out of his way to mock the loons, and over the years, he's acquired a number of different ways to accomplish this. If we were at Belle Isle and he heard a loon singing on the bay, he would go down to the beach and he and the loons would sing to one another. He has a loon call that at best sounds sick, but for some reason the loons respond. When Ken communicates with them, he looks like he is pretending to play a harmonica. He cups his hands over his mouth, vibrates one hand over top of the other, and does a yodel-like whistle between his pressed-together thumbs, using them like a mouthpiece. I'm not sure who is acting more looney during these choruses.

However, it is when we are fishing that he gets serious about mocking National Park loon policy. If he spies a loon sitting on the lake ahead of us, he sarcastically asks me if we should turn around to avoid disturbing its privacy.

"Leave the loon alone," I'd say.

"Why? Why should I have to change my trolling pattern for a goofy loon?"

"Because." I knew he knew why and didn't want to get him started. But, having already baited me, he'd push it.

"They'll move or they'll get run over."

"By a canoe?"

Ken would then mockingly thrash after the loon, pretending to pester them, sending our fishing rods into convulsions. I have little control over the canoe from the front seat, unless I want to turn around and paddle backwards against him, which is even more ludicrous than our argument. Besides, the loons were hardly in any mortal danger nor did they even appear to notice us, not changing their trolling pattern either.

"You're twisting our lines up," I'd complain. His fishing is the only thing that will take precedence over teasing me. He'd ease off, and we'd reel in to untangle our lures.

Ken knows I like loons. Two birds symbolize the North Country—Canada Geese and the Common Loon. Both birds have a call that reverberates across the quiet coves and inland lakes on Isle Royale. When I hear either of their songs, pictures of uninhabited shores immediately spring to mind. Knowing this about me, Ken takes great enjoyment in mocking the loons. We do constant verbal battle about it. After a few days together—day and night—conversational topics can sometimes come hard. We both take these arguments with a great deal of salt. I don't ever recall us actually becoming angry over National Park Loon Policy. These pseudo-squabbles allow us to vent. It's easy to get on each other's nerves when spending all day together in a canoe and all night in a ten-by-sixteen shelter. I can't help but wonder if our discourse on the lake sounds as odd to the loons as their warbling does to us.

In one regard Ken has great respect for loons. They're great anglers. Considering they primarily subsist on fish and have to outswim them to eat, they are an impressive bird. Anything that can catch fish on a regular basis is one-up on us.

Almost every night and during quiet evenings at dusk, the loons on Robinson Bay will commence to sing. Robinson Bay, on the north shore of Isle Royale, is five miles long and a mile wide. Inside its arms are several small islands. The loons' half warble, half-yelp can be heard echoing across its waters, rebounding within the bay's wooded shores. It is as if they're saying good night to one another. At such times, they make me think they are lamenting a wilderness lost a long time ago. It can be a particularly eerie sound at the end of the day.

Back home, seeing or hearing a loon is a rare occurrence. They are shy of humans and flee highly populated areas. The park's stance on keeping one hundred yards from them is good science, since, on average, there are forty-four nesting pairs scattered across the island. The Common Loon Monitoring Program was completed in 1998 at Isle Royale National Park. Part of its mission was to maintain continuous data on the size and productivity of the island's loon population. During this study, they discovered that overly stressed loons will desert their eggs or young. Thus, the warning notices posted in the outhouses at lakeside campgrounds.

Loon anatomy is uniquely fitted for their lifestyle. Their large webbed feet are placed farther back toward their tail than on other waterfowl. This gives them extra propulsion under water. It also makes them look awkward and unbalanced on land. They rarely leave the water. Only when nesting do loons come ashore. When they do, I expect them to fall on their faces at any moment.

A loon's bones are not hollow, and adults can weigh as much as fifteen pounds. The bone structure for most birds is very light, which improves their ability to fly. Loons, on the other hand, require a wingspan of up to five feet in order to lift off the water. The extra weight also allows them to dive to depths of eighty feet, and makes it easier for them to stay submerged. Ken and I have seen them dive and resurface hundreds of feet from where they disappeared. I'll be admiring their seamanship and get anxious at their failure to resurface after submerging for what seems like an incredible amount of time. I'll do a 360, swiveling my head to find them, having no clue where they might pop up.

Canada geese are different. They are not shy and are a nuisance for golf courses, parks, and lakeside cottages in southern Michigan, where they contemplate all over the place. However, on Isle Royale they are wary of people. During the daytime, I've watched them travel in their famous V formations so high in the sky that if I hadn't heard their barely perceptible honking, I'd have never known they were migrating overhead by the thousands.

Oddly enough, my favorite geese encounters are at night when they can't be seen but only heard. In September, on clear nights, when the wind is blowing hard from the north, Ken and I have witnessed them streaming across the moon and stars, departing for their winter homes. We can't actually see them. We only see the stars wink on and off as they pass between the stars and us. It's a strange experience. We'll stand in a clearing and look up at the night sky, sensing them more than seeing them as they catch a ride across Lake Superior on a cold north wind.

Geese are such social birds, seeing one alone on the lake or in the air causes me to ask what's wrong. Loons, however, neither gather in flocks nor migrate in large groups. Males and females have strong family attachments. The drakes assist with nesting and the feeding of young. In the spring, it's not unusual to see families swimming by in small coveys and sighting a family of loons on the water is the material of postcards. Chicks will ride piggyback on the backs of their parents.

Birds of prey and otters make raising chicks difficult. I've seen eagles chase geese in flight, though never catch one. I've also seen otters spot a loon swimming in the bay from hundreds of yards away. The otter appears to stand in the water, half his torso lifted above the surface, straining his neck to see clearly. He then submerges and reappears seventy yards closer. He rises again from the lake like a periscope to locate a bird and then submerges once more. He will travel like this across a half mile of water until he nabs his loon or more normally they flush and fly away. The otter doesn't hesitate in these chases, as though swimming across the whole width of the bay, back and forth, takes no great effort. Unable to fly and barely able to dive, young loons must be easy pickings.

If forced to pick a favorite, geese versus loons, I'd choose loons. I can relate to their preference for wild lonely northern lakes compared to hanging together in throngs.

What strikes me most deeply is the loon's call. I've read that it's tougher for people to lose their hearing than their sight. Either must be terrible. I tend to believe they're right about the loss of hearing. If I hear a loon, I can immediately picture him sitting on a glassy cove with the reflection of conifers shimmering on the water and I can smell the clean, evergreen scented air. But seeing a loon does not immediately bring to mind their remarkable song.

Their haunting wail cannot be adequately described in words. Their song pulls at something so deep, so true, that to just "hum the tune" is a mockery of their talent. Better to recommend hearing it live. And, lest I mislead anyone, no one appreciates their music more than Ken.

The fishing had been great. A stringer of lake trout hung off the side of the canoe so now it was strictly catch and release.

"Keep an eye out for the reef," Ken said from the back. The lures were running eight to twelve feet deep and we didn't want to get snagged.

"Yeah, I see it. We're okay. Just edge right a little."

Ken knew I wasn't paying attention to the rod or water depth. Stationed at the front of the canoe, as is my habit, my back is always turned to him. But even without seeing him, I could tell he was focused. A fish had made a hit on the last pass through this stretch of water, and he'd missed it. Trolling beside Dead Horse Rocks, just beyond the drop-off, we'd been circling the string of three, small, loosely connected islands, working the breaks.

"Ken, there's got to be a story behind a name like Dead Horse Rocks. Do you suppose some dead horse washed up here? They don't look like a dead horse."

Glancing back over my shoulder, I saw he was playing out more line.

"Who knows?"

The sun had just set, the sunlight remaining on the tree-tops. The lake was calm, and it was one of those all too rare evenings when the wind dies to just a whisper. We paddled west into a glowing sky reflected on the water. Ducks, geese and gulls had been winging in the past half hour and landing just beyond the rocks. They were settling in for the evening, taking their night residence behind the last set of boulders.

When winds die and the big lake goes flat, it becomes a highway for canoes. At such times, we could paddle all the way to Canada or Duluth or even paddle out the St. Lawrence Seaway if the lake would sit still long enough. With water as our roadway, the world seems to lie at our feet on calm days.

Where Dead Horse Rocks melt into the lake, the chain of three small islands descends into the lake and forms a reef that runs all the way to Belle Isle Pointe—a distance of one mile. We come here when the wind allows. It is a good spot and we've caught some nice fish here. The downside is it's outside of Robinson Bay and partially exposed to the lake. Only Captain Kidd Island lay between us and big water.

"We're out late tonight," I said without turning around. "You'll never be up for a cribbage game by the time we get back, clean fish, and have dinner."

This wasn't true and we both knew it. We had a regular nighttime routine. We ate dinner, cleaned up, played cribbage, made popcorn, and read if we could still keep our eyes open. Ken didn't bother responding. The smooth lake, the evening's calm, and the resting birds left both of us on the quiet side.

Dead Horse Rocks weren't the only interesting names here. Amygdaloid Island, Crystal Cove, Captain Kidd Island, Belle Isle, Cork Island, Green and Dean Island, Lane Cove, Hill Point and farther out beyond the north shore, Net Island. The names rolled through my mind. We'd fished them all except for Net Island—too exposed for a canoe … maybe one day.

The scenery held my attention, and the fishing remained far from my thoughts. I mostly fish for food. We'd already caught dinner. It was floating in the lake beside me. Ken, on the other hand, fished.

"Vic, look, the eagle is flying off Captain Kidd Island," Ken said, breaking into my musing.

"Where? I don't see him."

"Just off the water, between Captain Kidd and us."

In the growing dusk, I looked harder and picked him up flying just a couple of feet off the surface. "That's strange," I said. "They don't normally skim across the lake like that."

The sunset, the peaceful bay, and the quiet evening spent on the water, seemed an idyllic setting for the bald eagle sweeping across our bow. I slowed my paddle stroke, watching him fly toward the near end of Dead Horse Rocks. His flight path would bring him as close as a hundred yards away. As he neared, I realized he was hunting the waterfowl roosting on the other side of the rocks. The eagle was flying low to use the rocks as a screen. I could see the ducks and gulls from my vantage point through a gap in the boulders.

When the eagle was ten feet from the rocks, he swooped up and over the boulders. He stretched his legs down, talons out, and fell upon the resting birds, which bolted in panicked flight.

"Vic!" Ken shouted, "your rod."

I swiveled around and saw my pole bent backwards as if it would break. "Oh my God."

I slammed the paddle into the canoe behind me and reached for the pole. "I can't get it out of the rod holder." The rod throbbed violently. The inset holder strained hard against its mounting bracket. I leaned into it and pulled it out. The fish almost jerked the rod out of my hands.

Ken reeled in to prevent entangling our lines. "Fight him," he said. "I'm gonna have to chase him. You should have seen that strike. This is a big one."

My reel whirled as line peeled off, despite the tight drag.

Ken set his rod away and picked up his paddle, following the fish to take some stress off the line.

"This can't be happening." I looked back over my shoulder. The eagle had missed his prey. The fish felt heavy. I'd gain a little line and then he'd pull more out—more than I'd taken in. I was losing. Like a tug of war, he was pulling us into deeper water, which in this case was good. If he went shallow, the line would cross a rock on the shelf and snap for sure.

"Hang in there. Don't horse him. That's as hard a strike as I've seen you get."

Lakers normally go deep and landing big ones is like trying to haul up an anchor on twelve-pound test line. The rod tip bowed right into the lake. The old Shimano reel and rod had never failed me, but this was more strain than I'd seen them take.

I glanced back one more time. The eagle was gone. "Can you believe it?" I said to Ken. "This fish hit exactly the same instant the eagle sprang on those ducks."

Ken worked to get me over the fish. "Vic, try to bring him around to the left side. Have you seen him?"

"No."

The fish had pulled us well out into the lake. Ken had chased him down and gotten directly over the top of him, but I couldn't reel in any line. We'd reached a deadlock.

"Quit reeling," Ken said. "You'll just twist your line. Reel down and pull up slowly."

"It's not working," I complained. My drag whirled for proof as I lifted. "Am I snagged?"

"No, just keep pressure on him."

I did, and there we sat. Twilight fell around us, the stars not quite visible. The sunlight had disappeared off the top of the far ridge. I tried reeling down and pulling up more slowly, trying to inch him up from the bottom of the lake. "He must really be hooked," I said cautiously, fearing the comment might jinx us.

I gained line, little by little. We both stared down into the lake trying to follow the line into the clear but darkening waters. Finally, a large green shadow moved far below us as my rod tip jerked into the lake. He'd spotted us too and was off and running.

My drag whined. My arms were getting tired. "Try again," Ken said. I had expected the run. Lake trout are like pike and walleye. You drag them to the boat in one long steady pull, without much fight, but once they see you, they go spastic. I slowly and carefully pulled him around and we got over the top of him once more. I tried to ease him up and he took off a second time, but not as far. "He's tiring," Ken said.

"Get ready, it won't be long." I said. He was coming up.

"Go easy, he's too big for our net. I'm gonna have to grab him." Ken was good at landing fish, with or without the net. He has an iron grip. I'd never seen a fish slip out of his hands. But this fish was huge.

"Wow. Look at him," I said. It was as big a lake trout as we'd seen on Isle Royale. They come bigger, much bigger, but we'd never caught one.

He looked tired. The tail swept slowly back and forth. I kept pulling up and reeling down until all I had was about twelve feet of line left. Very slowly, the fish rose to the surface. I swung him toward Ken. He laid there for a second, dove a couple of feet, splashing us, but he was spent. I pulled him up and around again. Ken lunged. He grasped him hard behind the gills, snatching his tail with his other hand, and hauled him over the side of the canoe.

"Perfect!" I cried.

"Quick, get your camera. I don't want to keep him out of the water long."

I fumbled for my camera in my life vest's chest pocket. My hands were shaking. "I hope he shows up. The light's pretty low."

I snapped two pictures, and Ken lowered the fish back into the water.

Ken was beaming. "What a beautiful fish. What a damn big beautiful fish. He should be all right."

Ken moved it gently back and forth in the lake to get water to flow through its gills. The big lake trout flashed its tail, Ken let go, and he was away. He swam into the depths and was gone.

I shouted in triumph, the sound echoing across the bay.

Ken looked up at me after watching the fish fade out of sight and shook his head. "I don't think you'd have ever known you had a strike if I hadn't yelled at you."

"I'm not sure either," I said. "Can you believe this? I wouldn't believe it if I hadn't witnessed it myself."

We both sat there in the canoe, silent for a long moment. Ken then leaned over and washed his hands in the lake. I put my camera away. We had drifted out into the lake a bit, but there was hardly any breeze. We picked up our paddles and started back toward camp.

The stars were coming out and the air was noticeably cooler. Belle Isle Harbor was a sheet of glass when we canoed in. The campground was dark. We were the only ones staying there and had been all week. The canoe crunched on the pebbled beach. I hopped out and pulled it further up so Ken could get out.

Standing on the beach, we both turned and looked back out at the lake. I had looked for the eagle on the way in, but it was too dark. He'd be back at his nest by now. The evening star shone bright in the eastern sky, resting just above the Greenstone Ridge.

"It's going to be a cold night," I said.

# TOP OF THE FOOD CHAIN

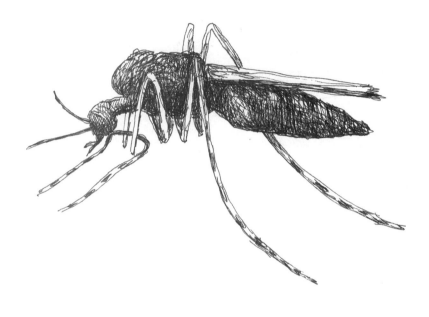

ONE OF THE FIRST THINGS A PERSON LEARNS AT ORIENTATION AS THEY ARRIVE AT Isle Royale National Park is "more people visit Yellowstone Park in a single day than visit Isle Royale all year." The island is promoted as one of the least visited Wilderness National Parks in the lower forty-eight states. From the nirvana-like descriptions used in books and on web pages that depict Isle Royale, a person could be led to ask why it doesn't see hordes of tourists. The low turnout should be a big draw for the I-want-to-get-away-from-it-all crowd.

Between the 4th of July and Labor Day weekend, peak season at Isle Royale, someone could easily question this boast about the solitude. They might doubt it, not because of the number of campers, which are indeed few, but because Isle Royale is as beautiful as the literature advertises. If this was the only time of year I visited Isle Royale, it could easily be confused with a Caribbean paradise. There may be no sandy beaches or T-shirt shops, but the park is dotted with sparsely populated islands clad in green hillsides, all surrounded by sparkling blue waters.

The weather is all I could ask for. Better than the Caribbean, days are longer, eighteen hours at a stretch from May through July. Nights are conveniently short. This allows for prolonged stretches of daylight for photographers, birders, researchers, and outdoor enthusiasts. Temperatures are also ideal. Highs are in the 70s and lows in the upper 50s, just right for rigorous activities like backpacking, canoeing, and kayaking.

However, I get suspicious when I find myself in a deserted paradise. I have a tendency to look over my shoulder to see if someone is sneaking up on me. *What's the catch?*

After spending a little time at Isle Royale, the reason for the limited park visitation became obvious. Besides the isolated setting and the sometimes long, rough boat ride across the lake to get there, Isle Royale has only two seasons. There is winter, which can last from November until early May. It's not uncommon for there to be ice floes in the bays and snow in shady pockets of land on the north sides of wooded ravines as late as June. I once had to skim off ice from the surface of a water bucket in September.

Then there is the bug season.

Ken had visited Isle Royale over Memorial Day weekend— once—and told me if we were going to the island, we would go at the end of summer when the bugs subside. When we showed up in early September, I couldn't help but notice the park staff had a dazed look about them. It was something in their eyes. They wore an expression of someone who's survived a terrible battle. When I arrived at the island and asked the rangers about how their summer was going, they hedged their replies with an unconvincing "Fine" or "August was busy but nice." It was obvious that much was left unsaid, and I wondered what I missed.

What I missed, of course, were the mosquitoes. *Culicidae* is a large family of two-winged dipteran insects. The females have a skin-piercing mouthpart used to extract blood from animals, including humans. The males extract only plant juices. The true monarchs of Isle Royale are not the alpha male and alpha female wolves. Neither is it the Park Superintendent and her husband. The Rulers of Isle Royale are, in reality, the hordes of brooding, hungry female mosquitoes.

Their presence is felt on every islet, every hilltop, and definitely in every lowland. They cause wolves to cringe, fleeing to the windy crests of ridges to escape. They make moose tremble. The moose run for the lakes, preferring to shiver in water that still holds ice than suffer the mosquitoes' presence. They drive humans inside thickly screened shelters and tents where campers curse their dictatorship, forced to hole-up and cower submissively.

Crowds do throng to Isle Royale, and they arrive in numbers that make the vacationers on a spring break at Fort Lauderdale pale in comparison. Only with gallons of arrogance do I imagine myself at the top of the food chain. Measured by quantity alone, one square mile of mosquitoes far outnumbers all of humankind on the planet. They mastered the art of biological warfare long ago. Malaria and yellow fever—just two of the diseases they can carry—have killed as many people as all wars combined.

If allowed, and even without using her biological arsenal, the female mosquito will extract enough blood to kill. Caribou, cattle, deer, and other ruminants are known to run over the edge of cliffs or stampede into rivers and lakes to drown, or stumble in a perpetual circle until they become so weary they are brought to their knees and eventual death. Death is preferred to the torment.

Working outdoors in the woods as an arborist, I've witnessed men who are as tough as they come, and for all appearances, immune to pain and toil. They flinch, however, when they hear the word "mosquito." Playing with their minds, I'll say in passing, "Hey, how were the bugs this spring?" They will pause for a split second in their hefting of a three-hundred pound log or in greasing their skidders. A tic in one eyelid trembles. Not able to speak of it, they fire-up a chain saw or rev their truck in order to drown out any further conversation.

I once asked my brother-in-law, who worked for seven years on Isle Royale on a trail crew, how he managed to work in the swamps to repair the boardwalks. "What do you do about the bugs?"

He replied, "It's a frame of mind."

"A frame of mind?" I asked.

He smiled at me and said. "Why don't you come for a visit in May."

I asked his dad the same question. He'd also worked there for two summers back in the 1960s. His answer wasn't much different.

"Cigars help." He said.

My own solution is to avoid them. I've never been to Isle Royale in May or June. Insect repellent slows them down, but that's mostly irrelevant when the difference is a hundred of them biting me versus a thousand. I'd spent enough time at work in the spring under trees sacrificing my blood. I wasn't going to donate more vital juices on vacation.

For those who have never experienced the whining drone of trillions of "skeeters" in the middle of the night while trying to sleep, I suggest recalling the most annoying commercial jingle you know and hum it all night long. The expression you will wear in the morning will look similar to the staff's on Isle Royale, as you disembark from the passenger ferry in the springtime. You and the other three visitors will look around wondering where everybody is, suspicious at the overly friendly rangers, and puzzled at the buzzing in your ears, you too may find yourself wondering why the staff looks at you with an expression that shouts, "misery loves company."

When you disembark, a park ranger will greet you with a warm smile and a twinkle in his or her eyes. "Welcome to Isle Royale, one of the least visited National Parks in the lower forty-eight states."

Did anyone mention the black flies?

# AN OFF SHORE WIND
## (A CAUTIONARY TRUE TALE)

RICK HESITATED, A SPLIT-SECOND'S INDECISION ALL THREE BOYS NOTICED. "I
… don't think so, Randy," Rick said. "It's getting late."

Randy's two older brothers, Steve and Teddy, who sat in the
back seat, quickly rallied to their brother's support. "Just a short
canoe ride, Dad. There's time."

"I don't know guys. It's too much work to take the canoe
down off the van again. Are you going to help me carry it to the
lake?"

"We'll help, we'll help," the three boys shouted.

"Come on, Dad," Randy begged.

Rick glanced at the lake. The sun was a couple of hours above
sunset. The water looked calm enough. Three young faces stared

at their dad. For full effect, the two older boys slid together in the middle of the backseat of their mini-van to be sure he'd see their pleading expressions in the rear view mirror.

Randy tugged at his pant leg. It was his turn to sit up front. "Come on, Dad. I don't want to go home yet."

Rick reached over and tousled Randy's hair. "Well, I suppose. It'll feel good to get some air, won't it?"

They were returning home from a day-long car tour of the Copper Country which lies at the northern tip of Michigan, the Keweenaw. A hundred years ago, the area had been extensively mined for copper. Rick was taking the scenic drive, the road that hugs the coast of Lake Superior between Copper Harbor and Eagle River. It's a jagged shoreline. The scenic drive makes several hair-pin turns to stay close to the water. In the summertime and during the fall color season its a big tourist destination.

They'd stopped at Fort Wilkins State Park in Copper Harbor and paddled around Lake Fanny Hooe, the small, scenic lake behind the fort. The boys had taken turns riding in the canoe with their dad, each boy getting a chance to paddle from the front seat. They'd also stopped in town for ice cream and bought T-shirts and some bracelets for Emily, their sister. Rick had even sprung for a small greenstone for her collection.

He pulled into the small parking lot at the beach in Eagle River. Everyone piled out of the van and he untied the straps holding the canoe. Between them, they managed to take the canoe down. As they trooped to the lake, Rick carrying the canoe at the bow and the three boys at the stern, they lugged the Old Grumman to the lake. They'd put on their life jackets and tied the paddles to the canoe to avoid making two trips. Blowing sand swept across the beach as they marched in procession from the parking lot to the lake. The beach sand blew straight out toward Lake Superior. The wind was so strong it left a film of sand and dust on the surface of the water a full twenty-five feet from shore. The lake gently lapped the beach front with barely any noticeable rise and fall to the surf.

A strong gust swept sand into Randy's face. Only four-years-old, he let go of the canoe and covered his face to shield it from the grit. His older brothers, who were eight and nine-years-old, didn't notice. They'd thought Randy was more trouble than he was worth for this chore, and had told him to stay out of the way.

Randy ran ahead as if leading them, pointing toward the lake. He put his other arm over his eyes to keep sand from swirling into them, peeking over the top of his forearm. As the shortest, the blasts of sand, which flowed across the ground like snow in a blizzard, affected him the most. No one else noticed the blowing sand and its telltale warning.

Lake Superior was deceptively calm close to shore. A more experienced canoeist would have known the danger. He'd have noticed the patches of riffles that streaked across the water, spotted the occasional whitecaps that started only a few hundred yards off shore, seen the jagged horizon where waves had built to significant size. Despite their sleek appearance, canoes are difficult to paddle against the wind. The air shoves the nose of a canoe aside as if it's a giant rudder and quickly turns you broadside to the wind. Once it has you broadside, the wind gains the full length of the canoe to push against. In a storm, you become no more than a sheet of newspaper caught in a breeze. You're turned one-way and then another, and while you're being spun around attempting to gain control, you rapidly get blown downwind.

Even two full-grown men struggle to paddle into the teeth of a gale. Ken and I, once, pushed our luck too far trying to cross Robinson Bay in a strong headwind. Belle Isle campground lay a half mile away and enticingly close. To reach camp, it would mean paddling at a 45° angle into the wind. After our usual pro and con debate about the crossing, we decided to go for it.

When we were halfway across, we realized too late that we'd underestimated the challenge. The waves were so large that we didn't dare try to turn around and go back, risking putting the canoe broadside to the waves. If we didn't reach Belle Isle, there was no recourse but to allow the wind to carry us out of the bay, into the lake, and try to catch the next outer island as we swept by. If we missed, the next stop was Canada. We barely reached Belle Isle, just catching the very tip of Belle Isle Point.

Rick and the boys shoved off. They hugged the shoreline at first, paddling right next to the beach, canoeing in front of The Eagle River Inn and Fitzgerald Restaurant. As they wandered farther away from shore, they started to struggle to turn and point toward land. Enjoying the battle at first, they put their full effort into it. But a strong gust blew them farther out where they were even less protected from the short bluff above the beach. It blew them no more than a hundred feet from shore. They were already too far to get back. Driven by an adrenaline rush acquired when your family is in peril, Rick's burst of energy was no match for the gale. They paddled as hard as they could. Steve, the oldest, paddled from the front seat. The two smaller boys sat on the floor and used their hands for paddles, all to no avail. Despite the calm waters, within a half an hour of fighting the wind, they were exhausted.

Rick quit paddling. The boys turned and looked at their Dad. "Steve, get off the front seat and sit on the floor. Stay low. It will make us more stable. Let's wave the paddles in the air and pray someone sees us."

In less than an hour, they blew a mile off shore where waves were one to two feet tall. Rick only had enough strength now to wave his arms. Randy sat between his legs, shivering. Two miles out, waves were two to four feet tall. Six miles out, they were eight to twelve. It would be dark soon. It was Monday, June 12, 2000. Water temperatures for Lake Superior in June are in the forties. The beach was cold and empty of tourists.

If you look at an aerial photograph of Lake Superior, the largest of the Great Lakes looks amazingly similar to the profile of a wolf's head. It's an interesting detail that schoolteachers love to point out to hold students' attention during geography lessons. Isle Royale represents the eye. The Keweenaw Peninsula is the wolf's gaping mouth. It's an apt description of the Keweenaw. Watercrafts ranging in size from skiffs to freighters have floundered off its northwest shore. Douglas Houghton, Michigan's first state geologist was one of the victims. He drowned within sight of Eagle River back in 1847. His team of explorers was surprised by a sudden offshore wind. Their skiff blew farther and farther out until they were swamped in high seas. *The City of Bangor*, loaded with 248 new Chryslers, went down in a storm back in 1927. All of the crew safely made it to land but the cargo was a total loss.

Mr. Houghton died shortly after verifying the area's wealth in copper. During the peak of the copper boom the nearby city of Calumet lost the nomination for State Capital by just one vote. Today, Eagle River is a town of three hundred residents during the summer; in the winter, less than a hundred.

Gitchee-Gummee Bible Camp is located in Eagle River. The camp sits atop the short dune that overlooks the lake and the town beach. The cabins are rustic, in keeping with the frontier feel of the tiny northern community. The relaxing sound of surf can be heard throughout the Bible camp. However, when northwesters pound the Keweenaw, you have to shout to hold a conversation.

On June 12, 2000, Kurt and Ginger Loosenort were packing their van to go home after attending a retreat at Gitchee-Gummee. Home for the Loosenorts is Grand Rapids, Michigan, a journey downstate of over five hundred miles. Ginger had grown up near the Eagle River Bible Camp. Her father, Pastor Hart of Calumet Baptist Church, ran the camp for four decades. Ginger spent several summers playing on its grounds as a child.

When Ken and I were in college at Michigan Tech, we attended Pastor Hart's church in Calumet. Ken briefly dated Ginger before he became more serious about her younger sister, Patty. The Hart girls were a big draw for Tech men. They may have done more to bring students to church than Pastor Hart's best sermons. Ginger was helping Kurt load the family van. She regretted having to leave. With so many friends and family nearby, she could easily have stayed longer. Kurt, on the other hand, was anxious to get on the road.

Kurt and Ginger went every year to this retreat. Kurt had come fully prepared to fish, camp, teach, and visit family. Kurt had taught a couple of the workshops. He is a bundle of energy and a gifted speaker. He's also a notorious pack rat. It has been a long time since he could park a car in his garage. It's stuffed to the ceiling with supplies.  A former youth director for Campus Crusade for Christ at the University of Wisconsin at Eau Claire, he'd learned a long time ago how kids always forget something. He'd picked up the habit of packing extra clothes, spare blankets and towels and ball gloves, and he always carries a well-provisioned First-Aid Kit. He'd retained his "prepare for everything" practice long after he left the campus job for his current work with area churches back in Grand Rapids.

Their van was almost loaded and, as expected, crammed full: sleeping bags, laptop, Coleman stove, palm pilot, dry socks, CDs, and more. Behind the van, he pulled a fifteen-foot boat fully equipped for fishing on Lake Superior. He'd fished the day before, trolling for lake trout in Eagle Harbor, a port located up the coast. On top of the van was a canoe.

As he shoved the last suitcase into the van, he said to Ginger, "Let's check the cabin one more time." They trooped up the path to the small log cabin where they'd stayed. It offered a fine view of Lake Superior from the top of the rise. On the way up the path,

Ginger glanced at the lake. The sun was setting. In the golden swath that sparkled across the darkening water, a black speck in the heart of the glare caught her eye. She paused, shielding her eyes. Kurt kept walking, unaware his wife had stopped. Ginger was about to comment on the sunset when a hiss of breath escaped her lips. "Oh no, oh please … Kurt, wait," she yelled up the path. She gained volume as she saw Kurt about to enter the cabin.

"What?" Kurt asked, holding the door open. Ginger had turned her attention back to the swimming speck on the water. She squinted and stared hard. Kurt tried again. "What?" he said more emphatically and with an edge of annoyance. "Come on, Ginger, we need to get going."

"Something's wrong. I think it's that dad and his boys. They're way out there."

Kurt hesitated. A frown crossed his face. Kurt and Ginger had seen them earlier when they were paddling in front of the Fitzgerald Restaurant.

Ginger said more emphatically. "No, honey you have to look. Something is terribly wrong. They shouldn't be out there. I know it. Get your binoculars."

He walked inside the cabin and grabbed the binoculars, which were still on the table. Stepping back outside, he put the binoculars to his eyes. "Where do you see them?"

"Directly below the sun, right in its reflection."

He found the sun easily enough. Quickly lowering the binoculars after getting blinded. An object dropped through the glass' field of vision. Scanning slowly upward, he saw a long shiny cylinder with fuzzy objects on top of it. When he adjusted the focus, an aluminum canoe with an adult in the stern and three children stared back at him. They were so far away they couldn't possibly see him watching them. Two boys sat on the floor toward the front. Their Dad sat in the backseat holding one arm around a very small child who appeared to be on his lap. The father weakly waved his other arm over his head. The canoe was turned sideways to the waves. They looked to be about a mile out and the waves were so big that the canoe almost dropped from sight in the troughs.

Ginger watched Kurt grip the binoculars more tightly. He clenched his jaw. His face turned white. When he finally lowered the binoculars, he turned to her and said, "We have to do something, now. The phone! Where's a phone?"

"There's no phone out here," Ginger answered. "Where's your cell?"

"In the van, but I'll never get a signal. We've got to do something. They're blowing farther and farther out. The waves will only get bigger."

"At least try it."

Kurt ran down the path and then stopped short. "Wait, we should pray, Ginger." Without waiting, Kurt bowed his head and said, "Oh Lord, please help them, please do something. Lord … please help us know what to do." With no amen or reverent pause, they both hustled to the van. Kurt opened the door, reached inside and grabbed his phone. He powered it up and waited. Nothing— no bars, no signal.

Ginger watched over his shoulder. "Try it on top of the hill."

Kurt sprinted up the slope. His long legs kicked sand backwards down the dune. Ginger tried to catch up. At the top, breathing hard, Kurt stared at the miniature screen on his phone. One bar showed, then two, and then one, wavering between the two weak indicators. "Oh my God, a signal." He quickly dialed 911. Nothing happened.

As Ginger reached him, she said, "There's no 911 service out here."

"Who do we call?"

Ginger thought for a second, "The Eagle River sheriff's office. They're the closest police and rescue."

"What's their number?"

They looked at each other and realized neither of them had any idea what the phone number was. "Mom and Dad will know," Ginger said. "They're in their cabin." Kurt raced off to his in-law's cabin across the camp before Ginger could finish speaking.

Bursting through the door without knocking, Kurt talked fast. "Dad, I need the sheriff's phone number. There's a family in a canoe. They're in trouble. Can't get back to shore. Hurry, please!"

Pastor Hart may have been eighty-five, but he was still sharp. He pulled the phone number from his wallet, which he put there when he used to manage the Bible Camp, handing the slip to Kurt.

Kurt tried the number. No bars registered on the phone. He flew out the door, shouting back to Dad as he ran, "I had a signal on top of the hill. Can't wait." He ran to the top of the rise, redialed and heard one ring before the phone died. He tried again. This time the phone died before he could press send. The low-battery indicator glowed. Kurt groaned.

"Where's your re-charger?" Ginger asked, who'd quit chasing after him, guessing he'd need to return to the hilltop.

Running over to the van, he pulled the cell phone connector out of the glove box. But when he went to plug it in, he discovered their old van had no plug-in socket and the cigarette lighter didn't work. Kurt was close to losing it. He sensed that every second counted, that the next wave could be their last. His sense of urgency was so strong he was having a hard time containing his emotions.

Seeing Kurt stand there, holding the cord, doing nothing, Ginger yelled, "What … what's wrong?"

"There's no receptacle for the charger."

They fell silent. "Wait a minute." Kurt slapped his forehead. "I've got a portable battery charger in back. I think it has a plug-in socket." Kurt popped the van's back hatch open and started pulling out suitcases and supplies. Buried with the spare tire and jack was the charger. He ripped it out of its case.

"It's got one!" Plugging one end into the charger and the other end into his phone, they waited, watching for the low-battery indicator to quit blinking. To their surprise, it did immediately.

"The number, where's the number?"

Ginger read off the sheriff's phone number and Kurt dialed as she spoke. When no bars showed, he groaned again. "We've got to go back up top."

They climbed the rise. Kurt carried the charger under one arm and thumb-dialed as he crested the hill. The phone rang through. "It's ringing!"

"Eagle River Sheriff Department," a woman's voice said.

Panting, Kurt rifled off, "There's-a-dad-n-three-boys-canoe-in Lake … Superior. You've got t'do something. They're getting blown out, can't get back. You've got to help!"

"Slow down sir, please slow down. What's your name?"

"This is Kurt, Kurt Loosenort, staying at Gitchee-Gummee. A dad with three boys, they're a mile out—in a canoe. Can't make it back to shore, wind's too strong for em. Please do something."

"Oh my … the closest boat launch is at Eagle Harbor, six miles away. By the time we trailer a boat there and motor back, it'll be at least an hour and fifteen minutes."

"That's too long. You've got to do something now," Kurt said, his voice rising.

"That's the best we can do, sir. But we're on our way." There was a click and the phone went quiet.

Ginger looked at Kurt. She'd reached him in time to over-hear what the dispatcher said. "An hour and fifteen minutes," she repeated, shaking her head. "What else can we do?"

Thinking hard, Kurt said, "I'm gonna try my marine radio. Maybe somebody's all ready out there." He'd been fishing yester-day but had seen no other boats all day. There'd been no chatter over the marine radio either, but he could try.

He ran to the boat, unlashed the cover and threw it aside. His well-packed vehicle and boat were starting to look ransacked. Raising the antenna, he switched on the radio. Pulling the Mic out of its slot, he said, "Mayday! Mayday! Is anybody listening?" When he let go of the key, all they heard was static. He tried again. "Mayday, Mayday, Mayday, there's a dad with three sons on Lake Superior in front of Eagle River. They're in trouble. Is anybody listening?" He stood there, thumb poised over the key. Ginger's Mom and Dad had now joined them, walking over from their cab-in. They all hovered over the marine radio. Static crackled from the speaker. Then the static stopped.

"Dollar Bay Coast Guard Station," a strong, clear voice replied.

Kurt went through his rapid-fire description again. The Coast Guard had to ask him to slow down, too.

Kurt said slower, "I'm telling you—there is a canoe—a mile offshore—Eagle River—with a father and—three small boys." He forced himself to breathe between phrases. "They can't get back to shore, I tell you. The wind is too strong. They're getting pushed farther and farther out. I almost can't see them with the binoculars anymore. Please hurry."

"Sir, the fastest we can get there is if we trailer a boat to Eagle Harbor and launch from there. It's twice as fast as steaming through the canal and up the coast. It's still going to take at least an hour and one half."

"Oh God, I don't think you'll make it in time. Alright, al-right, but please come."

"That's the best we can do. We're on our way."

Old Pastor Hart picked up the binoculars Kurt had set on the boat seat and scanned the lake for the canoe. Finding the canoe in the glass, Pastor Hart studied the young dad, who appeared to be talking to his boys. He only occasionally waved an arm now. He was no longer trying to use his paddle to slow their drift. The canoe completely disappeared between waves. Pastor Hart slowly lowered the binoculars and said more to himself than to his family, "They won't last that long."

When the phone rang, Anne jumped. It had been quiet all day around the Boggio's house and the sudden noise startled her. She quickly collected herself and picked up the phone on the fourth ring.

"Hello? ... Oh, hi Dick," Anne said into the receiver. "Good to hear from you. Yeah, Jim is right here, hang on."

Jim Boggio got out of his recliner and took the phone from his wife. Jim Boggio is the unofficial mayor of the small village of Eagle Harbor. He has a big voice and half bellowed—half spoke into the phone, "Hello Dick, what's going on? Haven't talked to you in six months ... you're down at the marina ... No, no, of course it's all right. Come on up. It'll be good to see you. You drink Manhattans if I remember right ... See you in a few minutes."

He hung up and said to Anne, "He's working on his boat down at the marina. Said he's ready for a break and thought he'd see if we'd like some company. He'll be right up."

When Dick Lantz arrived at the door, Anne let him in and hugged him. "How are you Dick, we're so glad you decided to call. Jim's so bored he's crawling out of his skin today. You're doing us a favor by stopping over."

Jim was in the kitchen fixing drinks and hollered to Dick from the other room, "Sit down, man. Take a load off. Haven't done a damn thing all day. You putting your boat in the water for the summer?"

Dick started to shout back and then dropped his voice as Jim walked in with drinks. "Hi Jim, boat's not really running quite right. Engine sounds a bit rough. Might just be old gas—sound familiar? I haven't run her since last September, not since I pulled her out of the lake. Treated fuel or not, that's a long time for gaso-line to sit in a fuel tank."

The Boggios and Dick Lantz were soon discussing boat me-chanics, mutual friends, their health, and their kids and grandkids. Both long-time residents of the area, the Lantz now wintered in Florida. While in the midst of their catching up, the phone rang again. Anne answered.

"Hello? Well, hi Steve. What a pleasant surprise. How are … oh … oh my," Anne's, normally pleasant features turned seri-ous. "He's right here. I'll get him."

Both Jim and Dick halted their conversation, turning to Anne. The tone of her voice caught both their attention. Jim mouthed to Anne as he took the phone, "Steve who?"

"It's Steve Kowaleski, Ron's boy. He's calling from the bar at the Fitzgerald Restaurant. Somebody needs help on the lake down at Eagle River. Here, take it. Tell him to speak up. It's hard to hear."

Jim took the phone and said, "Hi Steve, what's going on? … What? Wait, I can't hear you. What's all that racket? Sorry man, you're gonna have to speak louder." … Really? … Well … Dick Lantz is right here with me. He just put his boat in the water … Yeah, sure … of course … let me ask him."

Jim turned to Dick without putting his hand over the re-ceiver, "Dick, Steve's tending bar down at the Inn, you know the Fitzgerald Restaurant in Eagle River. Old Dave Murphy's perched on his favorite stool. Guess there's a wedding party going on. Dave told Steve to call me and get down there quick. Some guy and his kids are blowing out into the lake in a canoe and can't get back to shore. Dave told him, 'You call Bojo. Call the mayor. Get him out here right now. Don't wait. Just call him.' Anyway, Steve said Dave thinks we better hurry. What do you say?"

"Boat's not quite right yet, Jim, but yeah. I guess we better go. Tell him we're on our way."

Jim said into the receiver, "Steve, we're leaving now."

After the Coast Guard signed off, the Harts and Kurt and Ginger stood there looking at one another, feeling powerless. Kurt said to Ginger and her parents, "I'd be no faster getting to them in my boat. I'd have to trailer my boat to Eagle Harbor, too."

Ginger took the binoculars from her dad to see how the family was doing.

"Wait a minute." Kurt said. "How about our canoe? Marty's canoe, I mean. It's borrowed, but the little outboard for it runs good. If I can reach them I could tow them in. We'd have to hurry before they blow too far out." Without waiting to discuss it, Kurt began to unlash the canoe on top of the van. "Come on. Help me carry this stuff to the lake."

Kurt and Ginger hustled from their van to the beach and back again. It took several trips to carry everything that Kurt thought they might need. The canoe, paddles, the four-horse motor, fuel tank, two ropes—in case one breaks—flares, a searchlight and extra batteries, a bucket for bailing, lifejackets. Kurt radioed the Coast Guard one more time on his marine radio to inform them of their plans. The Coast Guard warned them to be careful and not risk themselves needlessly. Kurt told them to hurry and asked for their telephone number. He couldn't help but ask, "Don't you guys have a chopper?"

"Yes," the dispatcher replied. "But the closest one is in Traverse City. We notified them. They're coming. But it'll take three hours before they arrive."

As Kurt and Ginger were about to climb into the canoe and head out, Kurt spotted a couple taking a sunset stroll down the beach. They were heading toward them. "Aaaah, wait a second," Kurt said. Let me see if this guy can help." Kurt was far from comfortable with Ginger going. A rescue attempt was very likely to get dangerous and he knew it.

Running down the beach, Kurt pulled up to a stop right in front of the couple, panting a little. Feeling as if there was no time for polite introductions, Kurt blurted out. "Would you help me tow a guy and his kids off the lake? I hate to ask, but there's a dad and three kids in a canoe. The wind's too strong and they can't paddle back to shore." Kurt looked disheveled from all his running around. His request for help didn't come out as smooth as he'd wanted it to.

Don and Pam Adams had never met the Loosenorts before. They didn't say anything at first, taken aback a little. Rick's canoe was no longer in sight from the beach. Glancing at the lake and seeing no one, Don finally asked, "Who'd you say needs towed to shore?"

Kurt slowed his speech, took a breath and said, "You can't see them from here. But they're right about where the sun is setting. You can see them from our cabin up there." Kurt pointed to his cabin on top of the rise. "They're waving for help."

Don said, "We saw those guys, earlier. Three younger boys … with their dad … aluminum canoe?"

"That's them."

Don looked over at his wife, Pam. Their eyes met and she nodded.

"Okay, I'll go."

"Thanks, man. I can't tell you how much I appreciate it." Kurt ran back to tell Ginger. Don and Pam continued to walk up the beach together, discussing something the Loosenorts couldn't hear. Don leaned over and kissed Pam.

At that moment, a waiter from the Fitzgerald Restaurant stepped out of the door of the outdoor deck area and shouted to them to wait. Walking over, the waiter said as he approached them, "Hold on, someone's on their way from Eagle Harbor. We saw the canoe, too."

Kurt and Don looked at each other. "Do you know who's coming?"

The waiter shook his head, no.

"Any idea when they left?"

"Sorry, that's all I know."

"Don," Kurt said slowly, with a concerned frown on his face. "We have no idea when they'll get here. I don't think we can afford to wait."

Don nodded agreement.

The waiter wished them good luck and jogged back to the restaurant.

Don got into the canoe, climbed over the gear, and took the front seat as Kurt held the canoe steady. Kurt noticed that Don knew to stay to the center of the canoe to keep it from tipping. He noticed, too, that Don was a big man. When he sat down, the back end of the canoe raised off the sand.

"Love you, Ginger," Kurt said as he clambered in and pushed off. He fired up the outboard and shouted to be heard above the motor, "Where you from, Don?"

"Portage, Michigan, down by Kalamazoo."

"We're from Grand Rapids. Are you a praying man, Don?"

100

Don remained quiet.

They cruised straight toward the sun, which was now falling into the lake, the bottom of the sun appearing to dip into water. The farther they got from shore, the choppier the lake grew. At about a half-mile out, Don pointed ahead and slightly to the left. "There they are. I see them."

When Rick and the boys crested each wave, a silver glint flickered on the horizon. "I see them," Kurt said.

By the time Kurt and Don motored a half-mile closer, two-foot waves splashed against Kurt's borrowed canoe. They could clearly see Rick and his sons, who in turn, could now see Kurt and Don approaching. Rick and his sons were still a quarter-mile away. The boys waved excitedly, their shouts only barely heard, being shouted into the wind. Don waved back to let them know they'd been spotted.

"Don," Kurt said, "I'm going to call the Coast Guard. I'm having a hard time holding us straight. The wind wants to push the back end of the canoe sideways to the waves. I'm not sure I can trust her much farther than this."

Without turning around in his seat, Don said, "Yeah, it's getting pretty rough." Neither man had spoken much, intent on searching the lake for the dad and boys and then once spotting them, keeping them in sight.

A solitary loon swam ahead of Kurt and Don, maintaining a parallel course with them. Don pointed toward it and shook his head. "That's strange, don't you think?"

Kurt slowed the canoe to a crawl. He'd brought his cell phone and charger with them in the canoe. He called the phone number the Coast Guard had given him. After making the connection, he shouted into his phone to be heard over the wind and motor, "We see them. We're about a mile out. They're straight out from Eagle River. They're maybe another quarter-mile farther out than us."

The dispatcher said with a note of authority, "Do not imperil yourselves. I say again, do not put yourselves at undue risk."

"Well frankly, sir," Kurt said, "I feel imperiled already." Kurt was getting increasingly nervous. He felt that their own situation was growing precarious. Past this point, conditions could quickly go from precarious to worse. Kurt had been on Lake Superior before when it was rough. He had been in cold water before, too. He knew no one was swimming back to shore from way out here in

40° water. Hypothermia would set in long before they even got halfway.

"Do not hang up," the Coast Guard told Kurt. "Keep this line open."

"All right, but I have to set the phone down to operate the canoe."

Kurt and Don didn't move, floating there on the lake. At the tiller, Kurt used the motor to hold them perpendicular to the waves. The wind streaked the lake with long, parallel lines of foam, a sure sign of strong winds. Large swaths of riffles swept quickly across the surface and out toward the open lake. Small whitecaps were breaking around them. Kurt thought about the dad and boys. He was in no position to endanger Don any farther without permission. It's too much to even ask, Kurt thought. Normally not reluctant to ask for help, Kurt didn't. He remained silent and they sat there, bobbing up and down on the building waves watching Rick and his boys continue to drift farther away.

Don broke the silence first. "Kurt, if we're going to do this, we need to go now. I'm willing if you are."

Kurt swallowed hard. "All right, Don." Kurt paused and then said, "Don ..."

"Yeah?"

"It's very risky. You know that, right?"

Don didn't turn around, just nodded.

Even with the wind at their backs, the small outboard could only do five knots. Kurt picked up the phone off the seat. He notified the Coast Guard of their plans to push ahead and quickly set the phone back down. The winds kept wanting to shove the canoe sideways. At times it took two hands on the tiller to hold a straight course. Waves splashed a little water over the bow as they plowed ahead. A couple of inches of water soon sloshed back and forth across the bottom of the canoe.

As they approached the young family's canoe, they could barely see the tops of the three boys' heads. They sat on the floor hunched over. Kurt said to Don, "If they're sitting in water they must be freezing."

Don waved at them again. The dad appeared to bend over and say something. Three heads popped up. The oldest kid, Steve, waved back. When they got twenty-five feet away, Kurt slowed and then stopped.

"Are we ever happy to see you guys," the dad shouted through chattering teeth. "Didn't know if anybody saw us."

"Is everybody all right?" Kurt asked.

"Yeah, just cold. What now?"

Rick's light nylon jacket zipped up over top of his life jacket fluttered and snapped in the wind. Kurt moved in closer so that the two canoes were only ten feet from one another. It was still hard to hear over the wind.

Don shouted, "Kurt, I don't think you can tow them into this wind. We need to use the paddles to build a catamaran. Lay them across the top of both canoes. Tie the paddles to the crossbeams. Then you can use the motor for both of us."

"We're going to have to get their canoe pointed toward shore, first," Kurt said.

"What?" the dad asked cupping one hand to his ear.

"I said we need to get you pointed toward shore," Kurt shouted, cupping his hands like a megaphone. "We're going to link the two canoes together. My motor isn't strong enough to tow you into the wind." The dad nodded. Kurt wasn't sure he'd understood.

"What's your name?" Kurt asked. They quickly exchanged names. "Rick ..." Kurt shouted, "Do you think you can get pointed toward shore?"

"I don't know. We'll try."

No matter how hard Rick and his son paddled, they couldn't hold the nose into the wind and point toward Eagle River. The wind kept pushing them sideways and it took several precious minutes to straighten out again.

Kurt waved his arms over his head and shouted to Rick, "Stop! That won't work. Son ..." Kurt yelled over to the oldest boy, "You paddle backwards on the right side. Rick, you paddle forward on the left."

They tried again, but over-paddled, spinning the canoe around so quickly, they'd spun all the way around—broadside to the wind the other way. They switched sides with their paddles, immediately catching on how easily they turned, easing their canoe around to point toward shore. Randy and Ted cheered. It was the first time they'd said anything.

Kurt edged closer and pulled alongside. Working as fast as they could, they laid the paddles across the top of each canoe and tied the paddles to the crossbeams with Kurt's ropes. Rick's hands shook so badly he was having a hard time pulling the knots tight.

When the lines were secured and the canoes linked together, both canoes jarred less violently from the waves. Rick's canoe, however, was riding dangerously low in the water.

Kurt put the four-horse into gear. The motor labored from the strain. Looking like a poor man's catamaran, they cut through the water, slowly starting back for Eagle River. Kurt thought, *Lord, this might work, it just might work.* "What are your names, again? I have the Coast Guard on an open line on my cell phone. I want to let them know who you are."

Rick gave Kurt all of their full names and ages.

Kurt relayed the news to the dispatcher that they had reached the family. He also gave him everyone's name, including Don's. After going a couple of hundred feet, Kurt asked. "Do you pray, Rick?"

He was so tired his laughter sounded forced. "Man, we've been praying the whole time. You guys *are* the answer to our prayers."

Kurt smiled, and then looked at Rick's sons. They were shaking, their faces ashen. As he was wondering what to do for them, a large wave rolled under the canoes and when Kurt's canoe curled over the wave top, he could see deeper into Rick's canoe. It was half-full of water.

"Oh no … Rick!" Kurt shouted. Grabbing the pail, he tossed it over to Rick. "Bail, bail man, bail that water out!" Kurt talked fast. "Help your dad, kids, hurry! You have to get that water out of there. It will drag you under." The boys formed cups with their hands, flinging water over the sides.

But before Rick could empty three buckets, their canoe appeared to sag, water rushing over the sides. As the bow dipped beneath the surface, it pulled the rest of the canoe under. The paddles slipped from their knots and the boys and Rick all slowly dropped into the lake, their submerged canoe drifting away from them.

Four heads bobbed in the water beside Kurt and Don, their life jackets keeping them afloat. They gasped in pain, choking. The shock from the cold caused them to struggle to breathe. Water splashed into their open mouths. They flailed with their arms and legs, kicking frantically, trying to keep their faces out of the water. Teddy was first to reach up and grab onto the side of Kurt's canoe. Seeing him grab on, three other pairs of hands quickly followed. Randy's grip slipped and he went under for a second. His life jacket bounced him upward, and as it did, he lunged for the rail, just grabbing hold.

"Don't pull! Do not pull us over!" Kurt screamed. "Don't pull on the canoe!" He shouted so forcefully and with so much fear in his voice that the kids, despite their panic, obeyed. They stared up at Kurt, each resting their hands on the rail, kicking their feet to stay with the canoe. Puffs of steam escaped their lips. They trembled violently.

Rick's canoe resurfaced thirty feet away upside down, the hull barely showing out of the water. It bobbed for a couple of seconds. They watched in horror as it sank and disappeared.

"Kurt," Don shouted. "Let's throw all this stuff overboard. Make room!"

Looking into all of those terrified young faces, Kurt froze. He'd seen scared kids before, but this was far different.

"Kurt!" Don shouted louder.

Kurt glanced at Don. "All right," he slowly said, trying to pull himself together. He reached down and threw a flare into the lake. Don, seeing Kurt start to act, quickly threw most of the rest of the gear overboard.

"I'll lift the boys into the canoe," Don said. "When I do, Kurt, you *have* to lean the other way or we'll roll over. Rick, help push your boys up as I lift."

Kurt leaned as far as he dared. Don reached down, grabbed Randy by the scruff of his shirt and with one arm hauled him out of the water. He dropped Randy at his feet. He reached over, grabbed Steve and then got Teddy. Don's strong arm plopped the brothers behind him like sacks of flour. The boys hunched their knees up to their chests and wrapped their arms around their legs, shivering. The canoe rattled from their shakes.

Rick looked up at his three sons in the canoe. They stared down at their dad. Rick closed his eyes. His grip relaxed, his limp fingers starting to slide down the side. Kurt reached out and grabbed his wrist. Rick's eyes fluttered and then opened.

Kurt shouted into Rick's upturned face, "You hang on! Don't you dare let go."

Their canoe was now barely out of the water. Only six inches of freeboard remained. They'd slowly been filling with water. What Rick's extra weight would do nobody wanted to think about. A few waves slurped over the sides. Each time they did, the boys moaned. "We have one shot at this, guys," Kurt said. "We have to work together. Stay with me, now. Rick, when I lift, you have to kick as hard as you can."

Rick could barely speak. "I can't move my legs. Can't k-k-kick."

"All right, all r-right," Kurt's voice cracked. "Don't worry, we'll do this." Trying to stay calm, he took a deep breath. "When I count to three, everybody lean the other way."

"One—two—three—NOW!"

Kurt grabbed under Rick's arms. Don and the boys leaned the other way. Kurt lifted for all he was worth. He jerked Rick high enough for him to hook his armpits over the side. His legs hung limply in the water. "One more time!" Kurt grabbed Rick by the back of his pants, and screaming like a weight lifter, lifted. Rick curled his torso over the side and rolled his hips inside the canoe. Kurt flung Rick's legs over the side.

"Get us out of here," Don shouted.

Kurt helped Rick to sit up and then put the motor into gear. The canoe didn't respond. They had turned sideways to the wind during their scramble to pull Rick and his boys out of the lake. The weight of three adults, three young boys, the motor, fuel, and four inches of water in the bottom of the canoe was more than the little motor could push. Kurt pressed the tiller to port as far as it would go and held it there, praying and waiting for the canoe to turn toward shore.

The wind died for a couple of seconds. It was just long enough. The canoe started to come about and point toward land. Everyone sighed. They'd all been leaning right, unconsciously willing the canoe to turn.

"Find something to bail with," Kurt shouted.

The pail was gone. The paddles were gone. Everything had been jettisoned except the phone and charger. When nobody moved, Kurt grabbed the cover to the portable charger and started to bail.

Four-year-old Randy scrambled up onto Don's lap to get out of the ice-cold water. Don took off his coat and threw it over Randy's shoulders. Rick, Steve and Teddy huddled in the center of the canoe on the floor, sitting in a pool of water. Rick slung his arms around his two sons trying to shelter them from the cold wind.

Kurt looked toward Eagle River. It was growing dark. He could see flashing red lights on shore. Emergency vehicles had arrived. But they were still a mile and a half away. *If we can just get a little closer, the waves will shrink*, Kurt thought.

Motoring against the wind, they could only do one to two knots. The waves marched against them now. Plowing through the waves, the canoe appeared to travel faster than it really did. The wind didn't ease up. Strong gusts swept past them, and the wind flowed over the cold waters of Lake Superior, making everyone shiver except Don, who somehow seemed not to notice the cold. With all of the extra weight, the canoe was so heavy that the bow no longer rode up and over waves but thudded against them. Every so often, they'd strike one awkwardly, the impact momentarily stopping the canoe's progress. The canoe would labor, seeming to take forever to regain its forward motion.

Kurt kept bailing. But the water level inside the canoe continued to rise. Unable to let go of the tiller, he had to keep switching hands as one arm tired. "Rick," Kurt said. "Can you bail?"

Rick held out a hand for the cover. He was shaking so hard he didn't want to speak, not wanting his kids to hear him stutter from the cold. Kurt handed him the lid and Rick started bailing. The work helped to warm him a little. As he warmed, he bailed faster.

"Good, good," Kurt shouted. "Keep it up. The waves will shrink if we can just get a little closer to shore."

Steve and Teddy started to fling water overboard with their hands, picking up their pace, encouraged by their dad's efforts.

*A thousand more yards is all we need.* Kurt prayed.

In fifteen minutes they traveled only five hundred feet. The sun had set. The white caps were growing, looking whiter in the darkening water. Larger waves kept halting their meager progress, but the outboard never wavered. The sound of its engine droned the same pitch whether the canoe moved or stood still.

Don looked at the distant shore. He watched the waves crash against the bow of the canoe right at his feet. A few waves surged over the bow. Looking toward shore, he saw the surface of the lake suddenly shred into a thousand-foot-wide patch of frayed water. A gale-force gust scooped up water off the wave tops and shot spray thirty feet. From Don's vantage point, he saw the riffled patch race across the lake, heading straight toward them. He gripped the sides, bracing himself, and shouted out, "Hold on!"

The blast swept over the canoe, stopping them dead in the water. Kurt yanked the tiller hard one way and then the other, fighting the wind, somehow able to hold the canoe straight. The gust raced past, speeding into the open lake. The riffles smoothed after it passed. Freed from the gust, they slowly started to move forward again.

But the wind-burst had done its work. The lake was whipped to a frenzy, the waves turned into steep-faced curls. They broke and trailed white foam. The nose of the heavy canoe rode up the first curl, and as it did, the stern dipped into the lake. Water flowed over the rails beside Kurt. He leaned forward trying to tip the balance forward. There was nothing anybody could do. Sinking stern-first, Kurt settled into the lake and watched the rest of the canoe in front of him follow. The canoe, full of water, slowly rolled and spilled everyone into the lake.

Randy screamed as they tipped over. Don bear-hugged him to his chest. Rick grabbed Steve and Teddy. The boys kicked wildly in their panic and broke free of his hold, dog-paddling, straining to keep their faces out of the lake.

Released from its human cargo, the canoe resurfaced, floating upside down beside them. The weight of the motor caused the stern to sink underwater six-feet deep. Filled with Styrofoam, the nose of the canoe rose out of the lake, sticking two and then four feet into the air. The canoe bobbed up and down in the waves at an angle like a submarine trying to surface.

Don reached over and pulled the canoe to him. He half-threw, half-set Randy on top of the nose of the bobbing canoe. Randy lay face down, spread-eagled over the nose, gripping the sides with his palms. Don swam to the end of the bow, holding the canoe steady, trying to keep it from rolling Randy off the canoe.

Seeing Randy on the canoe, Steve and Teddy tried to pull themselves on top of the bow, too. They kept slipping. Rick pushed from behind, but the wet aluminum was slippery.

Kurt treaded water a few feet away. Everything had happened so fast. *This is it*, he thought. He stared at Don. He watched Rick and his sons struggling in the water. The terror-stricken expressions, their rapid breaths, their trembling lips, white faces—Kurt saw every detail. The trauma etched the scene into his brain.

*We're done. It's a disaster. Twenty minutes, it'll all be over.* Everything seemed to unfold for Kurt in slow motion.

Kurt floated there, dazed. He kicked slowly, calmly moving his arms back and forth to stay upright. *Forty-degree water—five minutes for extremities to lose feeling,* Kurt thought, *ten minutes to go all numb ... fifteen to twenty a coma.* The old hypothermia data he'd learned long ago came to his addled mind unasked for.

*Stay calm. We need to stay together.* He shook his head. *Do something!*

"Stevie," Kurt shouted. "Get on the other side of the canoe!" Kurt swam two strokes, reached out and grabbed him, pulling Steve around to the other side of the canoe. "You boys, reach over top of the canoe and grab each other's wrists." They did. "Inch yourselves up higher. Straddle the canoe and hold on to each other. Don't let go!"

They wriggled as high as they could up the overturned canoe without shoving Randy off the nose. Their chests and arms were now out of the water. Their legs and waists dangled behind them in the lake.

"Rick," Kurt shouted. "You and I have to do the same. Grab my wrists." Kurt reached over the canoe. They grabbed each other's wrists and locked hands. Kurt looked into Rick's eyes. "Rick, let's try and keep the boys above us."

Don remained at the bow, pressing upward on the nose of the canoe, steadying it, helping to keep the bow as high out of the lake as possible. The wave tops swept up the bow as high as Steve and Teddy's necks. Randy clung to the nose, perched above the surges.

"Keep talking!" Kurt shouted and then lowered his voice. "Come on, guys. Stay together. We've got to stick together."

Kurt wouldn't give up. Hope ruled his actions, but his thoughts raced. There was very little chance they'd make it and he knew it. *I'm sorry, Lord. I was a fool. All I did was drag Don down with me.*

Kurt silently prayed and then he would talk to the boys trying to lift their spirits. Then he would pray again—sometimes aloud. Everyone else was quiet. Freezing cold, steam escaped their mouths in frigid puffs. Teddy choked and gagged, swallowing water, unable to time his breaths against the splash from waves.

Rick laid his head down on top of the overturned canoe and closed his eyes. Kurt squeezed his wrists. Rick slowly looked up at Kurt, not appearing to see him. Kurt noticed his own grip was already weaker.

*Please Lord… don't let them suffer.*

Deputy Sheriff Keith Jenich followed Kurt and Don's progress from Eagle River. He saw them reach Rick's canoe. Standing beside the patrol car, lights flashing, Deputy Jenich shook his head. Outboard or not, it was too rough out there for canoes. Only two weeks earlier, two fifteen-year-old girls had been swept off-shore in a rubber raft. They'd been lucky. After getting blown six miles out, the winds shifted. The girls landed twelve miles down the coast.

He radioed in, "Deputy Jenich to base."

"Go ahead, Keith," dispatch replied.

"Peg, did you contact anyone in Eagle Harbor to see if they can help?"

"No, Keith. Didn't need to. Ann Boggio called ten minutes ago to notify us that Jim Boggio and Dick Lantz are responding in Dick's powerboat. Anne said they got a call from someone at the Fitz Restaurant."

"How much longer till they arrive on scene?"

"Don't know. Their marine radio doesn't work. Anne said Jim's got a cell phone but it keeps losing signal."

"If you hear anything, let me know. Keep the Coast Guard posted, too. Thanks, Peg. Deputy Jenich clear."

"Base clear."

Ginger and Pam waited on the beach, along with Pastor Hart and his wife, and a few bystanders from the restaurant. The patrons kept walking over to ask the young Deputy for updates. Pastor Hart had gone back to the Bible camp to get blankets. He threw one over the shoulders of Ginger and Pam, who huddled together, talking quietly. Mrs. Hart stood next to the girls, staring at what looked to be an empty lake.

Keith rested his elbows on top of his patrol car to steady his binoculars, adjusting the fine-focus on the powerful law-enforcement-issued glass. He watched the two canoes link together and start back. Scanning the lake, he also saw in the distance, a couple of miles away yet and approaching from Eagle Harbor, a boat motoring down the coast. He didn't tell anyone, not wanting to get everyone's hopes up.

When Rick's canoe sank, Keith gripped the binoculars like he was going to squeeze them in two. He watched Don pull the kids into their canoe and Kurt haul Rick over the side. Keith breathed a little easier. But even from over a mile away he could see how terribly low the remaining canoe rode in the water.

Moments later, Keith sucked in a quick breath and swore. His cell phone rang and he snapped it open. "Deputy Sheriff Jenich," he said in a sharp voice.

"U.S. Coast Guard, Petty Officer Smith at Dollar Bay Station. We just lost our phone contact with Mr. Loosenort attempting to rescue a family at Eagle River. We understand you are monitoring the situation. Please advise."

"They're all in the water, damn it! Both canoes swamped. I repeat—all six are in the lake."

"Are they wearing life jackets?"

"Yes, I believe so. It's hard to tell in the waves. I can barely see them. They keep dropping out of sight. What's your ETA?"

"Thirty to forty minutes. There's suppose to be another Samaritan vessel helping. Do you see them?"

"I see a power boat approaching. I don't know whether they are aware of the situation or would know where to look for a canoe."

"Keep us apprised."


The Flyin Solo pounded toward Eagle River through waves Dick Lantz judged to be three-to-five footers. They had traveled as fast as Dick dared push his twenty-one-foot boat. He'd just put her in the water that afternoon. The radio didn't work, and the motor sounded rough to Dick's ears.

Jim Boggio phoned his wife from the Flyin Solo, sticking one finger in his other ear to hear her. "Where are they now, Anne?" he shouted into the phone.

The cell phone connection was scratchy. The motor thrummed loudly in the background. After several attempts, Anne managed to relay the two canoes' approximate location to Jim, getting her information from Peg at the sheriff's office. Peg, in her turn, kept calling Keith at the beach.

Inside the small cabin area, where Dick piloted the boat, it was impossible to see anything beyond a few feet. The plunge of the bow into the waves splashed the windshield with a constant slap of water. Dick used his compass more than sight to steer by. Jim stood up top as lookout. They were approaching Eagle River, and Jim could see the house lights on shore grow brighter in the dusk. The lake was taking on that dark slate color it assumes just before nightfall. He also saw the flashing lights of emergency vehicles at the beach next to the Fitz Restaurant.

"Slow down!" Jim shouted. When the boat didn't slow, he bent down to stick his head into the cabin. "Slow down. In this chop, we could pass right by them and never know it. It's getting awful dark."

Dick eased the throttle back and slowed the craft to an idle. They stopped bashing against the waves and the bow dropped out of plane, settling into the lake. When they did, the craft began to pitch in rhythm to the broadside waves. At a mile and a half from shore, the wind was stretching the waves farther and farther apart, building them into rollers. When the whitecaps tumbled, the wind sprayed the wave top for several feet.

Dick came up top and stood next to Jim. A gust of wind caught his throat and caused him to turn his head aside. Protecting his face with his arm, he leaned toward Jim. "See anything?"

"No, not yet."

The men set their backs to each other. Jim scanned the lake right and Dick looked left. They each searched the lake in a radius starting from the stern and moved forward. When they looked straight ahead, Jim said, "Oh my God! They're right there. They're dead ahead. We almost ran over them."

Dick stared hard for a second or two and then said, "I don't … wait. Are they *in* the water?"

Kurt heard the Flyin Solo before he saw it. A dull roar had grown in his ears until it rose above the metallic ringing slosh of water against the aluminum canoe and over everyone's moans. It was getting more difficult to distinguish sounds for Kurt. He lifted his head and tried to focus. The rise and fall of the canoe in the waves and his strangely fuzzy vision made him close his eyes tight and reopen them to clear his head. Only three hundred feet away Kurt saw a boat racing toward them. *A boat! They see us!* Kurt thought, unable to find his voice.

When the boat didn't slow and kept coming at full speed, his relief turned to fear, *They're going to run us over!* A hundred feet away, the boat slowed to a stop.

He turned to Don, who'd also spotted the boat. Kurt managed to mumble, "A boat—guys—they're here. They f-found us." No one else could move besides Kurt and Don. Rick could only groan. Steve and Teddy both weakly turned their heads to look, but didn't speak.

Randy didn't move at all.

Kurt stared at Randy's chest. He thought he noticed a barely perceptible lift.

Dick Lantz moved the Flyin Solo upwind of the canoe to block the waves and he drifted down to them. Jim stood at the rail, waiting. Just before they sidled up to the overturned canoe, Don pulled Randy off the nose. Don lifted him as high out of the lake as he could. Randy was limp in Don's arms. Jim reached down and grabbed Randy under the armpits and hauled him over the side of the boat setting him on the deck as softly as he could.

Dick came up to the top to help and together they hauled aboard Steve and Teddy. The two boys lay on the deck beside Randy. They were shivering, sobbing between catches of breath.

With the kids in the boat, Don grabbed each man's out-reached hands and pulled himself aboard, quickly turning to help with Rick and Kurt. Rick could no longer move. Neither his arms nor his legs worked. But he was conscious. Kurt let go of Rick's wrists, and when he did, Rick slid off the canoe into the lake. He briefly went under but then bobbed up. Rick looked up at the men in the boat, unable to speak, barely able to hold his head out of the water. All three men reached over the side and grabbed the collar of Rick's life jacket and then by the back of his life jacket and then his pants sliding Rick over the side and onto the deck.

It was Kurt's turn. Kurt pulled himself around the canoe to the side where the boat was. He reached up, took the men's hands and when he went to kick, realized he too could no longer move his legs. Hypothermia had numbed his lower limbs. He tried again—nothing. "C-can't move my l-legs," Kurt said.

"We got you," said Jim, and the three men pulled him into the boat.

For a split-second Jim and Dick stared blankly at everyone sprawled on the deck, half-stunned at what they saw. They looked up at each other and Dick shouted, "Get them below! There's sleeping bags down there, maybe a blanket or two." He jumped into the cabin and behind the wheel. He put the boat into gear and edged away from the canoe.

Jim and Don carried the boys below and dragged Rick into the cuddy-cabin beside them under the forward deck. They put the kids inside sleeping bags, throwing blankets over Rick and Kurt. Dick threw the throttle into gear, and the boat lurched forward.

After getting the boys into bags or blankets, the men wrapped their arms around each child, blowing lungs full of warm air down their backs. The men were not gentle. When Jim started to rub Teddy's back, Kurt told him to stop. Kurt had read that they shouldn't massage their limbs, possibly sending the cold blood from limbs to their torsos, stopping their hearts.

Steve and Teddy lay still, absorbing the heat. As feeling slowly returned, the cold and numbness were replaced by an ache that felt like they were being stabbed with needles. The two brothers started to complain, pulling back from the men. Their objections were greeted with smiles and tighter grip.

From the cabin where Dick steered, he shouted through the door into the cuddy-cabin, "Jim, I could use some help up here!" Jim hustled away to resume lookout for the ride back to Eagle Harbor.

Rick lay on the cabin floor, curled up in a blanket, watching the men warm his two older sons. He was starting to tremble, beginning to thaw. He could wriggle his fingers, but it took all his strength to move his arms, and he could do no more than lift them like blocks of wood. He stared into the corner of the cuddy-cabin, watching Don try to rouse his four-year-old son, Randy, who wanted to sleep.

Don hugged Randy. He blew hot air into the sleeping bag until his face was red. Rick could barely see Randy buried inside a blanket enwrapped by Don's big arms. Don looked up at Kurt. "Kurt," Don called. "Kurt!"

Focused on the two older brothers, Kurt didn't hear Don at first. When he realized Don was shouting at him, he turned, and with one glance at Randy cried out, … "H-how is he? Is he breathing?!"

"Yes. But he wants to sleep—not good."

Together, they pulled Randy out of the now damp sleeping bag. They stripped his soggy clothes off and hurriedly wrapped him in a dry blanket. His skin felt terribly cold, clammy. Kurt lifted Randy up into a sitting position, and sat down behind him, wrapping his long legs and arms around him, hugging him to his chest, using his own body as a heater.

"Come on, son," Kurt whispered.

Rick groaned and strained to move, slowly crawling over to his son, and said through his shakes, "R-Randy." Finding his voice, he said louder, Randy!" He reached out a trembling hand and placed it on Randy's shoulder. "Randy ... Stay awake. Talk to me."

Randy only moaned.

Kurt quit praying, closed his eyes and slowly rocked Randy back and forth in his arms.

Randy shuddered.

"Stay awake, son," Rick said.

Randy mumbled louder, "mmmMMM ..."

"That's it. Come on ... come on, you can do it."

Rick took Randy from Kurt. "You're all right. It's okay, son. Just stay awake. You've got to stay awake."

Deputy Keith Jenich watched until all six people were pulled aboard the Flyin Solo and the boat was heading back toward Eagle Harbor. He could tell when two of the bodies went over the side of the boat limp the situation was serious. He set the binoculars down on top of the car. He quickly radioed Peg, relayed the news and added. "Peg, tell the Coast Guard they still need to hurry."

He walked over to the families and gave them the news. "A private boat just pulled them out of the water. They're taking them to Eagle Harbor where emergency personnel will meet them." Looking intently at Pastor Hart, who had his car parked at the beach, Keith told him, "You should be able to beat them to Eagle Harbor. Drive safe. But go now. Don't stop on the way."

Walking back to his patrol car, Keith called Peg back and said, "I'm on my way to Eagle Harbor Marina. What did the Coast Guard say?"

"They're almost there. Said they'd head out immediately. They called off the chopper."

"Good. Thanks, Peg."

The residents of Eagle Harbor hadn't seen such activity since last year's 4th of July. At the marina, the State Police were standing by, a couple of Sheriff Patrol cars, and three ambulances—the entire Keweenaw County fleet—lights all flashing. The tiny village encircles the small harbor. Any residents who weren't already at the marina waiting for The Flyin Solo's return watched with binoculars from behind their lakeside picture windows. Many stood out in their yards.

Anne Boggio had called several friends and neighbors to meet her at the marina with warm blankets plus hot drinks, and instructed them to leave their car motors running, heaters blasting. Jim had been able to reach her. She could tell, despite the noise in the background and the poor connection, something wasn't right.

The Coast Guard arrived first. They had to clear a path to the launch and then snake their way through the crowd to back their boat down the ramp. For all the congestion, it was remarkable how fast they moved. In less than three minutes, they were away.

The *U.S.S. Dolphin* powered through the channel, ignoring the no-wake signs. Clearing the pier head, they turned left and headed west down the coast, but quickly pulled up. The Flyin Solo was only a half-mile away, racing toward the channel. The Coast Guard powered back up to intercept.

Jim saw the Coast Guard clear the pier head and shouted below. Within moments, the *Dolphin* pulled alongside. The ship bounced hard against the boat. Three crewmen set bumpers between the boats, leaped aboard ropes in hand, and lashed the two vessels together.

"They're below," Jim shouted.

Hustling down the steps, they checked everyone's vital signs, including Kurt and Don, who shrugged them off. "We're fine," Kurt said. "The kids, help the kids."

They gave each boy a swallow of hot tea to counteract hypothermia. The hot liquid tasted to Steve and Teddy like every bad-tasting medicine they'd ever taken. But they felt heat course through their bodies.

Randy coughed, the liquid spilling out of his mouth, dribbling down his chin. He shook his head to avoid drinking more, but the ensign forced a little down him. The crewmen then picked up the boys and carried them over to the *U.S.S. Dolphin*, wrapping them in heated blankets. With some assistance, Rick was able to follow. The crew untied the lines, shouted, "All clear!" and the pilot immediately pulled away, charging back toward Eagle Harbor.

Jim Boggio and Dick Lantz watched the Coast Guard race away. Kurt and Don joined them on the bridge wrapped in blankets. The Flyin Solo bobbed in the waves, and they stared after the retreating stern of the Coast Guard vessel. It suddenly felt very quiet. Jim put his arms around Kurt and Don. "I think they're gonna be all right."

By the time they reached the marina, the *Dolphin* was tied up at the launch, and Rick and his sons had already been loaded into ambulances. One of the ambulances pulled away as Dick eased the Flyin Solo into its boat slip.

Anne Boggio and her friends waited at the end of the dock, along with half of the town's residents. The four men stepped out of the Flyin Solo and walked single-file down the narrow dock, Kurt and Don wrapped in their damp blankets, their clothes still soggy. A crowd of well-wishers met them. Thermoses of hot chocolate were pressed into their hands. Janice Maki, a good friend of the Boggios, winked at Jim and said, "This one has something extra to take the chill off."

Anne hugged Jim, stepped back, and placed her hands on top of his shoulders. She patted his arms and studied his face. "How you doing?"

Jim looked down at her, swallowed hard, and glanced away, noticing for the first time all of his neighbors. Finding his voice, Jim Boggio—Mayor of Eagle Harbor— pointed at Don and Kurt, and barked, "Get these guys some dry clothes! Warm'em up for God's sakes. What are you standing around for?"

Before Don or Kurt could protest, they were swarmed with jackets, blankets, and hot drinks. Total strangers began to rub their backs to warm them. Kurt tried to peer around the heads to see if he could see what was going on inside the other two ambulances. At the back of one of them, it looked like a couple of paramedics were working on someone inside.

A deputy was also standing at the back of the ambulance, writing on a notepad, evidently listening to one of the occupants. He then closed his notepad. The paramedic climbed inside the back of the van, turned and shut the doors. As it pulled away, the deputy scanned the crowd, spotted Kurt and Don, and walked over. "Excuse me. I'm Keweenaw County Deputy Sheriff Keith Jenich. I need to get some information."

Kurt nodded, still shaking a little, more from nerves and adrenalin than from cold.

"Why don't you get in the backseat of my patrol car where you can be warm and I can hear better. This won't take long. I just need to finish my report."

Kurt and Don climbed in back. Deputy Jenich got behind the wheel and asked them questions. He filled in his report as Kurt and Don took turns recalling the events of the past two hours. When they finished, Kurt asked the deputy the question he most wanted answered.

"Do you know how they're doing? Are they going to be all right?"

Keith hesitated, and said, "From what I could tell ... they all look like they're going to be fine. They're on their way to Keweenaw Memorial Hospital. The EMT said they'd probably all be kept overnight for observation."

"And Randy?" Don asked.

"The youngest boy? He was talking with his dad when I saw him. Seemed wide awake, crying a little—good sign."

Kurt and Don looked at each other. Don reached over and patted Kurt on the back, then had to look away.

Kurt was trembling all over. Tears filled his eyes. Not needing to contain his emotions any longer, he started to weep. He tried stopping and couldn't. Bending forward, he put his face in his hands.

"It's all right," Deputy Jenich said, dropping his voice. "This isn't unusual after an incident like this. You're probably still in shock. Just let it go. It'll pass in a moment."

Kurt did let go, not that he had any choice. All of the pent-up fear, all of his resistance to panicking, his fight to think clearly and control his urge to turn around and let someone else come to the rescue—every bit of self-control melted. His whole body shook. Tears flowed down his cheeks. Unasked for, Kurt began to vividly relive the horrific events of the past two hours—how terribly close it had been. He remembered it all so clearly he feared he'd never be able to think of anything else again.

Then ... the scenes slowly faded, ebbed and disappeared.

He took a deep breath, lifting his face out of his hands. He was no longer on Lake Superior. He was sitting in the dark in a patrol car, the motor running, and for the first time in what felt like an eternity, he was no longer shaking.

Kurt sat up and turned to Don, "Don, why weren't you cold?"

"What?" Don asked, looking over at Kurt. There was a twinkle in Kurt's eye. Don smiled. "Of course I was cold. What are you talking about?"

"No, seriously, you were like a polar bear out there."

Don chuckled and patted his belly, "Insulation, plenty of insulation."

Deputy Jenich turned around to face the two men and closed his report folder. "I'm finished here. And, it looks like you two have a couple of people who'd like to talk with you."

Don and Kurt looked out of their side windows. Standing outside, on either side of the patrol car, were Pam and Ginger.

"You guys take care of yourselves," Keith said. "If I need any more information, I have your numbers."

Rick and his three sons were admitted to Keweenaw Memorial Hospital, and as the paramedic predicted, kept overnight for observation. They suffered no permanent physical injury and were released in the morning.

I can vouch for how easy it is to get into trouble on Lake Superior. Whether you're a seasoned freighter captain or just piloting a canoe, you certainly don't have to be a novice to push your luck too far. Rick and his boys learned a hard lesson, a lesson learned several times each year around the Great Lakes. Most of the time, everyone walks away unscathed.

Sometimes you don't. In fact, you don't even have to be on the water to be in harm's way. While attending Northern Michigan University, two girls who lived a few rooms down from my wife's dorm room, and the guy they were with, all drowned when they were swept off the pier in Marquette. One of those infamous November storms was blowing. The roar from the surf could be heard all the way to campus, a mile away. They walked down to the lake to watch the storm—not an unusual thing to do on a slow night in Marquette.

No one knows for sure what happened. But it is likely they decided to risk walking out on the pier to take a closer look. One of them probably got too close. Often in these terrible accidents, a person either slips and falls into the lake or is knocked off by a wave. When friends attempt a rescue, they drown, too.

The evening of the rescue, Roger Wickstrom, a press reporter from the Houghton Mining Gazette, was listening to his police-band radio. Getting quick approval from his editor to pursue the story, he reached Eagle Harbor just in time to talk with several of the people involved—the Boggios, Dick Lantz, Deputy Jenich, Kurt and Don. When he interviewed Anne Boggio, she told him the quick response by Jim and Dick was reflective of Eagle Harbor's way of doing business. She said, "The town cares about each other. When something happens, somebody's there."

Each person told the reporter their version of the rescue and each person down played their own role. As he listened, Wickstrom became so intrigued that he asked Kurt if he could follow him to Gitchee Gummee to hear more. By now it was after midnight, and Kurt was past the point of exhaustion, but said okay.

Back at the cabin, Wickstrom listened while Kurt filled in more of the details of the ordeal. As Kurt slowly went over the events with him, the reporter ticked off a laundry list of facts he'd acquired. He double-checked his notes with Kurt.

"So, you say Ginger spotted the canoe in the sun's reflection on the lake on your last trip from the cabin to load the van?"

"Yes."

"Despite no working phones, you sort of "MacGyvered" a phone together and were able to contact authorities?"

"Yes, that's right."

"You happened to have a motorized canoe, and someone with Don's knowledge and capabilities happened to walk by on the beach just as you and Ginger were about to set out?"

Kurt nodded.

"Someone from the restaurant placed a call to the Boggios, who'd just heard from Dick Lantz for the first time in months, who'd just put his boat in. *And* … the rescue boat almost ran you over, pulling up just short after traveling six miles from Eagle Harbor?"

Mr. Wickstrom put his pencil down, stared at Kurt over his eyeglasses, and asked, "Is all of that correct?"

"Yes," Kurt replied. "That's correct."

Kurt shuddered. It was one of those holy shudders, a life-changing shiver, when you realize that something larger than yourself was at work. It wasn't until now, with the reporter connecting the dots for him, and in the quiet of their cabin, that Kurt saw how each piece of the rescue had come together.

Kurt and Ginger continue to attend the Gitchee Gumee Bible Camp Retreat every third week of June. At sunset on the 20th, they walk down to the beach to pose for a picture in front of one of the new warning signs. One year they asked a passerby to take the photograph for them. The passerby happened to be Peg from dispatch.

While in Eagle River, Kurt also makes a point to visit Jim Boggio and Dick Lantz. During one such visit, Dick Lantz asked Kurt if he'd like to go fishing with them. Kurt loves to fish. The next day they were trolling somewhere between Eagle Harbor and Copper Harbor, about a half-mile from shore. Kurt noticed fourteen, small, smiley-face stickers stuck to the dash of the Flyin Solo.

"What are those for?" Kurt asked.

Dick didn't say anything at first. He then cleared his throat, and said, "Well, they're for each boater we've retrieved from the lake—most of them kayakers, actually. They seem to think they're invincible in those things. You see that one?" Dick asked, pointing to the tenth sticker.

"Yeah."

"That one's you."

The piers and beaches all around the Great Lakes are dotted with warning signs cautioning people to keep away from the water during high winds—whether blowing on or off-shore. There were no warning signs at Eagle River in June of 2000.

There are now. As a direct result of the incident with Rick and his sons, the Keweenaw County Sheriff's Department posted warning signs on the beach at Eagle River. They also purchased a motorized rubber raft that can be launched from the beach in under ten minutes.

# INTO THE WIND

WHEN KEN AND I RETURN FROM ISLE ROYALE, THE FIRST QUESTION FRIENDS ask is, "How was your weather?" Given the island's reputation for cold and rain, not to mention bugs, I suspect the interest in our weather is, in part, a desire to hear how miserable we were. Nothing makes for better vacation tales than disaster trips. Whatever their motives, we answer the weather question by talking about wind. We have an oft-used expression that goes, "When on the water—wind is everything. Everything else can be dressed for."

Because paddling a canoe can sometimes feel like you're trying to stay atop a log in a log-rolling competition, we study the wind before we venture onto Lake Superior. We'll climb to a ridge top, walk down to the beach or find some other vantage point where we can get a broad view of the lake and sky. We'll take as much time as necessary to assess the wind's direction and speed.

I like the way Ken and I handle these go or no-go decisions. Where one of us is bold, the other is timid. It's not always the same person, though I'll admit to normally being the more hesitant one. One of the lessons I learned working at the tree service is that you don't ever just go for it. Whether climbing trees with a chainsaw strapped to your belt or canoeing over hundreds of feet of ice-cold water—caution should prevail. The law of averages eventually does catch up to risk-takers.

For the past few years, Ken packs in a battery-powered, pocket-sized marine radio. The weather service provides around-the-clock marine forecasts for each section of Lake Superior on a designated radio band. Now whenever we want to venture onto the open lake, we also listen to the weather. Even with their forecasts, however, we still take a long, hard look at the lake and sky.

We have one simple rule. If either of us says no, we don't go. Over the years, it's remained our one inviolate rule.

This time, however, neither Ken nor his radio was here to help. I stood, alone, on the beach at Belle Isle, staring at the lake. The skies were clear, but the wind was brisk and blowing west, the very opposite direction I was going. I needed to catch the passenger ferry tomorrow afternoon. If I left now, it would mean a difficult paddle right into the teeth of the wind.

I could wait to leave in the morning in hope that the stiff breeze might let up. But without Ken here to help shoulder the load, I wanted to allow plenty of time to reach Rock Harbor. If I didn't make it in time, the next boat wouldn't depart for four more days. If it was at all doable, I should go now.

There was something else, too. I felt this inexplicable urge that I shouldn't miss that boat—that I needed to get back home.

Ken had remarried in July and felt he shouldn't take a week away from his new wife, Terri, only two months after the wedding. I decided to go to Isle Royale anyway. I'd always wanted to do a solo trip. Now, after spending the past week on the north shore, it was time to start back. Standing there, I analyzed the wind. I also walked out to Fish Rock to get a different perspective. I even climbed up onto the ridge behind the shelter. I stared at the water for an hour, doing an internal wrestling match.

I finally decided it was safe enough to go.

While I was hauling my packs down to the gravel shore that serves as a beach at Belle Isle, four campers walked into the clearing in the center of the campground. They started to toss a football around. I stopped packing and sat down on the shelter step to watch. Their play felt out of place. People hunt for firewood here, or clean fish, tend fires—not play games.

They'd all been sick last night. We had arrived at Isle Royale the same day, taking passage together on the *Isle Royale Queen*. However they didn't reach Belle Isle until the day after I did. I found out why that night. They somehow managed to portage two cases of beer over the Greenstone Ridge, causing a day's delay to their arrival. One of them, the biggest of the four, had sounded like he wouldn't live through the night. Dry heaves are never much fun, let alone when you're sleeping outdoors far from the comforts of porcelain. His retches and moans reverberated across the quiet campground until the early hours of the morning.

Despite their hangovers, they were having a good time, and I had to admit that they made me want to jump into their game and "go long." Deciding against it, I got up and finished loading the canoe. Tom, evidently their spokesperson, walked over with a concerned expression on his face, glanced at the lake and asked, "Are you really heading out?"

"I'm going to try it," I said. "The winds are rough but the waves are small. If I get into trouble, they'll blow me straight back to Belle Isle."

Tom looked doubtful. "We decided not to go anywhere today. None of us is feeling well. It's nice here." He hesitated for a second and then said a little softer, "Hope we didn't bother you too much last night. Do you really need to go?"

"Yeah, I do. I'm taking the *Queen* back to Copper Harbor tomorrow afternoon. I'm afraid if I wait until tomorrow morning. I might not make it in time or not get out at all. If I can just get across Robinson Bay into Lane Cove, I should be all right the rest of the way. After Lane Cove I can hug the lee shore."

"You gotta be in Rock Harbor by tomorrow?" he asked with a surprised look. "Tell you what, we'll watch you from here and if you get into trouble, we'll see what we can do."

"Thanks," I said, genuinely grateful. Watching one another's back is an unwritten rule on the island. Knowing they were watching made me feel better about attempting the crossing.

His friends came over and helped get the canoe pointed into the surf. They even went so far as to wade into the lake to hold the canoe straight. I stepped in, took a seat, and they all shoved. I had no time to say thanks or look back and wave. A strong gust of wind caught the bow and immediately blew the canoe dangerously sideways to the breakers. Slashing at the water with the tip of the paddle through the shallows, I strained for deeper water where I could take stronger strokes. I barely made it past the drop-off and couldn't help but wonder how I'd ever manage this kind of effort all the way across the mouth of Robinson Bay.

I pointed the canoe straight into the wind. When I varied one way or the other, even slightly, gusts caught the bow like a sail and caused the old Smoker Craft to veer left or right. The farther aside I veered, the more difficult it became to straighten out. I paddled from one side of the canoe to the other and then back again, attempting to knife through the wind. I must have looked like a madman, whipping the paddle back and forth over the canoe.

I eventually struck a deal with the wind. By allowing it to blow me aside slightly, I'd paddle until I brought the canoe almost true, but not quite. I'd then ease up a little, and the breeze would nudge me aside again. By using the tension, I didn't have to continually switch sides, frantically swinging the paddle over the canoe back and forth. When my bottom hand on the paddle —the pulling arm—tired, I'd switch sides and allow the wind to take the canoe the other way.

Strong gusts can be seen in advance. The blasts of air cause large swaths of water to shred into frayed ripples. The islands of wind blasts resemble ruffled fur and travel faster over the lake than the waves. As gusts approached and then swept by, I'd hunker down in my seat to offer less resistance. The wind-scraped water streaks by like passing cloud shadows.

Some gusts would unexpectedly spring up right at the canoe in a whirl of spray, catching me off-guard. During that crossing of Robinson Bay, the lake looked like a blanket made from differing textures of silver and grey cloths that shifted without warning. It mesmerizes you if you allow it. I looked back only once, and noticed all four of them still standing on the beach, watching me creep across the bay. I paid for that glance when a gust spun the canoe around before I could correct it. I ended up facing them, my back to Lane Cove. It took five minutes to turn around and I lost fifty yards of hard-earned water.

An hour later, I reached Lane Cove, my hands cramping from my death-grip on the paddle. I wasn't sure they could see me anymore. Cork Island partially screens Lane Cove from Belle Isle. I turned and waved anyway. It was too far away for me to be able to see people on the beach. But Tom had binoculars. I hoped he saw me make it to safety.

I paddled across Lane Cove to the portage. The closer I got to shore, the more the land blocked the wind. Beaching the canoe at the trail marker, I stepped out and dragged the canoe out of the water. Lugging it and the packs the hundred yards down the path, I loaded back up and slid into Stockley Bay. Stockley Bay is only a couple of hundred yards wide, but a mile long. The wind funneled up Stockley into my face. However, by paddling just ten feet from the south shore, I caught some relief where outcrops and deadfalls along the shoreline offered windbreaks. Three more hours of hard paddling and one more portage later, I canoed into the next bay south, Duncan Bay. For once, I coasted with the wind at my back, west, all the way to the campground.

Tomorrow morning would be a tough portage over the top of Greenstone Ridge. It would take at least two trips to carry the canoe and all of the packs. However, returning is always easier than setting out. I'd eaten most of my food and used all of the stove fuel. At least the packs would be lighter. I felt good about my decision to leave Belle Isle. The upcoming portage would hurt, but I now had plenty of time to reach Rock Harbor.

The next day I reached the docks by one o'clock—two hours before departure. My brief, solo stay at Isle Royale had made me feel like a returning explorer. On the boat ride back to the mainland, I bubbled with success. Ready to celebrate, I quickly made plans to meet up in Copper Harbor with Captain Don and some other campers.

But despite my celebratory mood, something felt wrong. It was an odd sensation, and I told myself it was because Ken was not along. After disembarking, I grabbed my gear, found a phone, and called my wife. She and the boys were fine. My son Sam wanted me to meet him in Dollar Bay. The next day was my birthday and he and his grandmother had planned a dinner to celebrate. I also needed to call my dad. My mother was in the hospital again.

When I talked to him, Dad didn't seem alarmed but I knew both of my sisters were at the hospital. They live three hours from my parents and each have young kids at home. Debbie is a teacher and had left her class to a substitute. They must have sensed something was different.

Mom had Lupus which had gone undiagnosed for years. Lupus is a chronic inflammatory disease that causes inappropriate autoimmune reactions. It wreaks havoc with various organs, joints, the nervous system, and sometimes causes skin rashes. The symptoms of Lupus—a sensitivity to sunlight, achy joints, fluid around the lungs and heart, or butterfly-shaped rashes—appear similar to many other ailments, particularly arthritis, that early detection is difficult. The disease affects everyone differently, compounding the confusion. Diagnosis is often a process of elimination, when treatments for erroneous guesses refuse to give relief.

There is no cure. Once her doctors identified the Lupus, they prescribed Prednisone, a steroid used to give some control for the inflammation. The medication, along with a few lifestyle changes, provided a little relief. Unfortunately, the side effects from the drugs—bloating, more sensitivity to sunlight, and a rounding of the face called moon-face—plagued her. Mom had also suffered since childhood from damage to her lungs caused by rheumatic fever and pneumonia. She was in and out of school so often due to illnesses that she dropped out when she was only sixteen. Unable to catch up, frustrated and ostracized by friends who'd passed her by, she went to work. World War II was underway and there were plenty of jobs for women, even for a dropout.

Mom's dad, a Detroit police officer, kept a very tight rein on his kids, especially his daughters. Mom told us her early sicknesses and strictly controlled upbringing caused her to want a freedom for her kids that she never knew. "Be careful, but if you really want to do it … try it," she'd say. As a result, I got to play any sport and try any musical instrument they could afford. Most of my urges to explore, short of sticking a fork in an electrical socket, were not only encouraged but also enabled. Our yard was the neighborhood ball field in the summer and an ice rink in the winter.

Mom used to sing in the kitchen when she was cooking or cleaning up after dinner. She couldn't carry a tune, and my friends kidded me about her being tone-deaf, but that didn't stop her.

Until I was about twelve years old, and while playing Little League baseball, she'd allow me to practice my pitching by throwing a rubber ball against the brick wall alongside the kitchen window. As I aimed for individual bricks that represented the knee-high, outside corner of the strike zone or a brick for a high hard one, the pounding on the wall had to sound terrible from indoors.

She never complained. I could see her in the kitchen through the window, singing away to some old Sinatra or Johnny Mathis song. I never understood how she handled the noise until years later when my son, Sam, took up the drums. Sam's brother, Nick, would watch me taking a nap on the sofa as he practiced, and ask, "How can you sleep?"

On the phone, Dad reassured me Mom was feeling poorly, but he didn't see any need to hurry downstate. She'd been in and out of hospitals for the past ten years. I decided to stay in Copper Harbor, and stick with my plans to see Sam the next night.

The passenger ferry doesn't arrive at Copper Harbor until 7:00 p.m., so Ken and I normally stay the night. Having never stayed in Copper Harbor alone., I was on my own—an evening I seldom see. Ken has the gift of gab and normally carries conversations when we're here together. That night, however, I blathered away with everyone and anyone as if they were all long-lost friends.

The next day I left Copper Harbor for Dollar Bay and caught up with Sam and Grandma. It was Saturday, my birthday, and I planned to travel slowly through the Keweenaw, shopping for a few gifts to take home. I called Dad again. I talked with him and then my sister Debbie at their motel room. They had all decided to stay the night. Mom was at Munson Hospital in Traverse City. Dad said, "She's a little worse. The doctors want to monitor her condition to get a better read on what the Lupus is doing to her now."

I'd stopped to visit Mom and Dad on the way up north to go to the island. They lived in Houghton Lake after Dad retired. When we said our goodbyes, Dad wished me good luck fishing. Mom, however, said she wished I wasn't going. Surprised—shocked really—Dad and I looked at her. I thought she was just concerned that I was going alone this year. As she sat in her easy chair, where she now spent most of her time, I replied, "Don't worry, there's lots of other campers out there. I'll rarely be alone."

I noticed when I walked out the door she had an odd expression that didn't exactly look like concern. I shook it off, probably much like I'd done as a kid. "Don't worry Mom. I'll be fine," were words she'd heard more than once.

We celebrated my birthday in Dollar Bay with one of grandma's famous meals. She grilled steaks, baked some potatoes, gave us large glasses of milk (a luxury on the island), blueberry pie with wild berries picked that summer, and ice cream. We topped it all off with a Finnish sauna. I was glad to spend more time with Sam, and I went to bed clean and full—a great way to spend a birthday.

At two in the morning, I awoke unexpectedly. A great restlessness came over me and a strong urge to get up and leave. I normally sleep like a log after the kind of night I'd just had. I decided to get up. Quietly packing, I tiptoed down the stairs, put a note on the kitchen table thanking Grandma, and left.

Eight hours later I arrived at the Traverse City Hospital and after getting her room number from the receptionist, walked up to Mom's floor. She was in a private room in intensive care. There was no sign of Dad or my sisters. The nurse followed me in.

Mom looked to be in a very deep sleep, her breathing barely perceptible. I knew before the nurse told me. She asked who I was, and after I told her I was the oldest son, she said, "The Lupus has moved into her liver. I'm sorry." She studied my face and when I didn't say anything, said. "We've made her as comfortable as we can. It probably won't be much longer."

"How much longer" I asked, struggling to find my voice.

"That's hard to say, but probably today, maybe tomorrow. She's slipped into a coma. Your dad and sisters just stepped out for a moment. They should be right back." She walked out of the room, leaving me alone with Mom.

I sat down beside her, studied her face and said, "I'm back."

She didn't show any sign of hearing. She looked very quiet and still. The swelling in her face had gotten worse. Her color was far from healthy.

An hour later, Mom quit breathing.

My sister told me later she'd asked for me the day before. Apparently, before she fell asleep for what would be the last time, Mom talked briefly with my sisters. I'm convinced she held out until the day after my birthday. She felt that way about dates like birthdays, anniversaries, and evidently deaths.

Strangely, I didn't berate myself for not hurrying back to talk with her one last time. It may sound callous but somehow, I knew it was all right.

Her service and visitation lasted a couple of days. I was struck by how many people's lives she'd touched. Dad had wanted a small service with no visitation, fearing few would come. My sisters, brother and I changed his mind and were glad we did. Lots of people came, and the funeral felt more like a celebration of her life than a wake.

Stories came out about how she'd made newcomers who'd moved into the neighborhood feel welcome or how she consoled spouses of men from dad's firm who'd passed away. Several cousins revealed how they'd gone to her in private about problems they weren't comfortable talking about with their own parents. As a son, you tend to think your mother's world centers around you. At least I did. The funeral made me see her in a different light.

Mom had once shared with me, when I was going through a particularly difficult period back in high school, that Jesus, had appeared to her. It happened when Mom underwent surgery to remove a portion of an infected lung when I was just fifteen. Dave, the youngest, was only seven. She lay in the recovery room after the surgery, and she was losing her fight for air. Mom said she felt herself slipping away. She said that as she ascended through what appeared to be a tunnel of light, Christ greeted her. Mom told me that she asked Him to return, "To be allowed to finish raising her family."

During the family's meeting with the Reverend Ruth Billington to discuss funeral arrangements, the Reverend asked us to talk about her. "What memories stand out?" she asked. "If it's not too difficult, talking about her will help give me a better idea of who your mother was." She'd never met Mom and needed to prepare a sermon. I mentioned the appearance to the Reverend. Everyone turned and stared. Dad said that Mom had never told him. Aunt Helen, Mom's sister and closest friend, said the same. I grew quiet, unsure whether I'd betrayed a confidence.

After our meeting, Pastor Ruth pulled me aside. With eyes misting, she said, "I'm very glad you shared that with us. I, too, had the same experience as your mother. It's something that I don't tell to just anyone." She hesitated a moment and then continued. "I was in a car accident. I asked Him to return, too, and went into the ministry soon afterward."

At the visitation, I saw a lot of family and friends I hadn't seen for a long time. The gathering felt like a birthday party in many ways. A few people said as much. Several of the conversations started out, "Tough way to finally get together, but it's good to see everyone again." Remarks to the effect, "This is just the kind of gathering your mother would like," were oft repeated.

After the visitation, we went to a chapel for her memorial service. Just prior to the start, I walked in and sat down in the first row of the sanctuary, the pew reserved for immediate family. Dad, my brother and sisters, their spouses, and my wife and I were all crowded together. There was no casket at the front of the sanctuary, for Mom wanted no viewing. Instead of a coffin, on a table at the front, just to the right and slightly behind the podium, where flowers and cards are set, was a large photograph of Mom. The picture faced the congregation.

As the service started I was drawn to the picture. I'd seen it many times before. Dad kept it on a dresser back home. As I looked at it, my mother's face came alive. She was looking at me from … *the other side*. She glowed. It was her. She looked straight at me with a smile that held no trace of pain. She was so radiant I had to look away.

I turned to see if anyone else noticed. Everyone was listening to the pastor. I slowly looked back at the picture. She still looked straight at me.

We returned each other's gaze for barely a moment. I soon had to look away. "Thank you," I said quietly, and bowed my head.

When I lifted my head a third time, I watched the photograph slowly fade into a normal picture of my mother. The service continued as if nothing occurred. If anyone else saw her, I never heard.

Standing on the beach five years later, grateful to be here again, I couldn't help but think about her. *Was it really only five years ago?*

Can anyone adequately thank a person for the gift of independence? Mom's struggle to breathe and her constant toil for her own independence created an acute sensitivity to constrictions. She passed on that awareness to her kids. Her lifelong battle for air and her labors to overcome an overly strict childhood drove her to provide some space for her family. It was a space that allowed me room to thrive and flourish.

I'm sure I will never fully appreciate the effort Mom made to function "normally." But if her struggles were anything like paddling a canoe into a stiff wind for days on end, if it resembled knifing through gales where the slightest stray from course blows you broadside to the waves, maybe I understand—a little.

# THE WAVES OF MINONG

THERE WAS NO CHANCE OF MISREADING THE WIND TODAY. A SOUTHWESTER was turning Robinson Bay into a steel-colored froth. Long rollers careened up the bay and waves slapped against rock. The deep reverberated through the stone. I turned my back to the lake and returned to the shelter. Stepping through the screen door, I sat down at the picnic table I'd dragged inside and prepared for a day of repairing gear and some reading. This day's decision to stay or move on was an easy one.

I like "wind-days", as Ken and I call them. Marooned until the wind subsides, if we need to catch dinner, we will fish from shore. But more often, he fishes while I try to catch up on my journal. Even when we don't need to catch dinner, he still scrambles out to a place we'd dubbed "Fish Rock." There, he casts for several hours, standing exposed to the elements that speed past the promontory. He wears every piece of clothing he has in order to withstand the exposure. Fish Rock has become so special for him that he once told me he'd like his ashes spread there.

Ken would join me for the last week of my month-long vacation for our usual Isle Royale fish camp. I was taking a mini-sabbatical for my fiftieth birthday. As the month passed, I looked forward to seeing him more and more. From the relative calm inside the shelter, I could picture him. If he were here now, he'd be out there, jumping from one boulder to another to cover the full arc of water off Fish Rock. When he catches a fish he climbs up on top of the short bluff, shouts, and lifts his prize. Barely able to hear him shouting over the surf, I have to step outside the shelter so he can see me. I'll raise my fists in celebration. He then holds the trout over his head and shakes it.

When he returns, he gives me a full report of his battle with the lake trout. He'd also scowl at me and say something to the effect, "Still inside? I live what you write about."

Wind is an amazing phenomenon. Spending so much time near the water and as an arborist who sometimes examines 36-inch diameter oaks sheared off at the ground like matchsticks, I learn a certain respect for the force delivered by something as seemingly empty as air. My mother's respiratory problems, my own asthma, canoeing Lake Superior, inspecting trees—they all sensitize me to winds. My attention to winds, however, pales in comparison to other mammals. Wolves read scents and movements of air as clearly as I read text, and when gales blow over Isle Royale, they, like me, seek their dens.

Despite my more dull, human and urbanized senses, I can feel the island grow tense on wind-days. I've noticed this same tension back home. During storms, people drive as if possessed. Traffic picks up. Drivers become reckless and distracted. Tempers are shorter, too. While traveling to inspect storm-damaged trees, it pays to be cautious on the road.

Tucked inside Robinson Bay, there is a large dock on Belle Isle where boats traveling along the north shore of Isle Royale can escape the big lake during rough weather. When these storms blow from the southwest, traveling half the length of Lake Superior before they reach the island, the gathering winds funnel up Robinson Bay. The damp air blasts through the natural wind tunnel formed by the steep-sided bay. The air streams past the dock as if through a venturi. At such times, I like to stand on the dock and feel the weight of the gale against my body as I lean into the wind. It's cold. But it is also invigorating. It's like I've been allowed to embrace something wild, something I'm rarely allowed to get near.

I walk away from these overdoses of fresh air fully awake. It's the best mind clearer. Nothing works better for that mental haze caused by sitting too long over a dull chore.

Big storms on Isle Royale produce a more intense reaction than mere anxiety. These are storms where you feel like you're at the ultimate fireworks show. These are storms where the thunder is so loud that rock musicians cover their ears. When these storms strike the island, I don't want to be anywhere near the dock. Zipped up to my nose in a sleeping bag, my hat pulled over my ears, lying in a corner of the shelter, I wait them out.

Nighttime is when this kind of storm reaches its full effect. The clap of thunder is amplified by the absence of sight. Jolts of lightning freeze-frame the scenery. It's like someone turned a flood light on inside a closet for a split-second. In the flash of light, the landscape resembles an old film negative. Colors drain into whites and grays. My vision snaps to awareness, all in sharp relief. The brain isn't able to process the information fast enough to see color. I can feel through the floor of the shelter the bedrock of Isle Royale taking a pummeling. I sometimes wonder if it isn't thunderstorms that hammer the island into rubble instead of the slow work of erosion. The crash of surf booms when it hits the beach. Trees creak and snap. Branches rattle as if an entire forest is trying to rub its sticks together to start a fire. It's easy to imagine that at any moment a tree will uproot and crush the feeble two-by-four rafters over my head.

During storms, and while lying alone in the dark, I ask what will get me first: a Superior wave that obliterates the island or a whole stand of trees getting back at me for every wrong treatment I've prescribed as an arborist?

Storms humble me to the point of feeling invisible. Living on a wilderness island in Lake Superior for an entire month verified something I'd long suspected. Mother Nature is completely oblivious to my welfare. As Robert G. Ingersoll once said, "There are in nature neither rewards nor punishments—there are consequences." I have a tendency to paint Isle Royale as idyllic, almost Eden-like. However, it should be pointed out, she's a cold partner.

If I swamp the canoe in a lake crossing, the lake will not come to my aid. If I twist my ankle on a rock or a tree root, the forest could care less. When nights are chilly, all I can do is wear more clothes and if I don't have an extra parka, the night will not take it upon itself to warm me. Nature's indifference is partly what makes the trip such a challenge.

This total disregard is perplexing. I stand in admiration of the roiling lake on a stormy day. I love to gaze at stars that almost speak on clear winter nights. I wonder at the tenderness of a moose for her calf. But I feel snubbed. The universe doesn't appear to return my admiration.

With each passing day spent without Ken or my sons, nature's ambivalence was driven home a little deeper. To say otherwise would be misleading and deny a harsh reality. It would quickly become dangerous to see this temporary island home in any other light. To throw myself at the mercy of the lake would not only be naïve but downright begging for trouble. It's something I'd seen before going to Isle Royale.

For all the care I give trees, not once have they ever thanked me. On a few occasions they almost killed me. In their defense—which I'm not sure they deserve—I was helping to remove a very large beech tree for a client and said those words that an arborist should never say when fifty feet up a tree: "Oh, just go for it."

We'd reduced an over-mature beech tree to a seventy-foot trunk. With the tree completely de-limbed, I was taking the rest of it down in eight-to-ten foot logs, working my way down the tree. The old trunk made an awkward twist at about fifty feet high. As I finished the back-cut, knowing I was less than sure about which way this piece was going to fall, I watched the log slowly teeter and then tip toward me. With no place to run, I thought the tree rather unforgiving. I watched it fall. My last profound thought in that split-second before the let-down line caught and fortunately caused the log to only glance off my skull was, "This is gonna hurt."

I like trees—a lot. They constantly amaze me. They teach me something new all the time. But whenever I'm on a job and a branch drops next to me, I've yet to see a limb veer aside and say, "Excuse me." There is a tendency to anthropomorphize trees. Trees stand upright. They are long-lived and often have a lifespan similar to ours. They are admittedly very easy to become attached to and some people use them as living memorials for departed loved ones. However, I have, by necessity, learned not to let them fool me. This hardening of my heart makes me wonder whether surgeons develop callous attitudes toward their patients. Hope not. But until you've been bashed, bruised, knocked unconscious, scraped, cut or almost done in, and in some terrible instances seen people killed by trees, don't ask me why I don't go dewy-eyed over them. I can empathize with Gordon Lightfoot's lyrical question in his ode to the *Edmund Fitzgerald*: "Where does the love of God go?"

Despite these sentiments toward Mother Nature, something remains unsaid. Whenever I am outdoors, whenever I'm alone in large uninhabited locations, and especially whenever a BIG storm blows across the lake, I get this feeling that someone is watching over my shoulder, someone who appreciates my admiration.

There are a few locations on Isle Royale where this sense that someone is watching is more evident. Where the Greenstone Ridge rises to its higher elevations, on clear days you can see a most remarkable view. Atop Mount Ojibway, if you turn north, the Canadian shoreline, which is only twelve miles distant, looks close enough to touch. It is a particularly rugged and wild-looking place. Cliffs rise hundreds of feet out of the lake, and even from twelve miles away, create a massive presence. The cliffs look as if the Canadian wilderness stretches for thousands of miles over the top of their crests reaching all the way to the Arctic—which is exactly what it does.

From the Greenstone Ridge, when I stand atop the mount and turn my head the other way and look south, I can see the tip of the Keweenaw Peninsula of Michigan. The first time we crossed the Greenstone Ridge, I asked Ken if that was really what I was seeing. It didn't seem possible that without being in a plane, there was anyplace where you could see clear across Lake Superior. We were about to hike over the rise and down to the north shore of the island. He stopped when I asked him if that was the Keweenaw. He turned back and gave me a questioning look and said in his understated way, "Yeah, it is."

Ever since, I pause whenever I cross over the Greenstone Ridge to take in the panoramic view and reflect once again on being capable of seeing a thousand square miles of Lake Superior. As I do, I wonder why it is, when standing there, feeling all small and insignificant, that this is where I feel close to God. Despite nature's cavalier attitude, why do I get a sense I have my finger on the pulse of someone I can't touch?

When Michiganders want to get away from the fast pace of the city and find some elbowroom, they head "up north." This northern migration over the holidays, weekends, and for summer vacations is also true for the residents of other Midwestern states. Newcomers to the Great Lakes region puzzle over this ambiguous directional expression. By way of explanation, we compare going "up north" to heading to the mountains if you're from the West, or to the desert if from the Southwest, or perhaps, going to the ocean. In Michigan, most of the people live in the southern counties, so when we want to find some space, we go up north where the longer winters tend to drive people away.

My grandparents, upon their retirement, bought a few acres on a small lake in the northern Lower Peninsula of Michigan. I was only five at the time. They built a summer cottage on the west shore of one of those famously clear-watered, birch-fringed, out-of-the-way lakes. The cabin was a small, cramped, two-bedroom ranch with a floor space heater and a brick fireplace that couldn't produce enough heat to warm the bedrooms in the wintertime. Grandma Foerster told me many years later that when we pulled up the two-track driveway for the first time, crested the rise, and looked down on their new place with the lake all sparkly blue in the background, that I looked at her and said, "I like this."

There were only two other cabins on our side of the lake. I immediately set off to explore the surrounding woods. As a kid, I didn't normally like to get up at dawn, but at their cottage I would drag myself out of bed to watch the sun rise over the lake. In the summer at that latitude, the sky grows light before five in the morning. The cool mists hovering over Cub Lake, the early morning quiet—so different than the constant drone of I-96 only a few blocks away back home—made me want to steal away to stalk deer. When I reached adolescence, I'd get up and be gone all day.

Our family spent every vacation there, as well as many weekends. My Dad would fight northbound traffic fleeing the city Friday evenings after he got out of work. Half the city of Detroit—or so it seemed—moved like steel cattle up freeway corridors that acted as cow chutes. He'd grumble and complain about the slower vehicles that traveled in the "fast" lane, slowing his escape.

My fascination with the woodlands surrounding my grand-parent's cottage was a big reason I went into forestry and eventu-ally became an arborist. Those vacations clarified, for me, what real "green space" should look like.

When our family stayed home weekends, we rarely went to church. I only remember a dozen times when we spent a Sunday morning gathered in a pew. I only recall going once on Sunday night. We listened to a guest speaker at the First Methodist Church in Farmington, Michigan. The speaker had served as a missionary in a small African village. His humility and sacrifice made such an impression on Dad during the morning service that we went to hear him again that night.

By the time I reached high school, however, we didn't go to church. This was neither due to some disenchantment with the church nor becoming great sinners and being too embarrassed to show up. We just faded out of what little we had ever done in the way of formal religious practice.

My parents are moral people. In hindsight, I know their Christianity played an important role in their strong feelings for what is right and wrong. Both Mom and Dad made moral distinc-tions clear for us. They taught us you don't lie. They told us you should care for everyone, regardless of their station in life. Hurting someone's feelings was wrong, and when we did we had to say we were sorry. My parents gave me a base for how I ought to behave that can still prick my conscience at inconvenient times.

Standing on the beach at Belle Isle watching Robinson Bay rage, I marvel that something as soft as water, when pushed by something as empty as air, will chew up something as tough as rock. Given enough time, Isle Royale will turn to dust.

My canoe is a frail craft. It would be lunacy to go for it today. When the natural world is neither moral nor immoral, neither kind nor unkind, and holds no deference for anyone at all where is the moral compass? Why should I have to be so good? The lake is cold. The water is deep. It is colder and deeper than my body can bear. To think differently is a dangerous form of denial. If I choose to ignore the waves and venture out, she shows no mercy.

# THE CROSSING

AT THREE-THIRTY IN THE MORNING, A SINGLE KAYAKER SLOWLY APPROACHED McLain State Park. The campground was full, but at that hour only a few fires still burned, manned by late-night summer vacationers unwilling to turn in. It's not reported whether anyone saw him paddle by or not. If they had, they would have seen a solitary figure wearily pulling himself toward the pier through a choppy surf. They would have seen him pass by the beachfront at the park and continue past the north pier. They would have seen him cross the mouth of the Portage Canal turn in at the south pier beacon ,and then head up the channel. At that point he would have disappeared from sight, screened by the breakwall.

If anyone was watching, he would have seemed a ghostly traveler riding low in the water in the dark. Unbeknown to the people staying in the campground that night and to most everyone else as well, the largest of the Great Lakes had just been crossed in a kayak.

The morning Brian Engman decided to leave Isle Royale, the marine forecast was for calm southwest winds turning northward later in the day and no rain. Mid-lake water temperatures were in the mid-fifties. Air temps were expected to be in the seventies by afternoon. Stowed in the kayak's tiny compartment holds were a sleeping bag, high-energy food bars, candy, a couple of sandwiches, a flask, and a mug. A well-used marine compass was mounted atop the bow.

He'd packed the night before, double-checking his supply list before lashing down his gear to prevent it from shifting in rough seas. His intent was to push off just before first light. The twenty hours he expected the trip to take to cross Lake Superior would get him home to Dollar Bay just before last-call at Partanen's, the small town's tavern. He had scheduled a checkup with his dentist in Houghton on the following morning. If all went well, he'd be able to keep both appointments. The last preparation he made prior to going to bed was to load his Walkman with his favorite tapes. He set it on the seat—good to go in the morning. It was August, 1987.

The weather around Isle Royale is notoriously moody, and at five the next morning, it was pouring rain. Getting up and walking down to shore, he saw the tape player sitting in a puddle on the kayak seat where he'd left it—ruined. Brian turned around and went back to bed. He kept getting up to check the weather, and by nine o'clock, the rain had stopped, replaced by a thick fog.

He waited, edgy, pacing inside the empty bunkhouse. He'd prepared for this for weeks. He had four days off and just enough time to get home and rest up before returning to work. Brian worked summers on the island on a trail crew. In the park, the trail crews keep hiking paths clear of downfalls, repair washouts, pick up litter, fix shelters, and prune back the vegetation.

Fogs are common at Isle Royale and they normally burn off shortly after sunrise. Brian waited two more hours for the fog to lift. When it didn't, he decided if he was going, he'd better get started. It was eleven o'clock—five hours later than he'd planned to leave. He set out from Windigo for the two-hour paddle down

141

the length of Washington Harbor to Lake Superior. The shoreline quickly faded from view in the fog, but the harbor waters were familiar, like his backyard, and he could have found his way in the dark. He'd certainly hoped for a better departure. He'd anticipated a flush of excitement at his launch with his trail crew mates waving from shore and shouting encouragement as he paddled in the sun's first golden light. But the crew had already left on a detail to cut firewood for visiting researchers expected at the park the next week. The late start, the ruined recorder and somber weather created an unsettling doubt.

He'd had doubts before and learned to push through them, so he paddled down the quiet bay and unexpectedly ran into a park ranger who seemed to materialize out of the fog in his patrol boat. He stopped Brian and asked a few questions about the trip. Word of Brian's plans to cross the lake had spread among the trail crew personnel and reached the ears of the ranger stationed at Windigo. He let Brian continue, apparently satisfied with his preparations or not believing he was really going to try to cross the lake. After all, Brian had worked on the island for several years. He'd know what he was up against. The ranger parted by asking whether he was carrying enough water. Soon to be surrounded by Lake Superior, Brian couldn't tell if he was serious or not.

When park visitors arrive at Isle Royale and complete their orientation session, the rangers tend to leave campers alone. They try to allow everyone a certain degree of independence to enjoy their own wilderness experience. Park rangers are trained to keep a certain professional distance. Maybe their reticence comes from dealing with visitors who come and go quickly. The average stay on Isle Royale is four days. This is longer than at most other National Parks, but hardly enough time to make friends. Whatever the reason, both visitors and trail crews alike seem to view rangers with a degree of mild contempt. The rangers are the park police and whenever they're present, people become a little guarded.

Two hours after leaving Windigo, with visibility less than a thousand feet, Brian emerged from Washington Harbor into Grace Bay at the very western end of Isle Royale. From there he turned south, staying close enough to shore to keep the island in sight. He traveled south past a cluster of small outer islands until he reached Cumberland Point. Here he beached for a moment to make final preparations for the lake crossing. Brian put on his wetsuit, turned on his marine radio and set the chemical lights in the cockpit snapped to the D-rings.

Pushing off, he continued to hug the shoreline. He headed east a few miles along the south shore of Isle Royale until he reached Long Point, which is more of a bump along the south coast of the main island than a point of land. Instead of rounding it as he normally would if circumnavigating the island, he turned right instead, pointed the kayak south toward the Keweenaw Peninsula, and headed out into the open lake. Brian was going home.

He set his course for 134 degrees, which is a southeast heading. He felt strong but had a headache. A couple of aspirin gave some relief. He hadn't participated in the partying the night before with the rest of his trail crew, who wanted to toast his adventure. Waves were two-to-three footers with an occasional four. The winds remained out of the southwest. Brian settled into a comfortable paddling rhythm and had to keep reminding himself to back off on his pace to conserve energy for the sixty-five mile journey that lay ahead. The fog refused to lift.

Four hours from Windigo and two hours from Long Point, he decided to take a break. Stopping, he allowed his kayak to drift in the mists. When he quit moving, the water stopped lapping on his boat. He held his breath for a moment and could hear the sound of his heart beating. All else was quiet. Fog hung in the air, the same color as the water that surrounded him. Living on Isle Royale all summer, he was accustomed to stunning sunrises and sunsets, but this was a perspective he didn't often see. Few have the opportunity to sit on the lap of Lake Superior while she sleeps in her watery dreams. The quiet lake made him want to nap, too. After finishing his sandwich and a candy bar, he dunked his mug into the lake and washed his food down. He stretched the sprayskirt over the cockpit. Winds were beginning to shift to the west and the lake was getting choppier. The cold water, food and rest gave him a surge of energy. Refreshed, he glanced at the compass and started to paddle.

After two more hours of traveling with visibility still only a few hundred feet, Brian thought he heard a familiar drone. He knew noises can be tricky in a fog. With no reference points, he listened intently trying to gauge the direction of the deep humming sound. Despite being miles from the nearest shipping lanes, he was afraid it might be a freighter. He gently dipped his paddle and pushed on as silently as he could. The reverberating motors didn't make any sense. The noise was growing louder and it sounded just like the engines of the *Voyager*, the Isle Royale water-taxi. He strained to see through the fog.

Sounds carry far over the water, but he could swear he also heard surf washing up on rocks. Paddling a little more, trying to peer through the grey air, he saw a craggy shoreline slowly take shape. A couple of strokes later, the *Voyager* came into view and the ship motored by close enough for the Captain and its first-mate to recognize Brian. They waved as they passed.

Brian had misread his compass and instead of heading toward the Keweenaw, he had inadvertently turned around after his break and paddled straight back to the island. Angry and confused, he wiped the dew off the compass and immediately saw what he'd done. The old marine compass directional letters were worn and hard to read. Coupled with the moisture on the dome, the hard black line he thought represented south was actually north.

It was a terrible mistake and he knew it. After the boat passed out of sight, he threw a tantrum: swearing, and thrashing the lake with his paddle. He wondered if someone was trying to tell him to go back. He debated whether he should return to camp and try some other time. He seriously considered giving up the whole idea. Sitting there in his kayak, floating next to the island, he tried to regain his composure, but his mind felt as thick as the air. The longer he bobbed on the swells, the more undecided he became. His frustration reached a point where he shouted, "Shit, I'm not stopping now!"

He ripped his paddle into the water, did a hard 180, and headed back out into the lake.

In the summer, the sun burns bright over the heart of Lake Superior. The mists rising from its surface created a glowing silver dome over Brian's head at mid-day. This time, as he paddled away from Isle Royale, the light steadily grew more brilliant, and after getting only an hour away from the island, the sun began to beam through. Even with polarized sunglasses, he had to lower and tip his head to one side to shield his eyes from the glare. Sitting amidst the cool waters, and in spite of the intensity of the light, the sunshine felt like a reward for his determination. He felt encouraged, finally able to see more than a few hundred feet. The sun also helped him stay on course.

The air continued to clear. Waves began to build, but nothing serious. His kayak handled the three-to-five chop without much notice, and after another hour, the fog lifted altogether. Isle Royale was still within sight. Twisting around in his seat to look back, he could see the entire length of the forty-five mile long island. The lighthouse at Menagerie Island in Siskiwit Bay rose from the lake like a pencil; the Rock of Ages Lighthouse at the western end of the island, close to where he left Washington Harbor, was now far behind him. The rollers made the tower seem to drop into the lake like a bobber being pulled under by a small fish. Straight behind him, in the remaining haze, the details of the island's near shore faded from view.

Everywhere else he looked was water. The Keweenaw Peninsula would not come into sight for several more hours. Brian kept paddling.

The lake bottom falls away sharply from the south shore of Isle Royale, quickly dropping to several hundred feet deep. Only a short distance from the island, Brian crossed into the deeper portions of Lake Superior, where depths can reach a thousand feet and more. Only Lake Baikal in Russia is deeper and holds more water. But the size that mattered most for Brian—surface area— is not matched by any other body of fresh water. Lake Superior is the size of Maine. If the water were spread across all of North and South America, it would still be a foot deep. "The Lake" as those who live near its influence call it, has swallowed some of the world's largest ships.

The water is also very cold. Year-round average surface temperature is 43° F, but due to its size, the lake rarely freezes over in the winter. Even in the warmest of summers, surface temperatures rarely climb over 70° F. The speed at which hypothermia overcomes a person in these waters makes life jackets merely a psychological safety net. They do, however, help rescuers find the body.

Brian knew all this. He'd thoroughly researched this trip. He had lived in the area all his life and he knew how fast the lake can change. He had been kayaking for several years, before kayaking became a popular outdoor activity around the Great Lakes. In the seventies and early eighties, it was rare to see them on Isle Royale.

Back then, he had paddled alone for the most part. Perhaps this was why he started building his own kayaks. During winters, when the park was closed, Brian began to teach kayaking classes and building fiberglass kayaks in his parents' garage. It took him a few trial runs, but eventually he made some top-flight crafts. When people came to visit him on the island now, they could paddle together around the numerous coves and bays and explore parts of the park few others could reach.

Brian built sea kayaks. They have a rudder/foot pedal system, which enables them to travel in a straight line over open water. The river or whitewater kayaks are rudderless and built to maneuver quickly around the obstacles found in fast moving water. River kayaks are awkward to operate on a lake and over-steer with each paddle stroke. Sea kayaks are also much longer than the river craft.

He became a self-taught expert. Brian had circumnavigated Isle Royale several times, which is over a one-hundred-mile trip. He had kayaked most of the south shore of Lake Superior. He had also traveled the twenty miles north across the open lake from Isle Royale to the nearer shore of Canada. But he had never strayed more than ten miles from land. As he got farther away from Isle Royale, a growing feeling of apprehension settled over him. The winds were becoming troublesome. As the last wisps of fog dissipated, the breeze steadily grew and the waves were becoming ragged, showing white caps. Winds remained westerly and refused to switch to the north, which would have given him following seas.

Some wind can help a kayaker. At the right speed and from a conducive direction, a tail wind would help push him along or allow him to use a paddle as an additional rudder. Canoes, and even sea-kayaks, tend to zigzag over the water with each paddle stroke. To counteract this motion, a good waterman can hold his paddle aft as an additional rudder and use it to remain on course. A following wind also prevents a kayaker from having to paddle the entire time and allows him to coast a little.

There are also winds that eliminate this small luxury. A strong enough breeze from the wrong angle will push the bow to one side, and continually cause a kayak to veer. Canoes, which stand much higher out of the water, are especially vulnerable. This was just such a wind. The freshening breeze increased until they reached a steady fifteen to twenty-five knots. They never died the rest of the way. When winds gusted, as they often did, all Brian could do to stay on course was paddle harder. The growing breeze also caused the waves to build until, only six hours away from the island, they'd grown to three-to-six footers. Occasional waves were bigger.

As afternoon wore into evening, and as he approached the halfway point, the haze completely burned off. The Keweenaw started to come into view. Mount Houghton, Brockway Mountain, and the ridge tops along the backbone of the peninsula peeked over the horizon. The sun, coming around to the west, lit the hills that still lay far ahead of him. Isle Royale had faded into a fuzzy, dark line that dropped from sight when he bottomed in wave troughs.

Brian was in a marathon where he couldn't stop and walk away if he went lame or got too tired or changed his mind. His earlier apprehensions over his trek had now turned to dread. Any thrill he had hoped to experience never came. It felt all wrong. A slow start, fog, contrary winds, no rest, waves that no longer allowed him to stop and drift so he could take a break—they all combined to leave him feeling he'd made a terrible mistake. Not for the last time, he wondered aloud to the empty lake, "What was I thinking?"

His back began to ache from trying to stay low in the kayak for better balance. His fingers started to feel glued to his paddle. He kept trying to maintain a certain paddling rhythm, but the lake wouldn't cooperate. As the Michigan mainland crept closer, waves moved against the westerly seas causing a mild bathtub effect. The result was he not only couldn't pause to coast, he also couldn't find a steady paddling stroke. It was like varying your running speed every two or three strides in a long distance race.

The sun edged toward the horizon, and there was no evidence of calm seas at twilight. To someone standing on the beach, watching the sunset over the lake, the evening might have had a peaceful demeanor, but not from where Brian sat.

About an hour before dark, over his right shoulder and bearing down upon him, he saw a squall line approach. Squalls are a narrow band of thick clouds that move swiftly across the sky. Usually carrying rain or snow, they deliver brief, violent windstorms. They are common over Lake Superior and last for only ten to fifteen minutes. If you're unfortunate enough to be on the water when they overtake you, the lake turns an ugly gray and winds whip violently. Brian prepared himself.

The water darkened around him, as if the lake itself was also gathering strength. When the bank of clouds overtook him, white-caps swirled into water devils that lifted from the surface. Winds tore at the wave crests, and Brian slouched as low as he could to offer less wind resistance. Water spilled over the top of his kayak. The cockpit skirt kept most of the water out—but not all of it. Cold water sloshed inside the kayak beneath the seat.

The windblasts quickly subsided as the cloudbank raced away. Brian watched the storm speed across the lake ahead of him. It moved so fast that it was out of sight within twenty minutes. Breathing a sigh of relief, he looked backwards and groaned. In the distance he could see another squall line approaching.

Within an hour, toward dusk, two more squalls went over-head. His already fragile resolve was shaken further. One squall he could accept, but three? He was very close to breaking down. All he could do was weather these tempests. *Stay focused*, he thought, *one wave at a time until there are no more waves to climb.* Using a sponge he'd brought with him, he tried to sop the water up inside the cockpit. But between trying to paddle and the rocking kayak, he was never dry again.

Daylight faded, and he still had a very long way to go. He be-gan to look for the beacon light at the end of the pier of the Portage Canal. He kept a close watch on his compass, making sure he had it on the correct line. This far from the Keweenaw, landmarks are de-ceptive. Each hilltop looks the same from thirty miles away and a mistake would cost time, which he felt he couldn't afford to lose.

On the horizon and slightly left of his current heading, a tiny, flash of light appeared. Straining to sit up tall in the kayak as he crested each wave, he peered across the lake. Was it real? It was. Within the next half-hour, as he mounted ensuing waves, the wink of light grew into a steady, thirty-second spark. Now that he could see his destination, he adjusted his course and aimed the prow at it. A sense of relief flooded Brian. Much like the sun finally break-ing through the fog earlier in the day, the beacon gave him hope.

He'd made it past the halfway mark, and whatever thoughts he'd entertained of turning back were behind him now. Wrestling over the wisdom of his venture was a waste of precious mental energy. His mission was clear. Perhaps it was all a mistake. Maybe he'd been a fool or worse. It really didn't matter now.

The stars came out and the color slowly drained from the water until it went black. The sound and smell of the water became more acute as daylight waned. The way waves splashed his kayak and lifted beneath him spoke instantly to his body. He still couldn't find a rhythm to paddle by. Instead, he became fluid. He became one with the movement of the lake—an aquatic beat. Brian was riding a membrane that stretched from Duluth to Sault Ste Marie. The surface tension spreads taut over a liquid realm often traversed by the Native Americans.

Where the Michipicoton River empties into Lake Superior in Ontario, pictographs of Native Americans making lake crossings in fifty-man canoes are painted on the cliff walls that border the lake.

The 'Witching Tree,' a white cedar at the tip of Minnesota's Hat Point, is mentioned in a journal written by voyageurs from two and one half centuries ago. The ancient tree was used as a landmark for early trappers, and is a holy place to the Ojibwe, who held it sacred long before the French arrived. Many still do. The tree is alive today and stands alone atop its promontory. Gitchee-Gumee, translated as the 'Great Water,' is a highway described in the earliest native oral traditions. Long before Bishop Frederic Baraga recorded his first visit, the natives traveled the famous lake.

Along the south shore of Lake Superior, there is a rock carving of a Native American member of the Ojibwe tribe named Powers of the Air. His image was carved there to commemorate him, his people, and their tragic final battle with the Sioux. As a youth, Powers of the Air made a solo canoe journey of two hundred miles, paddling from near present day Duluth all the way to Grand Island just offshore of Munising. He brought back to the waiting mothers, sisters and daughters of his clan, the horrific news of the death of all of their men. His father sent him ahead in order to relay the news prior to battle, knowing his band was trapped, and there would be no quarter given by the Sioux. Two decades later, an exploration party, carrying Lewis Cass, the future first Governor of the State of Michigan, and Henry Schoolcraft, the Michigan territory Indian agent, met Powers of the Air during their expedition. Their party listened as he and two women from the clan half-chanted, half-sang their people's story around the campfire. One of the guides was so moved by the epic story that he carved a likeness of Powers of the Air into a rock cliff within sight of Grand Island. The carving, known as Face in the Rock, may still be found in the rock cliff over looking Lake Superior at a rest area on M-28 west of Munising.

Brian kept paddling.

Lake conditions didn't improve. As he got closer to land, the rebounding seas caused the rollers to break into contrary waves that jarred his kayak. It was dark now and hard to see details. Balance became more difficult as his body stiffened from the constant tension. The uncoordinated waves knocked him about. He used his paddle for balance as much as for propulsion. Tipping over is not an option. Brian could Eskimo roll with the best of them, but tired as he was in those seas, flipping back upright would be extremely difficult.

At about midnight, a second blinking light appeared on the horizon. At night, lights on the water easily confuse. Distances are hard to judge. On clear nights it is hard to tell the difference between shore lights and stars low on the horizon. As he rose atop each wave, he stared hard at this new light. Strangely, it was to his right. The light continued to flash and then flash again. Brian kept heading toward the first steady lighthouse he'd seen earlier, but he couldn't help but wonder what the other flashing light could be. There should be no other lighthouses south of the Portage Canal.

A shadow of land was growing in front of him, which meant the ridges of the Keweenaw were climbing as he got closer to shore and the hills blocked more stars. The ridge at night appeared as a black void on the horizon between the stars in the sky overhead and their reflection in the black water. Against that shadow, the steady thirty-second flash of light felt like a godsend. In the dark, it was hard to focus and his compass was all but unreadable. Even with the headlamp he wore, he could barely make it out.

Checking his watch as he brought his wrist up across his face with a paddle stroke, he saw it was getting late—approaching one a.m. He seemed to inch toward shore. His legs trembled. Pinned inside the kayak, he could do little to relieve their spasms. He was still fifteen miles out, and the strain from sitting for so long, cloistered inside the kayak as if shoved into a cocoon, started to cause his entire body to go into uncontrollable shivers. Still, he felt some relief knowing it shouldn't be much longer. He could picture the pier heads of the Portage Canal in his mind.

As he approached near-shore waters, the waves grew. Winds were finally shifting northward and picking up, as the forecast had predicted. The seas rebounding off the Keweenaw Peninsula caused the rollers to grow jagged and steep, some waves pitched up twice-his-paddle-length tall. Straight ahead his beacon was flashing from too high an angle. Something was wrong. The light to his right remained at lake level, moving farther starboard as he traveled. Then, with an insight that comes from God knows where, a sickening realization struck Brian. He'd misjudged directions once again. He had turned toward the airport beacon atop the tower near Calumet. It had come into view first due to its elevation atop the peninsula. Thirty miles from shore, its tower light had appeared to be a lighthouse. From that distance, the change in direction and elevation was so slight it was all too easy to mistake its light for the beacon at the canal. Mistrusting his old compass, he had turned toward the airport. Instead of a few miles from the canal, he was eighteen miles northwest of the Portage entry.

Brian had kayaked straight into a portion of the lake that has seen its share of shipwrecks. The Keweenaw Peninsula protrudes north, eighty miles into Lake Superior. Any weather moving over the western half of Lake Superior makes landfall right where he was heading. The northwest coast of the Keweenaw is the final resting place for larger boats than Brian's kayak, and the list of freighters beneath the waves is long.

The natives who lived along the south shore of Lake Superior avoided these waters for centuries. They considered paddling around Keweenaw Point something worse than bad luck and rarely ventured north of the Portage. They named the island off the Keweenaw Point, Manitou Island, meaning Spirit Island.

Brian veered right, too tired to bother with another outburst. He had reached a point in his internal journey where he had quit questioning himself. Crossing into a dull, lethargic place, he seemed only capable of telling his body to keep moving. He continued more by habit than from hope of success. *"Paddle,"* was all he could say.

He briefly considered heading straight to shore instead of to the canal mouth. However, the idea of having to return to the lake in the morning repulsed him. The same resolve that pressed him forward earlier in the day propelled him now. Making the canal was so firmly set in his mind that changing destinations was out of the question.

Brian felt disoriented. The change in course turned him more sideways to the waves. He'd grown accustomed to the quartering seas sweeping under him after spending the past twelve hours immersed in them. Broadside waves are the worst. Brian needed to weather the flanking seas for at least two more hours. The change in the feel of the lake, the darkness, the exhaustion—all conspired to break him. A sense of impending doom grew. It soon became suffocating. Angry, exhausted, and in no place to indulge self-pity, he allowed his anger to simmer, using its energy to help him focus.

Brian's feel for the lake and his balance was getting worse. He was well past exhaustion. He knew he was tired, dangerously tired. *"Am I thinking clearly?" h*e wondered. *"Check your direction! Keep moving ..."*

He paddled. But his pull through the water was losing power. His waning strength was getting spent on keeping his balance in the broadside seas. The two-bladed paddle felt like it was made of lead. Raising and dipping it into the lake, he barely pushed the kayak. His mind was void of emotion. He was close to passing out.

He was barely moving as he approached the North Portage Entry. His legs were numb. He couldn't feel his feet at all. His hands were wooden. How his arms kept moving was a mystery.

Getting closer, Brian saw a few campfires still burning at McLain State Park. He imagined vacationers sitting around their fires, late at night, unable to pull their gaze away from the flames. Only one mile from the canal, the campfires looked like flickering red stars, swimming in his eyes, more dream-like than real. It was three-thirty in the morning.

He began to hear the sound of surf for the first time since he'd turned around at Long Point. The sound had a curious effect on him. It was the first time he'd heard anything besides his own voice and the noise of splashing water for several hours. The rise and fall of surf against the shore brought with it a feeling of confirmation. He'd stared at the Keweenaw for so long he couldn't help but wonder, *Is it a trick? Am I dreaming?* With his sense of hearing validating his eyes, he realized—it's there. *I'm close*!

The breakwalls extend into Lake Superior on either side of the Portage Canal. Swells rose and fell on the boulders piled against the steel riprap. Even at night, the spray from the breakers was bright against the black sheet metal. No one stood on the piers. It dawned on Brian he could *see* the piers. His arms continued to paddle, as if disconnected to his body.

Brian paddled by McLain State Park. He didn't want to talk to anybody. "Leave me alone," he said aloud to the campground. His voice sounded odd after not speaking for the past few hours. "All I want to do is sleep," he said aloud again, encouraged by the sound. He paddled past the north pier, continued across the canal opening, and then at the south pier, turned left toward shore. Paddling inside the two breakwalls, the waves died and the water grew quieter. He slowly kayaked alongside the south pier, and for the first time in over ten hours, he stopped paddling and coasted ...

He glided past the boulders and riprap that appeared to grow and then shrink in the smooth swells inside the canal. Taking two last strokes, he felt the kayak stop. His body lurched forward in the seat. In the dark, only half-awake, he'd struck land.

Straining to wriggle out of the cockpit, unable to stand, he crawled up the beach dragging his kayak with him. When he was satisfied everything was beyond the reach of the surf, he slowly tried to get to his feet. The ground swayed under his shaky legs. His terrestrial balance refused to return. Slumping to his knees onto a surface that didn't move, he dragged his sleeping bag out of a compartment and threw it down on the ground.

The last thing he did that night was pull out the flask of Canadian Club he'd bought for this moment. He lifted it toward Lake Superior, and slugged down one gulp. He then fell on top of his bag and slept ...

Brian woke a couple of hours later to flashing lights and sirens. The Coast Guard was beating up the canal out through the pier heads into the lake. It was five-thirty in the morning. He wondered if they were looking for him. He sat up and flashed his headlamp on and off, hoping they'd see him, just in case they were. The ships turned around and went back up the canal. They never came closer for Brian to discover whether he was the reason they were there. Sitting atop his sleeping bag on the beach, shivering, he watched until they disappeared. Chilled from the damp lakeside air, he roused himself to activity. He ate a sandwich and a Snickers Bar, drank some water, rolled the kayak over and repacked it.

In August, daylight comes well before six. The sunrise he'd hoped to see the day before, now dawned bright and clear. The star-filled sky faded into a dark grey and then slowly flushed to a dark shade of violet. He struggled to drag the kayak to the water. He couldn't make a fist. His hands were swollen and clumsy. He managed to shove himself back inside the cockpit, and push off from shore when a wave lifted him off the beach. Every part of his body ached. He barely could hold the paddle. *At least there's no mistaking the way*, he thought.

The Portage Canal is named after an old Indian portage route. For the natives, the portage created a short cut through the base of the Keweenaw Peninsula that saved them a hundred miles of dangerous open-lake travel around Keweenaw Point. The last three miles at the western end of the portage—the side Brian was on—was dug out around the turn of the century to connect the inner-waterway to ship copper ore from the mines from Houghton-Hancock. The mines have been closed for over eighty years. Today, freighters only use the canal during storms.

Three more hours and Brian would be in Dollar Bay. He decided to stop by the dentist in Houghton and get that out of the way. He knew once he went to bed, he'd never wake up for a dentist appointment. The quiet, early-morning paddle up the passage calmed Brian. Returning to the marine world, kayaking seemed more natural than walking. Mists rose from the surface as the cooler morning air caused the water to steam. Ducks swam along the water's edge. Seagulls and crows took up their shore patrol, looking for new discards. The canal paddle was a chance to decompress. Its gentle waves and nearby shores allowed Brian to slowly get the feel of land again.

Brian approached the Isle Royale Headquarters dock in Houghton. He pulled over behind *The Ranger*, the passenger ferry for Isle Royale. No one came down to greet him, nor did he expect anyone. It was still too early for any staff to be in the office and the boat wasn't scheduled to run until Thursday. Gliding up to the dock, he tied off, pulled himself out of the kayak and climbed up a ladder. He stood for a long moment on the dock to gain his balance. When he'd regained as much equilibrium as he was going to find, he walked into town.

Sitting in the dentist's chair that morning, Brian tried to tell the dental hygienists about his trip. They didn't believe him. Maybe they caught the scent of alcohol on his breath. Frustrated, and with dental instruments in his mouth, he decided to be quiet. He'd come a long way for this and submitted to the examination. The dentist seemed to look at him strangely and may have wondered about his unkempt appearance. When they were finished, Brian said thanks and walked out the door. Leaving the office he trudged down Sheldon Avenue in Houghton. It was ten o'clock and shops were just opening up. Turning down the hill toward the canal, he walked back to the dock.

Brian felt far more than numb. His legs wouldn't behave properly. His head was spinning slightly and he waited at the dock until he thought he could safely climb down the ladder and get into his kayak. Managing that, he untied, pushed away from the timbers, and turned east for home. It was just a few more miles to Dollar Bay.

A half hour later, he passed Julio's old boat yard on the point, went through the narrow channel in front of Sandy Bottom park where he'd played growing up, and stroked toward the far side of Dollar Bay. He landed behind the flooring mill, lashed his paddle to the kayak, picked it up, and somehow managed to carry it the three blocks to his parents' house. He set his kayak behind the garage, walked up the back steps, opened the door and stepped into the house.

Brian was home.

His dad was sitting in his chair reading the newspaper. He looked up and asked what Brian was doing home since the ferry to the island wasn't scheduled that day.

"I kayaked home from the island," Brian replied. "I'm going upstairs to bed."

After pausing for a moment to watch Brian's back disappear up the stairs, his dad went back to the paper.

News of Brian's accomplishment spread very slowly. There were no newspaper articles, no interviews for local TV or radio. He had to return to the island to work two days later and he spent most of that time recovering. Only a handful of individuals knew he'd paddled home and they were all back on Isle Royale. He had come and gone back to work so quickly that no one was able to throw together a party before he was back on Isle Royale. There was no dinner in celebration, no pictures, certainly no formal recognition, nor did Brian ever seek any.

His accomplishment, in true local fashion, eventually became a quiet adventure story told only by those who know him around Dollar Bay—a small town of roughly a thousand residents—or by those who work on the island.

He rarely speaks of it. When asked if he'd ever do it again, he responds with a sharp look and says with more than a little emphasis, "No."

His solo crossing is a remarkable accomplishment and perhaps even more amazing for the lack of fanfare it received.

Altogether, he paddled without touching shore at least seventy miles, the trans-lake portion of the crossing took over fourteen hours, beginning at one in the afternoon and ending at three-thirty the following morning. He spent about five hours of the journey in the dark and the first four hours in fog. The paddle up the Portage Canal took an additional three hours. Between departure and walking into the house, including the dentist appointment, the whole event occurred in twenty-four hours.

Lake Superior has been crossed where the lake narrows at either end by kayak several times. There are reports of Native Americans making lake crossings from Isle Royale, as well as a few voyageurs, centuries ago. However, by most accounts, they were in much larger crafts.

Technically, Brian didn't actually paddle all the way across Lake Superior, since he started from Isle Royale. If it is of any importance, he has paddled from Isle Royale to Thunder Bay, Ontario which would complete the journey. The outfitter in Copper Harbor I talked with doesn't know of anyone else who has kayaked from Isle Royale to the Keeweenaw. The Park Serivce says they know of only one other individual besides Brian who has successfully made the crossing.

In 2002 I spent an evening with friends at a restaurant in Copper Harbor. I mentioned that I had family who had worked on Isle Royale. Captain Don of the *Isle Royale Queen* and Mark, his future brother-in-law, were sitting across the table from me. Joining us were Linda and Bob Guiliani, who is past president of the Isle Royale Natural History Association. Mark had worked on the island with Brian, helping to build some of the staff facilities at park headquarters on Mott Island. Mark brightened when I mentioned that Brian was my brother-in-law. "He's a hard worker," he said and then paused with a twinkle in his eye. As if letting me in on a secret, he asked, "Did you know he kayaked across the lake?"

"Yes" I replied, "and I'll never forget how I first heard about it." I told him that, after a phone conversation with her sister, my wife told me that Brian had kayaked home from the island the previous week.

"Didn't she say anything else?" Mark asked.

"Yes, but barely. I remember sitting on the sofa, staring at her, waiting for more details. After she said nothing, I finally had to ask if that was all she knew. She said that her dad told her sister, but either couldn't or wouldn't provide any details."

Mark laughed and shook his head. "That sounds about right."

It took twenty years to get the rest of the story from Brian.

But a few years after the crossing, I was talking with my father-in-law after returning from one of my Isle Royale trips. He had worked on the island building shelters in the sixties. He asked me about the fishing, but before I got my answer out, he leaned over and said, "You know, Brian kayaked home across the lake once."

I smiled in response. It was the first time I had heard him speak of it.

He gave a little knowing nod of his head, and then let me finish my fish-tale. He never mentioned it again.

# THE HOWELLS

Mist and low-riding clouds scudded through the empty campground. I sat at our picnic table we'd moved inside the shelter and propped open the screen door to have a clear view. With forty-degree temperatures, there was no fear of bugs getting inside today. I'd come too far not to enjoy the scenery, even a dreary setting such as this one. The screen door would stay open.

I lit the backpack stove, adjusted the flame into a faint blue fire, and then set the coffee pot filled with lake water atop the stove. The dampness in the air, coupled with the wind, made it feel like November instead of the middle of September. We hadn't seen anyone for three days. The island felt deserted. Except for the occasional ranger cruising by in the distance on the lake, everyone appeared to have gone back to the mainland.

We were beat. Ken lay on his sleeping pad on the floor. He'd pulled his hat over his face and within seconds, snores rose from beneath the brim. I fumbled with the stove, cranking it up higher to heat the water for a little bouillon. We'd fished hard all day. Between the constant wind, the spitting rain, and the gray, dismal weather, we had finally decided late in the afternoon to pull around Belle Isle Pointe, reel in our lures, and point toward camp. Catching nothing, it would be Dinty Moore tonight.

I didn't care. I was glad to get in out of the rain.

Scanning the inside of the shelter, I spotted the journal. Inside each shelter is a notebook for campers to record their experiences while visiting the park. Sometimes during the evenings, I'd read these reports to Ken to fill in quiet moments after dark. Not surprisingly, many of the entries are about the weather. *"Rain, rain, rain … every night, and all the damn-day long"* is a common theme, especially in the springtime. Another frequent complaint contains variations of *"The mosquitoes are the size of hummingbirds. You can't walk to the lake without donating a pint of blood."* Ten exclamation marks usually follow that remark.

Far more graphic descriptions of the insect-filled, soggy weather move from the journals to the inside walls of the shelter in the form of graffiti. It's not difficult to picture the stranded campers, wet, cold, and restless, with the incessant drone of mosquitoes driving them over the line to do something, anything, even if it's to resort to vandalism. Isle Royale is a long way from anywhere. Making the effort to reach the island, hike to some distant campground, and then do nothing but sit caged within a hut is more than just frustrating. The rain and bugs can force you to watch your vacation time-clock slowly tick down to zero.

More days than we care to mention, the lake, the wind, and the fish, all conspire against us. They had been determined today. There are so many great places to fish and we'd tried them all. God knows how many miles we covered in the canoe. Isle Royale's inland lakes and its many coves and bays are long and narrow, just like the main island. The tall ridges on either side of these narrow bodies of water create wind tunnels. On windy days, which are almost every day on Isle Royale, it feels like we are forever paddling into the wind. We call it upstream because it takes three times as long to canoe against the wind and many times that in effort.

When Ken and I are here fishing from the canoe, I sit up front. My role from the front of the canoe is to provide power. Into the wind, I have to paddle with a steady, deliberate stroke in order to maintain the proper trolling speed. My paddling gives us enough speed for Ken to steer from his position at the stern. The forward motion I provide (he paddles, too) allows him to track our lures alongside the drop-offs that run parallel to shore. Downstream paddling, or with the wind in our case, is my chance to rest. There's little need for power since the wind does most of the work. There are even times when we move too fast. We have to set our paddles in the lake to act as sea anchors to maintain correct lure presentation.

The state record lake trout hails from Lake Superior and the lunker weighed sixty-four pounds. Our catches look like minnows compared to that. We've caught a small handful of twenty-pounders. But most of our lakers run in the two-to-four pound class. The big ones are too large to eat at one meal anyway, even for Ken and me, so we prefer the smaller fish for dinner fare. At two-to-four pounds, we only need to catch two or three fish per day. However, it's not uncommon to fish all day for just those two or three.

With so much at stake, getting a strike is a big deal and landing one essential. When we got a hit in the morning on the very first pass going around the point at dawn, and lost him at the canoe, we both groaned and cursed—not a good omen. Superstition and anglers are close friends.

Now, sitting at the table at the end of the day, I stared outside across the open field that is the Belle Isle Campground. Belle Isle, where we so often stay, used to be a 1920s version of a miniature golf course. The grasses remain, standing two feet tall. But small conifers are now scattered across the old course and beginning to return the campground to forest. A resort once stood on the side of the ridge behind our shelter and touted the recuperative powers of the air and water, a common advertisement for North Country lodges of that time period. Golf was an activity meant for the children or for days too windy to go fishing. Before 1915, the year Fred Schofield built his resort, Belle Isle's name had been Fish Island. The name change was another marketing ploy.

The American Fur Company came to Belle Isle in 1837 to establish a fish camp. The beaver, muskrat, mink, and other fur-bearing animals had been trapped out by then. It's reported that when they first arrived an Indian fish camp was already established. Every year thereafter, commercial fishermen lived on Belle Isle. The long history of people fishing from where I sat made me feel part of an on-going tradition.

Several families lived along the north shore of Isle Royale from the 1860s to the 1940s. They set up cabins tucked inside the protected bays, where they lived and worked for seven to eight months of the year before returning to the mainland for the winter. A few families even stayed all year. Isle Royale officially became a National Park on April 3, 1940. The resort on Belle Isle had been closed long before that, a casualty to the Great Depression. Over the following decades, the trees encroached upon the turf. Today, there is very little evidence left of Belle Isle's resort and its golf course.

A fresh gust of wind delivered shreds of mist that moved quickly through the deserted campground like wisps of spirits unable to form an image. I caught myself shivering. Getting up, I found my chook—a pull-over cotton hat and the northern Michigan version of the Canadian quque—and put it on my head to keep warm. Ken didn't stir when I walked over to get my hat. I needed to stretch my legs. They were cramping from sitting like a frog in the front of the canoe all day.

I looked out through the screened front of our lean-to shelter. The scene outdoors grayed even more behind the steel-colored mesh. Needing to go for a walk, I sat back down instead, unable to overcome my desire to hunker down in my cave with its small fire. My mind drifted into that semi-conscious state where strain, damp, and cold combine to dull thinking. I sat staring into the flame.

Ken continued to sleep, and I might as well have napped too. Sitting there in a daze, a familiar sound roused me from my stupor. I slowly turned to look out the door, and blinked in order to look outward instead of inward. Voices carried in the wind. I tilted my head to listen better. The words were indecipherable, but quiet mumbles could be heard in between the gusts of wind that sent the trees behind the shelter into a loud rustle, drowning all other sound but the surf.

As the wind died, I heard them again. There … that was definitely someone speaking, a woman's voice. I looked through the door and as I did, an older couple walked into sight. They were talking to each other.

"Looks like there's no one here, Fred."

He paused and then replied, "Yeah, late in the season for visitors to Belle Isle."

They stood together, gazing across the curved bay in front of the campground. They looked as if they lived here, or more accurately, they looked like they had just stepped off their front porch at home. Dressed in slacks, loafers, and wearing only light nylon zip-up jackets, they could have been standing on their veranda, drinks in hand, admiring the view. I froze, immobilized by the urban normalcy of their behavior against the wilderness background.

At that instant, Fred's wife, who was scanning the campground, swiveled her head my way and looked straight across the field through the open door of our shelter right at me. I stared back.

"Oh Fred, there's someone here after all," she said with a nonchalant shrug. Fred turned and saw me, but said nothing.

I rose from the picnic table and said to Ken, "Hey, someone's here."

He mumbled, lifted his hat, and propped himself on an elbow to see through the bottom of the screen. Hearing the voices, he crawled out of his bag and got up.

I stepped outside, and they walked toward me.

"Well, how are you guys doing?" the woman asked as she approached. "Kind of a dismal day out here today, but it's supposed to blow over this evening. I'm Maude, and this is Fred."

Pulling myself together, I said, "Hello. I'm Vic, and that's Ken. He'll be out in a second."

They looked me up and down, like I'd seen customers judge me at a first meeting before letting me inside the house to discuss their trees. What they saw couldn't have been impressive. Both of us had the tired, soiled appearance of guys who'd fished all day.

Fred was quiet, but Maude broke the silence after a short, uncomfortable pause.

"You boys look like you could use a drink. I see fishing poles leaning against the wall. Do you have any fish? I could cook them for you."

I shook my head.

Waiting again for a reply, she then said, "That's okay. Come anyway. It'd be nice to have some company."

Ken, who had just joined us, saw my blank look and quickly rebounded.

"Thank you. That sounds really good. Where are you staying? We haven't seen anyone for days. How'd you get here?"

Fred turned his attention to Ken, dismissing me as too slow for normal conversation. "We have a boat tied at the dock. Thought this place was empty when we motored by the beach."

"We were fishing in Amygdaloid Channel," Ken said. "Guess we missed each other. You must have arrived while we were out. We haven't been on the south side of Belle Isle or down to the dock since early morning."

"We'll see you in a half-hour?" Maude asked. She seemed to be truly looking forward to entertaining us.

Ken nodded, "See you then. Thanks, again."

They turned and sauntered up the path that leads to the dock, disappearing around a curve in the trail. Ken and I looked at one another and walked back into the shelter.

"Well, let's get ready," I said. "Maybe I should change shirts or something."

"What for?" Ken asked. "I don't have any clean clothes, and neither do you."

I pulled a small mirror out of my kit, glanced at my reflection and winced. Well, at least I can brush my teeth and comb my hair. Ken did too, I noticed. These preparations took all of two minutes. We then spent the next twenty-eight minutes waiting to walk down to the dock at the designated time. We now had a schedule to keep, quickly relapsing into watching the time.

"This could be interesting," I thought aloud.

"Wonder what kind of boat he has?" Ken asked. "It must have sleeping quarters at any rate."

"You ready?"

"Let's go."

We rounded the last turn in the path to the inside arm of Belle Isle and walked down the slope to the lake. Stepping onto the dock, we looked up and stopped. Tied to the cleats was no boat, but a ship. It was at least seventy feet long, a radar mast atop the bridge, and space for more than sleeping quarters. The ship creaked at its bumpers where they protected the hull from the thick wooden beams of the dock as it slowly rose and fell on the waves in the bay.

Maude was apparently waiting for us and immediately opened the rear cabin door and invited us in. Ken's head swiveled forward and aft, checking the ship out carefully. Over the years, Ken had slowly moved up in size with his own boats. His current twenty-three-foot Tiara is a great fishing boat. It's just large enough for Terri and him to sleep in when they choose to remain aboard in the fishing ports along the Great Lakes where they sometimes stay on summer weekends. He was impressed.

I was impressed. Maude opened the door wider, and as I was about to step in, I noticed the white carpeting and jerked my foot back.

"Oh, don't you worry about that," Maude said. "We love visitors and most of them look like you guys."

I almost bit and was about to comply when Ken grabbed my shoulder and hissed under his breath, "Take your boots off."

We did.

Maude smiled and escorted us to the forward area, where Fred met us and asked if we'd like a tour.

Maude excused herself to prepare drinks and appetizers, and for the next half-hour, Fred showed us around. Fred was trying hard not to show his boat off, but he shouldn't have. He was justly proud of her. She was immaculate, containing all of the latest electronics, which he and Ken poured over. Boat-lovers are a separate breed, and Fred found a kindred spirit in Ken. They discussed Lorans, autopilot systems, lake charts and ports. I mostly listened and admired Fred's hard work, which quickly became apparent. Fred and Maude were self-made millionaires, growing up in the Upper Peninsula of Michigan in the city of Marquette. They had moved away to make a fortune in the garbage hauling business at the four corners out west. Fred was well acquainted with dirt and hard work, and I sensed no pretentiousness.

Maude called us down from the bridge to a room that could have doubled as a plush living room from a mansion. We each sat down in cushioned easy chairs. She had already set out hors d'oeuvres of spinach and guacamole dips with chilled shrimp, crab legs, cold cuts, and a tray of crackers and cheese I normally don't see, even at home. She offered wine with European brand names I didn't recognize—no difficult feat—and served it from glassware she brought out from below deck and was visibly thrilled to use.

For the next two hours we sipped on drinks that never seemed to grow warm, discussed Lake Superior, our lives back home, children and grandchildren, and of course, boating. They were semi-retired and had spent the past few summers touring the Great Lakes, especially Lake Superior, which they still called home.

Fred and Ken switched from talking about boats to discussing the construction business. With their money, Fred and Maude had started a commercial construction company. Fred and Maude made a big point of saying they worked at it together. Back home, Ken works as a Project Manager for a large commercial contractor. The three of them were soon into an in-depth conversation about the state of the industry. Maude noticed me drifting out of the conversation and she asked me how I came to love the North Country. We were soon cross-checking each other's family members who live in the upper peninsula to see if we knew anyone in common.

We were all having a wonderful time, and with the help of the wine, were soon in great spirits. They too hadn't seen or talked with anyone for several days. They had been cruising along the north shore of Lake Superior and hadn't been in port for some time, anchoring in isolated coves instead. The four of us, perhaps relieved to have someone new to converse with, never stopped talking, except to refill a glass or to compliment Maude on her Isle Royale table fare.

The cabin where we sat was located at the rear of the ship, walled on three sides from floor to ceiling with glass. Fred had docked with the bow pointed toward the big lake, and the stern toward the end of Robinson Bay. We could see up the entire length of the bay from our easy chairs, which faced aft to take advantage of the view.

The weather was breaking as Maude had predicted. The low scurrying clouds were dissipating and the sun broke free near the western horizon at what couldn't have been a more perfect moment. A sunset, the likes of which is only seen from the middle of Lake Superior, unfolded before us. Sitting as if in a theater, we watched the sky slowly clear, washed spotless from the streaming, day-long mists. The sun beamed eastward upon retreating cloud-banks. Golds, reds, and flame colors of every tint grew in intensity as if Fred and Maude controlled the master dimmer switch, and were slowly cranking it to full power. The bay glowed and the retreating clouds were edged with an aura of bright light.

We were experiencing something we dared not take for granted. Our conversation grew silent as we gazed west. The sun settled atop the trees and then slid behind them, showering the surface of the darkening water with rays of violet-hued light. Sunbeams streamed through the branches. We watched the sun sink and the daylight fade into gray and then black. Not until we could barely see did Maude get out of her chair and turn the lights on inside the cabin. She offered to refill my glass and asked us to stay for dinner.

Ken piped up before I could reply, "No, you have been more than kind, and we should get back."

I looked over at him with a puzzled expression, and then realized he was right.

This was too easy. In just two hours, I'd re-acclimated to climate control, to sitting on sofas, and to food set within arm's reach. Ken got up and moved toward the door. I followed, both of us thanking our hosts profusely. We exchanged mailing addresses and said good night.

Stepping outside onto the dock, we said goodbye to Maude who let us out from the rear cabin door. Our eyes had grown accustomed to the light aboard the ship. When she shut the door, everything went black for a moment until our eyes could read adjust. The sharp wind coming down the bay quickly reminded us where we really were. Stumbling down the path back to the shelter, since we'd forgotten to bring our flashlights, we came back to a cold, dark campground and to the barren wooden box we called shelter.

After we returned, Ken talked about Fred's boat for a while, and finally said to me in chastisement, "What were you going to do, ask to stay the night?"

Thinking about it for a second, I replied. "If they'd offered me linen sheets and turn-down service, I'm not sure I wouldn't have accepted."

The Howells, as I came to nickname them after the Gilligan's Island wealthy couple, send us Christmas cards, and Ken has stayed in better contact than I have. However, neither of us has seen them again. That drizzly evening in September on the north shore of Isle Royale—where we shared wine served in crystal, hors d'oeuvres of chilled seafood and cheese, and the most inspiring sunset I've ever been privileged to see—is now only another memory of an odd adventure on the island.

They motored out of the bay early the next morning. We waved goodbye from the beach. Fred blasted his horn three times in farewell.

"I guess we won't be drinking wine tonight," I said as we turned to walk back to the shelter.

"You about ready to go fishing?" Ken asked.

"Looks like the wind's up," I mumbled.

Ken thought about it for a second. He hesitated in his stride, and just as I thought he was going to comment further on last night, he said, "Might rain too."

# SPRINKLED IN STARLIGHT

THE FISH WERE ON THE BITE THE DAY SAM LEFT ISLE ROYALE TO GO HOME. We'd spent the past five days together, fishing the north shore, using Belle Isle as base camp. Sam, the older of our two sons, had just turned twenty-five. I would turn fifty in a couple of weeks. My bosses at the tree service had been gracious enough to let me get away for a month-long, mini-sabbatical (a first for me) to celebrate our milestones.

Sam had recently started a new job and needed to get back to work. I was remaining for three more weeks on the island, and the preparations for living a month on Isle Royale took an entire year. I'd joined a gym to get into shape, wore hiking boots for weeks to break them in, gathered supplies, packed and repacked until it all felt just right.

In order to spend as much time as possible with Sam, I wanted to travel with him back as far as Rock Harbor where the passenger ferries pick up campers to return to the Michigan mainland. To accompany him and then return to Belle Isle would mean doing the awful portages over of the island twice in one day. Sam told me I didn't need to. Looking at the map we always carry with us, he traced out a new course that would avoid the portages. He pointed out how we could canoe to Lane Cove, just a mile-long paddle. From there, we could leave the canoe, and hike the Lane Cove Trail all the way into Rock Harbor.

"Dad, it's just a six-mile hike to the docks. In fact, you could just drop me off at Lane Cove. I can walk the rest of the way on my own. I don't mind."

I questioned his logic by pointing out he would have to carry all of his stuff in his backpack, instead of floating his gear for most of the way in the canoe. At twenty-five, he didn't seem to think that was a big deal.

"And Dad," he answered, "if you come—and really, that's not necessary—*you* will only need a small daypack."

When we arrived at Rock Harbor, the Lodge was still open. The Rock Harbor Lodge serves the island as a hotel for three months during the summer. Run by a concessionaire, it's the last vestige of the resort era. At one time, I wrinkled my nose at the "Inn" on Isle Royale—not in keeping with the true spirit of a Wilderness National Park and that sort of thinking. I've changed my mind in recent years. The Lodge provides a place to stay for those who are either unable to camp or choose not to. At the Lodge, guests can listen to Rangers give educational programs, go on short nature hikes or relax and watch the world unfold from a place with no motor vehicles.

It was early September, and the hotel was closing for the season the next day. Sam suggested we stop and have a hamburger before he boarded the *Isle Royale Queen*.

"Have a hamburger?" I asked.

"There's a snack bar."

"You've got to be kidding."

"Yeah, on my last trip, my friends wanted a change from freeze-dried meals, so we hiked to Rock Harbor following the same route we just took and had burgers. After hanging out for awhile, we walked back to Lane Cove, picked up the canoe and paddled back to Belle Isle."

"You make it sound like you went to town for the day."

Sam shrugged and smiled in reply.

He and some friends had been to the island three weeks earlier for a ten-day trip. Ken and I always blow out of Rock Harbor as fast as we can in order to avoid all the people. In all of my years of going to the island, I never knew there was a restaurant.

After we'd *dined*, I told him I wanted to get started back. "It's a three-hour hike and who knows what the weather will do. All of my stuff is in the shelter at Belle Isle. If the winds pick up and I can't paddle across Robinson Bay, I'll be stuck." Although true, this was mostly an excuse. I really wanted to avoid standing alone at the dock watching him sail away.

He understood. We walked a short way up the trail where we said our goodbyes.

He hugged me and wished me luck. Seeing my growing realization that I was about to be alone for the next couple of weeks, he tried reassuring me and said, "You'll be fine, Dad."

He then turned and walked down the path to the dock. The trail looked empty when he disappeared around a bend.

The return to Belle Isle was a quiet one. It was a beautiful day, sunny and cool, a perfect Isle Royale day. The trail for the first three miles out of Rock Harbor is mostly flat and smooth, and well worn from steady use. The path I was on runs beside Tobin Harbor, a six-mile long, blue finger of Lake Superior. An eagle keened from his perch in an old pine on one of the many islands in the skinny bay and small birds sang from the trees as I hiked. Deep in thought, it was all background music turned too low to catch the words. Carrying no extra weight, I had one of the most comfortable walks I'd ever done at Isle Royale. Despite the leisurely pace, I hardly noticed the beautiful setting, thinking mostly about Sam.

Following high school, he'd left home to attend Michigan Tech, located in the Keweenaw Peninsula at the northern end of Michigan. He dropped out after a couple of years, much to his mother's and my objections. Sam stayed in the Keweenaw, not returning downstate where good-paying jobs were easier to find and where he'd be closer to his family. He was forging a life for himself "up north" as we call it downstate, facing the difficulties, plus a few extras, a young man encounters when getting started. Difficulties his mother and I hoped to soften.

Sam and I had caught up on "news" over the past five days. After dark, sitting together in the shelter by candlelight, our conversations ranged from what was happening back home to talk about how his brother. Nick had also moved away and had just started a new job as a youth pastor. We discussed all of the unique challenges he'd face and how hard it was to imagine his little brother as Pastor Nick.

Sam and I also covered how much it cost him to pay rent, own a car, buy all of the toys he wants, and still have enough money left over to eat. Fishing was discussed too, of course. Sam struggled financially when he broke the home-strings, but without saying it directly, told me the independence was worth it, which was a little hard to hear. Somehow, you think your own kids will prefer to stay, at minimum, within an hour of home.

When we talked, he shared cautiously. He had his own secrets to guard now, and phrased things carefully. It wasn't as if I wanted him to become a small child again. On the other hand, I missed those endless, bare-hearted questions young sons ask their fathers. He'd acquired that adult ability to say only as much as he wanted me to know, a self-defense mechanism we all, unfortunately, have to learn.

Our time together seemed all too short. My grandfather and then my dad had both warned me time flies. They were right. After five whole days of being within a few feet from Sam, I had a hard time saying goodbye—again.

A solitary venture on Isle Royale spread before me and for the next two weeks, I planned to experience it at my own pace. Two whole weeks of fishing, camping, canoeing, and soaking in as much of the island as I could absorb. Ken would join me at the end of two weeks for our usual fishing vacation.

However, after leaving Sam in Rock Harbor—the start-up to my solo trip—I wasn't as excited as I'd hoped. Hiking alone down the trail alongside the bay, I looked back over my shoulder from time to time, half-expecting to see him running down the path to catch up.

The return trip took me up and over the Greenstone Ridge. Without the Smoker Craft or heavy packs, it was no more difficult than walking up a long hill. The final leg of the hike is a three-mile walk from the top of the ridge to the north shore of the main island. Coasting downhill, light on my feet, despite walking six miles to drop Sam off in the morning and six miles to return in the afternoon, I cruised into Lane Cove still feeling strong.

*What a great route, Sam,* I thought.

The canoe was right where I'd left it. Despite Sam's reassurances that nobody on Isle Royale would ever steal a canoe—especially that canoe—I had worried all day about leaving it unguarded in Lane Cove. Being from Detroit, I'd been taught to lock all doors, going so far as to hide the paddles in the woods. Sam had wrinkled his nose at that. With a sense of relief, I dragged the canoe into the lake, threw my daypack in, and shoved off.

Winds were light and the solo-paddle across the bay presented no problems. When I rounded Cork Island an hour later, the Belle Isle campground came into sight. At a couple of hundred yards offshore, I could just make out the sound of a harmonica over the splash of water. Music is such a human sound. After seeing no one since leaving Rock Harbor and canoeing across a mile of empty lake, the sound of a harmonica felt out of place.

The tune was unclear, but as I got closer, "The Yellow Rose of Texas" drifted over the water. I thought, *Strange song for someone to play way up here.*

A couple of kayaks and one of the park's rental canoes were pulled up on shore in front of the campground. Someone was banging pots, and I heard the squeak of a shelter's screen door as I approached the beach. No one was in sight.

Gentle rollers from the big lake moved across the surface of the protected cove, only evident by their slow rise and fall at shore. They lent a rhythmic lift to the canoe. Wash from surf created a muffled prattle as water tumbled through the gravel when the surge receded. Canoeing the last fifty feet, I watched the bottom rise quickly from its depths and then shallow-off. The nose of the canoe ground against the pebbly beach. I got out, pulled the canoe all the way up the bank, and flipped it over in case it rained in the night.

Back at Rock Harbor, I had picked up a can of corned beef hash at the store, another park convenience I'd never noticed before until Sam pointed it out. I would have no time to go fishing, and I'd be hungry when I returned to camp. Sam's more pragmatic attitude, similar to his mother's, had rubbed off on me.

Dinner was on my mind when I walked up to the shelter. As I stepped inside and saw Sam's stuff missing, it hit me all over again that I was all alone—alone for two whole weeks. "Better stay busy," I said, and commenced to reorganize the shelter. Sam worked for a year as a cook in his attempts to subsist in the Keweenaw, and he'd done most of the fish frying and made most of our meals. I now reorganized the kitchen and set supplies where I was accustomed to having them.

At the center of the Belle Isle Campground is a pavilion. In it, a small group of campers gathered, poking at a very dismal, smoky fire that smoldered in the big stone fireplace. One of them was playing the harmonica, and he was starting into another rendition of *The Yellow Rose* … "This could get old," I muttered. I unpacked the few items from my daypack, lit the stove, dug out the can opener, and poured the ingredients into a saucepan.

While I was cleaning dishes after dinner down at the lake, two guys around thirty-five years old, looking a bit weary and bedraggled, and a young boy, perhaps ten, walked over to say hello. With an unmistakable Texas drawl, the friendlier looking of the two said, "Hi, my name is Paul. This is Gerald, and this is my son Mark."

"Hi," I said. We all shook hands.

"How'd you get here? We didn't see you come in." Paul said. "We're staying in that shelter … over there." He pointed to the shelter next to mine. "We just rolled in earlier today. Didn't know if we'd make it. Sure is beautiful. Have you been here before?"

I was in no frame of mind for conversation. Their friendliness, like their accent, clashed with the surroundings. Most campers keep to themselves at Isle Royale, and Midwestern accents are predominant. I chalked up their openness to Southern manners.

"Well … actually," I began, "I'm staying in the shelter next to yours. I just returned from Rock Harbor an hour ago—where I dropped off my son. He had to go home today."

They looked like they were trying to piece that information together. While they paused, I added, "We've been at Belle Isle for the past five days. All of my gear is already inside the shelter, so you probably missed my one trip up from the beach. I guess I've been to Belle Isle about a dozen times."

They didn't say anymore, as if still wondering how I snuck past them.

"You're obviously not from around here. If it isn't too forward, how did *you* get here?"

They all gave me broad smiles as if thrilled to find someone willing to talk. "We're from the Dallas area, and it's blazing hot. I called Gerald and said 'How about a little vacation? I got some time coming to me, and we're slow at work right now.' Gerald said, 'Where do you want to go?' I said, 'Somewhere cold.' We looked at a map, and this was as far north as we could get without leaving the country."

"You just looked at a map and happened to pick here?" I asked.

All three of them nodded.

Paul continued. "Mark doesn't start school for two weeks. His mother and I are divorced, and she said he could come along. Said it might do him good. We drove all day and all night, boarded the boat at Copper Harbor, rented a canoe, and here we are."

I scratched my head and then stopped, thinking it might imply an inappropriate amount of amazement. Paul and Gerald didn't look like they could handle the hike over the Greenstone. I studied them more closely. They appeared a tad portly, like they never got off the couch.

As tactfully as I could, I asked, "Which way did you come to get to Belle Isle?"

They'd obviously been itching to tell this story. Gerald jumped into the conversation and quickly piped in, "We were gonna backpack, but I twisted my knee unloading all of our supplies from the ferryboat. We decided to rent a canoe. Never been in one before, but what else could we do? We paddled around the point."

"You paddled all the way around Blake Point?" Blake Point was notoriously rough. I'd never risked paddling around it.

They enthusiastically nodded in unison.

Paul said, "Yeah, the guy who rented us the canoe said we were sure to drown. Shook his head at us when he saw the sides of the canoe only stuck four inches out of the water. As we were paddling away, he yelled after us, 'You put your lifejackets on and don't take them off!'"

Gerald sheepishly said, "We nearly did drown, too. That's crazy water off that point. Waves kind of smash into one another. We swamped once. Had to get to shore quick-like. After dumping the water out, we tried again. Water slurped in a couple of times, but we managed."

Paul finished their story. "It took forever to get all the way here. When we landed, we all kissed the beach. Our stuff is still drying out."

I was a bit stunned, but managed to finally say, "Well I'm very glad you made it," meaning it more than they knew.

The whole while we were talking, Paul's son Mark never said a word. He almost clung to his dad and looked painfully timid. I could only imagine what his day had felt like. I looked straight at Mark and said again, "Glad you're *all* here. I hope you enjoy yourselves."

Mark gave me a shy smile.

We each returned to our respective shelters. It was getting dark and I tried to do some reading before turning in. I couldn't focus. The wooden walls felt bare and camp dreary. Closing the book, I decided to go for a walk.

Stepping outside, I waited until my eyes adjusted to the dark, and then strolled down to shore. The lake was still calm. The evening star was rising over top of the distant ridge. Mars glinted bright and prominent in the black sky, tinged red, unless that was just my imagination. Directly overhead was Ursa Major, and I followed the line of the big dipper until I located the dim north star.

"Polaris, they call it. No Northern Lights tonight, though— too bad. Lake Superior's quiet, maybe she's brooding too," I said aloud and then shook my head. "You're reading way too much into all of this. Go to bed. You're already talking to yourself."

On the way back to the shelter, I could hear Gerald playing his harmonica from the pavilion. Some other campers had joined him and were laughing quietly, their voices carrying over the slight rustle of leaves.

*It's too early for bed.* I thought to myself.

Paul greeted me warmly as I stepped under the roofed, open-air pavilion and into the light from the fire. Six picnic tables were tucked inside. The pavilion is a remnant of the old resort at Belle Isle that closed in the 1930s. Journals from that time say the guests would gather here to listen to fireside stories or do sing-a-longs. The Park Service tore the resort down when they created the campground but retained the pavilion, pouring a new concrete pad and rebuilding the sagging roof. The mammoth stonework fireplace was all that was left of the original structure.

Gerald and Mark were there too. Mark ventured to say "hi" when I said "hi" to him. There were two new people. They were a young couple, kayaking for four days before they had to return to Wisconsin. When introductions were finished, we talked about the park and our homes, wildlife sightings—the usual camp conversation. Gerald entertained us with his harmonica. He tried to get us to sing "Oh Susanna," but we sounded so weak and pitiful, he, thankfully, gave up.

He also told the story of the *Windigo*. The *Windigo* is an Ojibwe legend about a monster disguised as an old woman who entices people into her home where she then reverts to a monster and proceeds to eat them. The story was meant, in part, as a lesson to Ojibwe children to avoid overly friendly strangers. The Sioux and Ojibwe raided one another's lands for centuries, kidnapping each other for slaves. Gerald, for not living anywhere near the Great Lakes, did a pretty good job telling the local legend. He howled and whistled like a wolf, aping the ghouls that accompany the hag, who wait hidden in the trees until her captives are secured.

After the Wisconsin couple retired to their shelter, and Mark and Gerald turned in, Paul stayed behind nursing the fire. We sat there, silently watching the embers glow as the last flames died.

Paul broke the silence. "Mark's mother and I split about a year and a half ago. It's been real hard on him. She moved away shortly after that, and I don't get to see him much any more. They live with her sisters, and they all pick on him." He paused, frowned and then said, "Poor kid can't fart without them telling him how he did it wrong."

I didn't respond.

"Not sure how much longer my job's gonna last either," he continued after I remained silent. "When I left for this here vacation, I got the feeling I wouldn't be missed."

"Mark seems like a nice kid," I ventured. "It must be awful rough living that far from your son."

Paul nodded slowly, blinked, and said, "I don't know if you noticed or not, but Gerald kind of teases Mark too, and not all too kindly. He can get nasty."

I had noticed. Trying to change the topic, I said. "You guys came an awful long way to get here. That was pretty bold."

"Yeah, kind of surprising, really, and it's even more surprising Mark's mother let him go. She don't care much for me, and not afraid to say so. I'm sure she ridicules me in front of him."

"Maybe so, but he seems to hang on you for all of that. I don't sense any disregard for you."

He didn't respond at first, as if checking if that were true. "Maybe," he finally replied.

We sat staring into the red and orange coals that shimmered in the hearth.

After a long pause, Paul said more to himself than to me, "I hardly sleep anymore. Even now, as tired as I am, I hate to go to bed."

"Well, maybe you should try," I suggested quietly. "We both have had a long day. I'm gonna hit the sack," I yawned. "Tomorrow's another big one. See you around."

"Good night," Paul said.


The next day I planned to fish. I needed to catch dinner and the sooner I got after it, the sooner I could relax. Waking before dawn, I rigged the canoe, setting the rod holders in their brackets, and the stringer and landing net inside with all of my tackle. I also filled a sack with rocks, placing it at the front of the canoe for a counter-weight. With no one to offset my weight, the bow sits too high out of the water. Every little gust catches the nose like a sail. Some people, when they solo paddle, paddle from the middle of the canoe. I've never cared for it. It causes the canoe to lean too far to one side for my tastes.

I trolled all morning with no success, but about mid-afternoon, I got a strike. I was running tight to shore alongside a steep drop-off, well inside Robinson Bay. On one rod, I was trolling a shad-rap on a bullwhip, Shimano fishing pole. The rod and reel—my favorite—had been a gift from the guys I worked with when I left a former job. I set it in the rod holder, mounted to the crossbeam directly in front of me within easy reach. The second rod, an even older, seven-foot Shimano Quickfire, trailed a shallow swimming Raapala. The pole was stationed on the canoe's stern deck, directly behind me. The drag was set loose so I would hear the whine if it hooked a fish, which it did.

A nice seven-pound laker rose for the bait. The whirl from the reel startled me so much I almost tipped over. I tightened the drag and reeled him in. He was big enough to provide three dinners. Sliding the stringer through his gills and securing him to the canoe, I pulled lines and paddled for camp.

When I arrived, my new friends came down to greet me.

"Where you been all day? We were getting worried," Paul said.

Not accustomed to such concern out here, I answered, "I was fishing." For proof, and to show off a little, I lifted the trout out of the water.

They were duly impressed. Mark, for the first time, stepped forward from his father.

"What kind of a fish is that?" he asked.

"*That* is a lake trout."

"You gonna eat it?"

"That's the plan. Want to watch him for a second, while I go get my fillet knife?"

He nodded his head. His dad and uncle walked back to their shelter, where they'd evidently stayed all day.

"He should be fine," I said to Mark. "I've lost fish to seagulls and otters and fox. All you have to do is stand here. I'll be right back."

At the mention of the scavengers, he hesitated. "I don't know."

"It's okay. I'll only be a second. Just shout if you see anything."

I jogged up to the shelter, grabbed my knife, a plate, and a couple of baggies, and hustled back down to the lake. He was standing guard over the fish, tugging slightly at the stringer to see if he could get it to move.

"Thanks," I said.

"Can I watch?"

"Sure. It'll be nice to have some company."

I cleaned the fish, something he'd never witnessed before. He was genuinely interested, following my explanations of why certain cuts went where, and in what order. Thinking I'd like to encourage him, I kept talking, attempting to hold his interest. We talked about the types of fish found at Isle Royale. I told him Sam had out-fished me on a windy day when we couldn't get on the lake in the canoe and dinner depended on our success. "He cast from shore long after I quit," I bragged. "Wish you could have met him."

Mark behaved as if no one ever talked to him as an equal. He listened well, asking questions about the animals that "steal fish," which seemed to pique his curiosity. He also wondered, "What do you do when you're here all by yourself?"

"Well … fish, read, write … finally have some time to just think and look around. I've never done this before, set off alone without family or friends. Guess I wanted to see if I could handle it."

He seemed to understand.

"I better get these up to the shelter. Thanks for the help."

"Bye," Mark answered.

Paul and Gerald cornered me the next morning. Paul picked up where he left off the night before and Gerald chipped in his version of life back home. In addition to hating their jobs, they were both divorced and bitter. "Treat us like minions," Gerald described his workplace. "It's just like Dilbert's cubicle world and his pointy haired boss." They didn't like their apartments. The weather was too hot. The economy was bad, and so on. I think they would have continued all day if I'd stayed to listen, reinforcing one another's gripes. I finally had to interrupt and say I needed to get on the water.

Gerald had agreed with Paul's assessment of Mark's mother and aunts. He said they hounded the kid. "Even his sisters rail at him," Gerald complained. He seemed unaware of his own belittling of Mark.

We spent the next four days at Belle Isle, and despite their tendency to obsess over their problems, their friendliness was contagious. Every night under the pavilion around the fire, we'd gather, along with several other campers, to discuss the day's events. Due in large part to their blunt questions, over the course of the next four evenings we got to know several new people.

Previously avoiding people with Ken, I discovered everyone has their own reasons for being at Isle Royale.

Hans and his canoeing partner Jorge were entrepreneurs, recently selling their lucrative manufacturing business. They were taking several months off, and Isle Royale was just one of many remote locations they were taking in. Hans said he was in search of ideas. "Need something new to sink my teeth into," is how he put it. He went so far as to pull me aside to tell me if I ever had any ideas for new inventions to be sure to email him. Nothing came to mind. I did try emailing him when I got home. My message bounced back.

Another father/son tandem showed up while we were there. From Minnesota, Dad was a Lutheran minister, the son a firefighter. They moved with a coordination that reflected a long-established knowledge of what each other was thinking. Conversation seemed to only slow them down. Even the Texans had a difficult time denting their polite, but reserved, answers to their probes.

Steve and Yohanna arrived in a motor boat. Married, Steve fished and Yohanna spent most of her time sun bathing. They hummed with activity around camp, anxious to see more of the island, and apparently happy to have visitors. Paul and Gerald, along with the rest of the mostly male contingent, stopped by their shelter on a regular basis to see if they needed anything. Yohanna was extremely attractive. Steve and Yohanna remained cordial, never once hinting at any distaste to the attention.

Another young couple arrived, engaged. They were canoeing, planning to travel in the same direction I'd soon be heading. They were bound for Birch Island. I was to see more of them in a few days.

One night, Paul, Gerald, and Mark decided to sleep outside instead of their shelter. They spread a tarp on the ground at dusk and threw their sleeping bags on top. When I went to bed, the three of them lay in a row in their sleeping bags with only their heads sticking out staring wide-eyed at the sky.

At about two in the morning, they were rewarded for their nightwatch with a brilliant display of Northern Lights. Their oohs and aaahs woke me. I scrambled out of my bag and peeked outside. The Aurora Borealis was so bright it lit the campground as if it was early dawn. Greens, blues, even some reds and purples, streaked from horizon to horizon. Some rays shot across the sky like phasers. Others hovered in the air, pulsing. Several people had also left their warm bedrolls to stand in the clearing, necks cranked skyward. Everyone cheered as if at a sporting event when one spectacular shimmer parked overhead.

The lights were much discussed the next evening around the fire.

"What are they?" "Why don't we see them in Texas?" "Do you know when they'll appear?" "What are they again?"

I tried explaining what little I understood about them. Somehow, I'd become the resident expert.

"Northern Lights are still somewhat of a mystery," I said. "Has something to do with solar radiation reacting in the ionosphere when it passes through the earth's atmosphere at the magnetic poles, or so I've read. They used to think they were the sun's reflection off the polar icecaps, sort of a prism effect. But that's not the case."

They couldn't get over how silent they are. "All that glory with nary a whisper," Paul said.

"Yeah Dad," Mark responded. "Like fireworks without the boom. One second the sky's starry, the next it's blasted with color—made me shake all over."

The Texans, as they came to be called, were amazed at almost everything they saw. They couldn't get over Lake Superior and "all of that water," which they would only wade knee-deep into. "Too cold to swim, that's for sure," Mark said. They also marveled at the camp fox, which quickly found them a soft touch for handouts.

However, their favorite pastime was visiting with all of the campers. They conversed freely with kayakers who came and went, and especially looked forward to visits from the Ranger. Socializing is how they spent most of their time. Despite the natural wonders that surrounded them, it was the people they found fascinating, acting as if they were in a foreign country where everyone had strange accents. It took all three of them a day to recover from their expedition north. By day two, however, they began to rouse themselves and pursue their individual interests.

Gerald was the photographer in the group. He snapped pictures of wildflowers and of sunrises that the eastern-facing Belle Isle campground affords. Some of the cynicism faded from Gerald when he smiled, as he did when asking campers to pose for group shots.

Paul threw himself into caring for Mark and Gerald. He became camp foreman. He made meals, organized their supplies, studied the map to create the day's itinerary, and he slept. He told me when we sat around the fire that first night that he couldn't fall asleep, and constantly felt tired. However, after only the second night on Isle Royale, he said he was sleeping much better. The dark circles under his eyes disappeared and he no longer shuffled around camp. He stepped with purpose. He grew more alert, and started to notice the fox squirrels who scolded him when he got too close or the Canadian Jays feeding on crumbs fallen from the picnic table.

I could almost swear Mark was losing his baby face. He began to stray from camp, getting braver and bolder each day, stretching his explorations to farther reaches of Belle Isle. One day, I saw him venture alone atop an outcrop, climbing among the boulders on the knoll that overlooks Robinson Bay. He jumped from rock to rock, and then edged out to the lip of an overhang, daring to teeter at the prow of Belle Isle. His young face reflected the wild expanse of Lake Superior with its rugged headlands.

Paul asked me earlier if I'd lend them a couple of casting spoons. Mark was too shy to ask directly, he said. They brought fishing poles but only had tackle for bobber fishing, and there are no worms at Belle Isle.

Later that day, coming around the point in the canoe, I found Mark fishing, all alone, breakers splashing his feet. Robinson Bay drops fast at the point, making it an ideal location for lake trout to ambush small fish. Mark reminded me of Sam, who caught the fish we'd needed for dinner just a week ago from exactly the same spot. Mark was casting the daredevil I lent him.

"Nice cast," I said, surprising him as he threw out. He was faced the other way and hadn't noticed me trolling up the shoreline. "Had any luck?" I asked.

"Nah, thought I had a bite once, not sure."

"What did it feel like?"

"Like someone pulled back and then let go."

"Could be," I said. "When you throw out, stay away from the left side. It's shallow over there. You'll get snagged."

"Okay. How are you doing?" he asked.

"About the same, that's where Sam caught his fish. Keep trying, Mark, you might get lucky," I said as I canoed past.

In the evening, when dinner and wash-up was completed, I heard Mark running through the undergrowth. Laughter spilled from him. Paul was chasing him around the campground. I'm not sure what Mark had done, but Paul was pretending to be angry and was imitating the *Windigo;* growling, baying, shuffling after Mark, his arms swung low like a pursuing ape, knuckles scuffing the ground. I laughed from the doorway of my shelter as I watched them. Paul finally caught up to Mark. He squealed when Paul threw him over his shoulder, mockingly dragging him off to his lair. He kicked and screamed until Paul set him down and Mark took off, teasing Paul to chase him again.

*Ten years old*, I thought, *what a great age.*

On their fifth and last night at Belle Isle, we sat around the old stone fireplace in the pavilion. All three of them now moved and spoke as if they lived here. It was nice to see them more relaxed, enjoying themselves, less focused on their troubles.

Gerald told ghost stories. Mark couldn't sit still and wandered in and out of the pavilion chasing strange night-sounds and other curiosities that caught his attention. Paul looked awake. And, for the umpteenth time, I listened to "The Yellow Rose of Texas."

Everyone in camp breathed a sigh of relief when the Texans decided to take the water-taxi to return to Rock Harbor. They had threatened to try canoeing back. Both the ranger and I had strongly encouraged them not to risk paddling around Blake Point again. They were reluctant, but in the end agreed.

The morning they left, they asked me to take their picture. Standing together on the gravel beach, canoe paddles in their hands, they smiled into the lens. I took three shots and said, "Gerald, when you get these developed, will you send me one?"

"Sure."

We exchanged addresses and said our good-byes. As they boarded the water-taxi, I said with a mock Texas drawl. "I know it's a long ways, but I hope to someday see *y'all* again."

"We'll be back," Paul said. Gerald and Mark nodded agreement.

We laughed and then waved until they steamed around the point.

# MEN, WOMEN,
## CANOES, AND KAYAKS

"How heavy did the guy at the Skampt Shop say the canoe is?"

"He said you don't want to know," I answered.

We hoisted our packs onto our shoulders and prepared for the portage. I shaded my eyes with my hand and looked up at the distant top of the Greenstone Ridge, and not for the first time, asked Ken, "Why do you insist on doing this portage in one trip?"

"We've been over this before. I hate covering the same ground twice. It wastes time."

"We have all day. What's the rush, *and,*" I said with a little extra emphasis, "why break our backs doing it?"

"To reach camp in time to go fishing today—of course."

Any sane person would take two trips instead of one to carry all of our gear and the canoe clear over the top of the Greenstone Ridge. During this trek I think of Ken as "A Man Called Horse." He and I are the same height, but he outweighs me by twenty-five pounds. Those pounds aren't fat. The packs I carry over the island have all the food, the cooking equipment, the paddles, and fishing gear for a week's stay. Sounds like a lot. It is.

Ken carries all of the clothes in his pack, making his pack bulky, but light. However, he makes up for it and then some by lugging the canoe on his shoulders at the same time.

We checked each other's loads and adjusted the straps. Standing there shivering from stripping to nothing but shorts, a tee-shirt, and hiking boots in the fifty degree sunshine, I took a deep breath as my heavy pack settled into place. I'd be warm soon enough.

I'd bought the heavy old aluminum canoe from my brother-in-law Brian, who worked on the island, and had bought it from someone else, who said it wasn't new when he got it either. Before venturing onto Lake Superior with it, I wanted to know how seaworthy it was. When I asked the pro at the Skampt Shop about the old Smoker Craft he said, "It's a great lake canoe, very stable, heavy and wide. They quit making those a long time ago. They're built from the same metal they use to build aircraft. You'll never put a hole in it, but I'd hate to think how much one weighs."

He had continued to tell me about the canoe, giving me more information than I'd ever be able to retain. His knowledge of canoes was impressive. He looked me up and down, wondering, I'm sure, how I managed to lift a Smoker Craft over my head. I didn't mention I seldom carry the canoe.

The battered craft would not have made it into Canoe and Kayak Magazine. We'd modified it, installing a portage yoke and fishing rod holders. The hull had lots of dents and creases, caused from the rocks and stones along the island's bony shoreline. A couple of struts were also warped. They looked suspicious, like someone had dropped it on a rock, no doubt from fatigue carrying it. Despite it being my canoe, Ken took it upon himself to get the struts reinforced. Over the years, the canoe had grown on us. We liked to think its rugged and weathered appearance and its unpretentious nature matched ours. More importantly, and just as the pro at the Skampt Shop told me, it handled big water like a small boat.

People don't come to Isle Royale for the gift shops. They come to experience one of the most pristine environments in the Midwest, and since the words "crowds and pristine" rarely go together, campers tend to avoid each other. After the initial park orientation, there's a rush of hikers down the two trails leading out of the Ranger Station at Rock Harbor. The newly released adventurers, attempting to flee from one another, look like a pedestrian rush hour on Madison Avenue as they scurry down the trail, carrying backpacks instead of briefcases.

The best way to avoid this herd is to take to the lake. But even then, anyone who canoes or kayaks must paddle out of the head of the bay in a fleet. Ken and I circumvent this by portaging directly over the top of the island to the North Shore. Five minutes after leaving orientation, we're all alone.

We've turned lugging the Smoker Craft over the top of the Greenstone Ridge into an island initiation. Every year we look forward to this hike and dread it at the same time. This is why we try to stay in shape the rest of the year. The portage is one mile of carrying our fully loaded packs, fishing equipment, and our canoe several hundred feet up and several hundred steep feet down over the most rugged portage trail on Isle Royale.

The park map grades the portages by ease of use. Many of them are described as "easy" or "up and over." The portage trail from Tobin Harbor into Duncan Bay and thus to the north shore—the one we were about to use—reads "extremely difficult." Being younger when we first tried this route, the designation made it seem all the more attractive. Over the ensuing years, the portage over the Greenstone had become a test for our fitness. In a good year, we make it all the way to the top of the ridge without stopping for a rest.

If we pack light, if we load our packs smart, if we balance everything atop our shoulders wisely, using our legs instead of our shoulders to support the weight, *and* if we stay in shape, we can do it.

Most years we don't.

We have an unspoken rule. Whoever carries the canoe gets to set the pace. So, on this trail, I try to stay close to Ken in case he gets into trouble. He can't see up the path with the canoe over his head. He can't hear very well either. Sticking one's head under an aluminum canoe, while trouncing along a rough trail, is like placing one's head inside a steel drum during a concert. Where paths intersect, it's easy to get disoriented and make a wrong turn. We made that mistake once trying to get into Chickenbone Lake. It took us half an hour to relocate each other after I finally realized Ken wasn't behind me any longer. Needless to say, Ken didn't appreciate having to carry the canoe a quarter-mile farther than necessary.

On the trek over the top of the Greenstone, we had found a few strategically placed, two-stemmed trees on previous trips where, if Ken wants to, can set the canoe down to take a break. I had made a promise to myself that when he carries the canoe, I'll never stop to rest until he does—no matter how tired I feel. When I carry the canoe, he does the same for me.

We made it to the top after only one rest. The pause came just before the last climb up the rocky knoll toward the top of the trail. The absence of any lichen on the normally moss-covered rock, caused by years of boots treading over it is the only sign of the path. It was sunny and dry out, which helps with traction. The worn rock can get slick when wet.

Cresting the ridge, I turned and waited for Ken. I leaned forward with my hands on my knees to catch my breath. He walked up and I helped him set the nose of the canoe on a large horizontal limb in a pine tree that's right at the apex of the trail. I set the paddles and kitchen-pack down and then we lowered our backpacks to the ground, propping them against a boulder. Glad to set aside our loads for a short break, we looked up and down the seldom-used hiking trail that runs along the ridge top at the east end of the island. There was no sign of recent hikers.

The Greenstone Ridge Trail runs the entire length of the forty-eight-mile-long island. The trail ends at its eastern terminus at Lookout Louise a couple of miles from where we intersect it. There used to be a fire watchtower on the mount, and the hilltop offers a spectacular view of the east end of the island. Despite the panoramic view, we've never seen anyone on this path to reach its summit.

This is one of my favorite spots. Standing atop the island, we could look backward over the terrain we had just climbed. Our day's journey up to that point lay at our feet. I could see Rock Harbor where we'd disembarked off the *Isle Royale Queen*. It was one of those cool, clear-aired September days and Lake Superior sparkled in the background. The Keweenaw, fifty miles distant, peeked over the far southern horizon. It seemed strange that I could literally see how my day unfolded, like being able to peer from a great height at my course on a map spread out on the floor.

Everything before us was in shades of greens and blues. The color of the lake and sky merged at the horizon, and the forested island fell away before us and stood out against the lake in stark evergreen hues. It was about two o'clock and the sun was just past its zenith. In its light, our world had grown vivid and bold.

Ken stirred, got up and tightened the cords on his pack, checked the bolts on the portage yoke, and rotated his shoulders to loosen up for the next leg. I took one more swig of water and handed him the water bottle. He drained it, handed it back and I snapped it onto my pack. We were ready to move on.

Our path drops from the ridge top down the north side of the Greenstone Ridge to Duncan Bay and is steeper than coming up the south side. This is true for most of the ridges that run the length of Isle Royale. The geology of the island is such that from the air, the island looks as if it was scraped with a hand-cultivator from west to east, pushing the soil southward. Going down the north side of the Greenstone Ridge is difficult and tough on the feet. Descending to Duncan Bay carrying eighty pounds of supplies feels like someone jumps on your back with each step. The path resembles steep, uneven stairs with risers that violate every building code. I always worry about twisting an ankle here because once I commit to stepping down, there's no turning back. This is where blisters are made and whole trips can be ruined. This is where you find out if the boots you're wearing are as good as the salesperson said they are.

We labored down the trail, and a half-hour later through the trees I glimpsed Duncan Bay. We made the last switchback turn and trooped down the path to the lake. I turned and said to Ken behind me, "We made it," encouraging him down the last slope.

As he caught up, I could see his face from underneath the canoe. He was wearing that determined, hard-working look he gets at times like this. Ken pulled up just short of the water's edge and I helped get the canoe off his shoulders. We set it down with a clang that only big old aluminum canoes can make. We dropped our packs, stretched, and gazed out at the bay. No one was in sight. When we quieted ourselves, we could hear loons singing from somewhere out in the bay. There was little wind and the lake looked good enough to jump into after getting into a major sweat, a heat developed in spite of the cool weather and stripping down to almost nothing.

Ken slapped me on the back. "Good job" he said, "One hour and ten minutes. If you hadn't brought those books, we could have cut off five more minutes."

I smiled. "You know you'll be borrowing one before we're finished."

The silence of Duncan Bay is a marvelous change. With the heaviest labor behind us, the sudden quiet of standing still and the release from heavy packs caused me to feel like I was floating on my feet, looking for the first time across an arctic lake. The stillness of the unpopulated bay demanded quiet in return. We obliged it.

This landing is one of the hardest places on the island to load and launch a canoe. The edge of the lake where the trail empties into the bay is blocked with boulders and rocks. I'd always wanted to ask someone from the Park Service why they chose this particular spot of all the places along the long shoreline to launch canoes or kayaks. The water is deep and the boulders make it extremely awkward to set heavy packs into tippy canoes. If we drop anything—including ourselves—while straddling the canoe and shore, it will quickly sink into deep water, deeper than we'd want to fish anything from, short of essentials.

We carried the canoe down to the lake, carefully setting it in the water. We then set our gear and packs between the two cross members. When everything was loaded, Ken lashed it all down with bungee cords. We brought several of these in order to keep gear from shifting in rough water and for tethering loose objects to our packs. They are convenient. Unhooking and hooking them to canoe struts or pack rings is as simple as snapping one in place. With everything secured and the Smoker Craft filled, we gingerly stepped into the canoe, one at a time, and slowly sat down. I shoved with my paddle but not too hard. We carried an extra paddle, but breaking one this early in the trip could be disastrous. Inching away from the rocks, we then turned the canoe to point toward the far side. As I raised my paddle to take that first determined stroke, I heard a clear and pleasant high-pitched voice say,

"Excuse me, I think you forgot this."

Ken and I spun around in unison. There, all alone at the portage entry where we had just been busy preparing for departure, was a woman standing on one of the boulders holding out a bungee cord. Apparently, we'd left one on the trail-path above the entry. But when we saw her, our surprise turned into a speechless, stunned silence. And, for a long paralyzed moment, a canoe packed with two grown men and a week's worth of provisions floated on the water stock still. She repeated herself.

"This strap, I think you left it here. I found it on the bank."

I couldn't have cared less about the bungee cord. The early afternoon sun poured down the ridge and spilled over her. With blonde hair pulled underneath a bandana over her head, wearing a small daypack slung over one shoulder, she literally glowed with a vitality that radiated sunshine, fair winds, and clean lake water. Trim and athletic looking, she had on leather boots with socks rolled over the top, wore cargo-pants topped with a snug, maroon polar-tech fleece jacket. She smiled down at us with a friendly, I-come-here-all-the-time look. But she also wore an expression that said, are you going to take this or not?

She looked fresh, like she'd just stepped off the *Queen*. When she still got blank looks in return, she held the cord out toward us as if to prove her genuineness.

Ken was still speechless, but he managed to turn the canoe around and push me, sitting up front, toward her. I struggled to find my voice and managed a meek sounding, "Thanks."

I glided toward her, and when I was just a few feet away, she tossed the bungee to me. It sailed through the air in a perfect arc over the water and struck me in the chest, falling in my lap. Only then did I reach out to catch it. More silence followed. She smiled at us in turn, her gray eyes coming to rest on me.

Unable to think of anything more to say—actually unable to think at all, I noticed her face went from a warm smile to a touch of wariness, as if unsure how to communicate with these two dolts. She finally shrugged, turned, and walked up the portage trail, disappearing behind the thick trees growing along the water's edge. Just like that, she was gone.

We sat there resting on the water, staring after her. Ken pulled himself together first. He backed the canoe from where we'd coasted to the rocks, turned it around, and began once more to paddle toward the far side of Duncan Bay.

"Vic, are you going to paddle?"

"But ... did you see her? Did, did you see how beautiful ... where did she come from? Who is she?"

Ken said nothing. I picked up my paddle and we stroked across the quiet bay, our shaken solitary resolve now dwelling on what had just occurred. Half way across the bay, Ken finally said. "She must have been day-hiking out of Rock Harbor, heard us cross ahead of her and then followed. That's the only thing that makes any sense."

Ken first came to Isle Royale in 1970. He went with three high school classmates directly from their graduation ceremony. They left the Kenowa Hills High School gymnasium in Grand Rapids, drove twelve hours through the night, and boarded the *Isle Royale Queen* in Copper Harbor at eight o'clock the next morning. They spent the next two weeks backpacking and fishing. It was a sign of things to come for Ken.

We met as freshmen at Michigan Technological University, located in Houghton, Michigan, only fifty miles south of Copper Harbor. The male-to-female ratio at Michigan Tech at the time was ten-to-one. Neither of us realized this little-advertised fact when we chose our school of higher education, and so when I arrived at campus, it surprised me to see so few girls in class. I lived in a dorm of 1,300 guys. Michigan Tech is predominantly an engineering school and in the sixties and seventies, very few women were studying to become engineers. The eyes of hungry males followed the few girls that did attend wherever they went. It was at college that I better realized how much visual attention women receive. I appreciated their presence too, but I wouldn't want that much scrutiny.

Ken and I didn't start to go to Isle Royale together until 1982, eight years following college graduation. As with college, there were very few women going to the island at that time. Whenever we did see a woman on the trail, it reminded me of those years at Tech. No matter how wonderful the scenery is on Isle Royale, it all fades to a blurry backdrop when a woman walks onto the landscape.

I mentioned this to Ken during one of our earlier September trips. I said to him, "You know, of all the beautiful things God has created, women are his best work."

Ken snorted and choked. After he regained his composure, he said, "I don't think so, Vic. Besides, I don't come here to watch girls."

He helped raise five girls, which helps explain his desire for a little distance.

I have all boys.

Twenty years later, seeing a woman on the island is no longer a shock, unless they jump out of the bushes in the middle of nowhere. Lately, it appears to me that as many women as men visit Isle Royale. I've seen no documentation to support this and doubt such statistics are kept. Captain Don concurs with my observation and if anyone should know, it would be him. He's been piloting the *Isle Royale Queen* for thirty years, has been a bachelor all his life, and has a reputation for excellent eyesight. He told me on my 2005 September voyage, "You know Vic, there was one trip this summer where I had all women aboard except for three guys!"

On one recent trip to the island, I met two women who circumnavigated Isle Royale in kayaks. Ruth and her friend paddled around Blake Point to reach Belle Isle. They were camping in a shelter next to my son Sam and me. Blake Point is the eastern tip of Isle Royale and is notorious for strong currents, large eddies, and fierce unpredictable winds. Anyone in a small boat times his or her attempt to round Blake Point with care before venturing around the point.

Ruth and Bess are in their upper fifties, married with grown children, and came to the island to decompress from the stress of nursing at a Mental Care Clinic. Ruth paddled clear out to Passage Island, which stands alone in Lake Superior twelve miles beyond Blake Point, and then kayaked back to Belle Isle, a journey of almost forty miles. Sam and I talked with Ruth around their fire that evening after she returned. I asked her what prompted her to risk the venture out to Passage Island, a place I too had wanted to reach one day, but from the safety of a real boat instead of in a canoe or kayak.

She hesitated and with a thoughtful expression on her face said, "I wanted to see if I could do it."

Couples can make interesting—as well as entertaining— people on Isle Royale. From a distance, Ken and I have watched many pairs come and go. We can normally judge, while still on the *Queen*, who will still be talking to one another on the return voyage.

It's not a great place to bring a date. We've seen several couples that start strong. They're confident they won't get seasick crossing the lake, that they can get past using the outhouses and withstand the bugs and sweat, only to be miserable by the end of the first day. It's a sad sight. He's angry because he's been waiting to do a year's worth of pent-up hiking, while she wants to pick every thimbleberry she sees along the trail. And conversely, she's upset because he won't stop to take any pictures or slow down long enough to enjoy the biological wonders that surround them.

From my experience, most men do have a Rambo mentality about achieving their mission, and that mission is normally to reach the next camp. The women seem to want to move more slowly and better appreciate the intricacies of Isle Royale.

Some couples come with amorous intentions, usually fulfilling them the first night to the embarrassment of the campers in the shelter or tent next to them. This once happened to Sam and me at the campground at the end of Duncan Bay. This is a very quiet, secluded cove with only two shelters. I'd seen the couple on the *Queen* on the ride to the island. He was slowly and meticulously tying fishing leaders while sitting out back with us on the stern deck. Unfortunately, they too climbed over top of the Greenstone and cruised into our campground shortly after we did. On one of those rare windless nights, when you can hear a fish rise on the bay, their cries of satisfaction, even suppressed, carried into our shelter.

Sam and I were playing cribbage by candlelight in the shelter next door and he glanced up at me over his cards at the sound of their laughter. Although only fifteen, he looked at me with eyes much too aware of what was occurring.

We have also seen couples who are true teammates and make as good an outdoor tandem as Ken and I. They are experienced at finding a compromise of pace and goals. A few partners come to mind.

One such couple is Steve and Yohanna. Married for eight years, they live in Copper Harbor, where she grew up. After living in Colorado for a couple of years, they came back to Michigan, where Steve started a construction business. Yohanna opened a massage and health spa. They are the very picture of health and vigor. If trees could capture their vitality, he would be a tall sugar maple in all his crowned autumn glory and she a white birch in her lithe, slender form.

As with Ruth and Bess, I met them while camping at Belle Isle. Courtesy of Steve, it was the one and only time at Isle Royale where I drank a beer. It was an unusually hot day for September. They were only wearing shorts, she with a bikini-top as they pulled up on shore in their rental boat. They could have just stepped from the surf on a California beach. Perfect tans, toned bodies, smiles as pure and friendly as the mountains of Colorado where they'd once lived. When they pulled a cooler out of the boat, I wandered over to their shelter to welcome them to Belle Isle.

Steve has one of the best tattoos I've ever seen. On his left arm is a map of Isle Royale. It is accurate to the smallest detail. The inland lakes are named. The ridges and valleys are colored in subtle shades of tan and green. I can't begin to imagine the kind of time and pain he went through to have it done.

Talking together in front of their shelter, I slowly sipped at my beer, savoring the unexpected treat. We talked of the island and the people we both knew in Copper Harbor. We seemed to connect in one of those all too rare moments where kindred spirits fortuitously cross paths. To this day, whenever I visit Copper Harbor, Yohanna will hug me if we see one another—all wonderful, innocent, and strangely friendly for a city boy.

I met another couple, Dean and Lynn, who also partnered well. They were young and engaged to be married in a few months. Despite their inexperience, they seemed to have already found an island rhythm. We'd met aboard the *Queen*. When I ran into them at Belle Isle, we talked a little more extensively and discussed fishing spots along the north shore. They told me they were traveling on to Birch Island, which seemed like a perfect setting for them. Birch Island is a tiny, isolated island with one solitary shelter.

"Good choice," I told them. "I'll be passing by in a couple of days on my way to McCargoe Cove. I'll stop and say hi."

Two days later, I set out for McCargoe Cove. Birch Island lies just within the mouth of McCargoe Cove. The weather was perfect for the long paddle except for a persistent light breeze I had to paddle against. It wasn't overly taxing, just enough wind to make me feel I was earning my way across the island.

The last stretch of water before reaching the narrow McCargoe Cove entry is a two-mile expanse of open lake. There are very few beaches to escape to on this stretch. The rock-faced shoreline is shear and drops fifty feet in some places. The stony shoreline is scoured from the winter ice-pack and from the countless storms that scrub the rock and then rinse it clean.

The north shore of the island appeared deserted. Paddling a mile off-shore, I felt like a lonely voyageur. I also felt vulnerable. When winds turn north, the swells ride all the way from Canada and strike the north shore of Isle Royale. Paddling for the McCargoe Cove entry, the smooth hills of water washed under me, lifting me over waves in long slow patterns.

To the west, broad sky reaches to meet the lake at the horizon. To the north, twenty miles away, the lake meets the wooded Ontario Buttes. To the south, the main island and its prominent Greenstone Ridge runs the length of the island. Its undulating ridgetop shrinks into the distance where it narrows to a green bump on the edge of sight. Behind me lie the cuts and bays at the northeast end of the island.

There are places on Isle Royale where I feel the immensity of Lake Superior more vividly. Sitting in a canoe in the middle of the lake crossing to the McCargoe Cove entry is one of them. The land recedes behind me as I paddle out into the open lake. The sky seems to expand overhead. I feel like a beginning swimmer venturing into the deep end of the pool, scared to let go of the sides. It's as if I'm a piece of driftwood, adrift, fearful that I'll become waterlogged and sink.

Trying to reach McCargoe Cove is similar to climbing mountains, or so I'm told, having never climbed a mountain. It forces me to focus on one hand-hold at a time or one paddle stroke in this case. Without that focus, if I allow myself to stop and stare around me, gawking at the lengthening vista, I'm sure my mind would shatter from the visual overload.

Halfway across this stretch of open lake, I glanced backward and noticed a fog bank cutting off from sight everything behind it. It seemed strange to see such a distinct line of weather. Even more peculiar, the fog was moving toward me across the lake from the northeast to the southwest, contrary to the prevailing direction of weather fronts on Lake Superior. It was a long way away, and even though I was confident of making it to the cove, I still decided to pick up my pace. I occasionally glanced over my shoulder and noticed the weather was gaining on me. It was going to be closer than I thought.

When I was a few hundred yards from the entry buoy at the channel, I looked back again and with some alarm realized this was no fog bank, but a racing squall line broiling backwards over the lake. It was going to be very close. The lake weather can do strange things, and although fully aware of this, I was still taken by surprise. The sky and water darkened and the storm gathered itself, preparing to slam onto shore. I'd been paddling all day with a fully loaded canoe and was tiring. With the storm right on my tail, I found extra energy and just beat the squall into the channel and then the winds and rain smashed around me.

Safe inside McCargoe Cove, but incredulous at how fast the weather had changed and grateful I'd made it into harbor, I stopped paddling and turned to look back at the lake. Bobbing on the growing waves about a mile out was the Park Ranger in his patrol boat. I hadn't noticed him. Seeing me make it to safety, he quickly turned and beat it back for Amygdaloid Channel where his sheltered dock lay. I lifted my paddle skyward to say thanks for being there—guessing he had seen me crossing the lake and had heard of the approaching storm.

Two days later, I ran into him at the McCargoe Cove Camp-ground, and he confirmed my hunch. I wish Ken had been there. It would have given him, as it did me, a better appreciation of the rangers.

I pulled my hood over my head down to my brow and turned to paddle for Birch Island. The gusts threw rain in sheets of large droplets, pelting the lake all around me, giving the surface a stucco finish. With the wind at my back, the squall pushed the canoe up the cove. The wind was so strong I could rudder in it.

Birch Island is just a thousand yards inside the two-mile long narrow cove and in the brief amount of time it takes to reach Birch Island from the entry, the squall raced past overhead and the sun started to peek through as I came abreast of camp. The rain fizzled and the wind started to die just as I pulled up to the small beach in front of the Birch Island lean-to shelter. Taking my hood off, I lifted my head to peer at the camp that faced me.

There, only thirty feet away, and completely naked, stood Dean and Lynn.

She was standing inside the shelter, bending forward to al-low her long hair to fall in front of her face, gently patting her hair dry with a towel. He stood a few feet from her, searching for clothes. Unaware of my presence, they were the very picture of a young attractive couple in an intimate moment. The storm had probably driven them inside after a swim in the secluded cove.

The nose of my canoe ground onto shore, a sound they couldn't hear due to the receding storm, and I thought it best to say something since there was little chance of sliding away without them seeing me.

"Sorry," I yelled and then looked away. "I was trying to get out of the storm and didn't see you until too late."

They both jumped, he more startled than she, and he quickly grabbed his clothes. Lynn, after putting some pants and a jacket on, said, "Come in out of the weather. It's all right."

"No ... no that's ok. It's blowing over."

She tried again, "We have a tent, if you want to stay here tonight. We didn't think you were coming until tomorrow. Are you sure?"

Yes, I was sure. Birch Island was far too small to not interact with one another. It seemed too awkward to remain. If I stayed, my now addled thinking would no doubt betray me during some innocuous conversation around a campfire. For several days, a mental picture of her dripping lake water onto the wooden shelter floor, so unaware and unguarded, so truly naked, was imprinted on my mind.

"No. Thanks anyway," I yelled. I pushed the canoe back into the lake. "McCargoe Cove Campground is only an hour paddle."

They walked down to shore, dressed now, and waved good-bye. I saw them once more, two days later, but only from a distance, and fully clothed.

I rested in Chippewa Harbor. My feet were swollen lumps and my shoulders raw. I had stayed at McCargoe Cove for four days. I'd then decided to cross the entire width of the island from the north shore to the south shore in one day. Knowing the *Isle Royale Queen* was due that afternoon at Rock Harbor with more campers, I wanted to reach the popular campground at Chippewa Harbor before the next load of hikers disembarked. I feared they might get there before me and fill the four shelters atop the bluff overlooking the lake. Hopscotching over the island, using several inland lakes and the portage trails in between, the hike south had worn me to the point of exhaustion.

Ken or Sam would normally have shared the load. They were sorely missed, and I barely made it. I was so spent I ended up leaving the canoe back at Lake Richie, deciding the last portage could wait until tomorrow.

The portages lengthened as I went south, the last one over a mile long and more than I could hike a second and then a third time. Going it alone forced me to walk each trail three times—once to carry the packs to the next lake, the return hike to retrieve the canoe, and then a final slog with the canoe over my head. As the crow flies, the distance across the island is only five miles. However, the meandering paths and misshapen lakes make the journey several miles longer. The fishing guides back at Quetico Provincial Park would have thought this an easy jaunt, but I had learned the real meaning of the word 'tenderfoot' that day.

Few people portage across the central part of Isle Royale, and the backpackers don't often use the same trails. There are better paths for them to get from campground to campground. I'd seen only two hikers all day, and it was while returning empty-handed to Lake LaSage from Lake Richie for the canoe. They were hiking the Greenstone Trail. As we passed each other going in opposite directions and noticed I wasn't carrying anything, they asked, "Traveling kind of light, aren't you?"

"I'm going back for the canoe. Where you heading?"

"We're hoping to reach Moskey Basin."

"Want to trade?" I asked.

They chuckled and kept moving. Neither of us stopped to chat—too much work to do. In less than a minute, they rounded a bend, leaving me alone in the center of the island.

It was a cloudless day, and the few gaunt trees and scrub along the rocky trail appeared to bask in the sun's heat. For most of the year, this windswept ridge looks cold and barren. But today there was only a slight breeze and the earth and rock radiated warmth.

As the pair of hikers had said, I was 'traveling light,' and it felt normal, and normal felt odd. Back home, I never needed to lug supplies on my back. But out here, I never go anywhere without carrying something. Seeing them on the trail, and saying "hi" as if we were neighbors passing each other on the street, caused me to notice that I was walking with no load, as if I was out for a stroll.

The irony was strong enough to make me stop for a moment to reflect. When I did, the seemingly deserted landscape came alive.

By pausing, I was able to catch the quick motion of small birds and insects among the foliage beside me. The birdsong, I noticed, didn't sound any different from the activity around the feeders off the deck back home. All it needed was the background noise of traffic. Closing my eyes, I listened more carefully. The swish of the wind through the leaves and over the hills grew louder. Without the distraction of sight, I detected the clicking spring of grasshoppers jumping off trail where they'd been sunning themselves on the bare path and the small movement of a chickadee when it bounced from sprig to sprig.

It struck me that this was Isle Royale, *terra firma*, and this was their backyard. I lifted my foot and set it down, hearing my own movement in order to better grasp what I might sound like to the creatures that live here. The pebbly trail crunched beneath my boot. What do they sense on the rare occasion when a human stumbles by?

The canoe was waiting. Opening my eyes, I stepped forward. A few strides later, the small wildlife faded into the background.

I finally made it into Chippewa Harbor late that afternoon. The campground had always seemed to be just around the next turn on the trail. I gratefully dropped my packs, scanned the area, and picked out a shelter. Moving my gear into the one with the best view, I then lay down atop the picnic table outside. It took only a couple of minutes before my sweat started to dry and I felt a chill.

I was hungry, tired, and sore. Dinner needed to be made, my feet and shoulders checked, and there were at least a dozen other important tasks to do before turning in. "Use whatever daylight you're given," I heard Ken say in my head. Giving in to the temptation to curl up inside my sleeping bag would have been a big mistake. Muscles would cramp if I didn't keep moving and drink some water. I got up.

Pulling the water purifier out of the pack, I went down to shore to fill the coffee pot and water jugs. Since I couldn't push the canoe into the lake to get clear of the backwash at the lake's edge, I took off my boots and socks and waded out thigh deep. The ice-cold goo on the lake bottom numbed my throbbing feet and I sighed.

While the purifier slowly filtered the water and drizzled into the jug, I examined my feet, which were slightly magnified by the sunlight shining through the shallows. They didn't look as bad as they felt. A few blisters had ripped open and my toes were swollen. But there were no gaping wounds like I'd imagined when I was limping along the last mile, fearing the worst. The sand under my feet slowly turned pink. If the lake waters had any restorative powers, like the old-time resort advertisements boasted, I hoped they'd work their magic because I couldn't help but notice that my feet were soaking in my drinking water.

Standing in the lake, working the pump, I turned around and looked back at shore. The campground is situated thirty feet above the lake on top of bedrock that rises steeply out of the channel. It's a strange place to put shelters. Only a hundred feet either way up and down the shoreline are nice flat sections of dry woodlands where it would have been far more convenient. Gazing about, it struck me that something was amiss. It was the canoe. Without it beached beside me in camp, I felt naked.

The next morning, every part of me ached and I struggled to get out of my sleeping bag. Stepping gingerly through the screen door of the shelter into another sunny day, I shuffled down to the lake, wincing with each step.

I'd slept late. It seemed like eight in the morning, judging from the angle of the sun in the sky. Chippewa Harbor lay before me. The forty-foot-tall cliff on the other side of the channel that faces the campground reflects sound as well as its own image from the surface of the water. I sat down on the dock, took my boots and socks off, and soaked my throbbing feet, again feeling them go cold. Listening to the peculiar, reverberating echoes from the waves lapping on stone as if inside a cave awash with surf, I heard in the distance the rumble of *The Voyager*.

*The Voyager* is the passenger ferry from Minnesota that doubles as the Isle Royale water-taxi. *The Voyager* departs from Grand Portage, Minnesota, at the Canadian border and transports passengers to the Windigo Ranger Station. Windigo is at the far western end of Isle Royale, closest to Minnesota. After the passengers check in with the Rangers at Windigo, the ferryboat circumnavigates the park clockwise, dropping hikers off at various campgrounds and also carries supplies for the work crews and island residents.

The rumble grew. A few seconds later, the boat appeared, chugging around the point, and turned into the narrow channel leading to the dock where I sat. It moved fast, like the pilot had done this tricky water-course a thousand times before. A moment later, he pulled up to the dock. A crewmember jumped out and hurriedly set lines. Three separate parties of campers disembarked.

There was a solitary hiker, who was quickly away and down the one trail that leads into Chippewa Harbor. A pair of guys also got off the boat with their canoe and left for Malone Bay within the hour. The third party was four women with their kayaks. The crew unloaded their gear, setting it on the dock. The four women looked to be staying the night. They moved their packs into one of the unoccupied shelters, pulled their kayaks up on shore and tipped them over. When done unloading, the crew swiftly untied the lines, and jumped aboard as the boat pulled away. Within a couple of minutes, the *Voyager* disappeared back into the big lake.

It's like that here. One instant you're all alone in a wilderness that seems to stretch forever, with no sound or sight to betray the perception, the next instant there's a rush of human activity.

I'd now been on the island for over two weeks, seeing no one the past 24 hours, and having company in camp felt good. The quiet conversation among the women from within their shelter was a welcome break from the silence. I noted the change in my attitude. There'd been a time I would have thought it an intrusion on my wilderness experience.

The next morning at dawn, I walked back to Lake Richie for the canoe. It hadn't been as bad a hike as I feared. My feet were healing nicely, and a couple of hours later, I paddled into camp from the portage site. The women were just getting up.

I talked with them at shore while they were filling their water bottles, and it turned out this wasn't their first trip to the island. They'd been coming for the past twelve years, some women missing the trip occasionally, but a few of them making it every year. They were from Minnesota and had arranged for the *Voyager* to take them to Chippewa Harbor, where they were going to start their kayak trip. From here, they would work their way to Siskiwit Lake, then to Lake Richie, and then back again to Chippewa Harbor where the Voyager would pick them up. It was an ambitious venture, given the five days they were staying, but they looked up to it.

They seemed very comfortable here, and their camp had a few amenities I don't bring like fold-up beach chairs. They were impressed with my candles, which they had never thought to bring before. Just a few candles throw an amazing amount of light, and at night, my shelter looks warm and inviting in their glow. Candlelight lengthens a day that only lasts for twelve hours toward the end of September.

Comparing camping equipment is a common topic of conversation among park users. It pays to be friendly. Much of the gear I now bring has been improved upon over the years. With each trip, I pick up something new. However, each addition requires that something has to go. I'm not sure the four women totally believed me when I told them how I got to Chippewa Harbor from McCargoe Cove. I felt a little proud to think they might doubt I could make the journey from McCargoe Cove in only one day. But I also wondered if they thought me foolish since they all went quiet after I complained to them how sore I was.

An hour later, they loaded up and got under way. I would be staying three more days at Chippewa Harbor if the weather allowed and the fishing remained good. I needed to catch dinner. They asked me to take their picture standing together on the dock, which I did, and then said good-bye. Paddling west across Chippewa Lake, they handled their kayaks expertly, holding a straight course. Their paddle strokes had no wasted motion. Five minutes later, as they too disappeared around a point, I was left alone again, and would be for the next several days.

Missy, the Park Ranger, took my itinerary tag when I returned to Rock Harbor a week later after exploring the island for three weeks. I was returning to Copper Harbor on the *Queen*. There, I would meet up with Ken, and then turn right around and come back to the island for a fourth week.

Sue, Missy's aide, assisted with the data entry. Two female Park Rangers—I looked at them curiously. They didn't seem to notice my thoughtful expression. Good thing, I probably looked a bit squirrelly after three weeks of living outdoors.

Much has changed in just a quarter of a century. Far more women go to Isle Royale now. It's a good thing. An entire half of the population now enjoys Isle Royale where they once seldom ventured before.

The small handful of park visitors who still canoe have switched to lighter canoes made from high-tech, synthetic materials. That distinctive clang that reverberates across the water when a paddle bangs against the side of an aluminum canoe is seldom heard any longer.

However, few people canoe. Most paddlers have switched to kayaks, which travel faster and can handle rough water better. They're admittedly ideal for Isle Royale. However, Lake Superior is synonymous with voyageurs and their canoes. Early native people traveled the Great Lakes in primitive dugouts. They improved their boat building until they eventually developed birch-bark canoes, which still offer some of the finest paddling on the water.

I recently retired the old Smoker Craft and oddly, didn't feel much regret. I couldn't quite bring myself to part with it either. It now rests on Portage Lake, where we occasionally use it to fish Dollar Bay in northern Michigan.

I went back to the Skampt Shop the other day to price a new and lighter canoe. They mostly come in day-glow colors, neon-reds, greens, or yellows. Slick, shiny and so light, I didn't believe the salesperson when she said it weighed thirty-eight pounds. She gave a long technical dissertation about the pros and cons of different synthetic materials and designs.

It felt all wrong. I finally had to cut her off and asked wistfully, "Do you have any scratched or dented ones?"

# FISHING FOR WORDS

I ran into a snag. Dangle the bait in front of them and see if they bite. He's laying in the weeds. Who's on the line? He's a good catch. We netted a bundle. That's deep. She's so shallow. Is he ever hooked. I came up empty. She's a keeper. You're over your limit. Did you get any nibbles? And, if you're simply looking for something, just fish around, you'll find it.

Ken fishes a lot. When I go to Isle Royale with him, I fish a lot too. With all of that time spent on the water trying to catch dinner, I discovered an unexpected fringe benefit. Besides the deeply enjoyable experience of eating fresh lake trout grilled over an open fire, fishing helped me to better express myself, something not always easy to do.

What I discovered was that fishing contains some of the best metaphors and analogies ever created. It finally provided a language to help me communicate. And, not only did the actual act of fishing help me find verbal handles for what I wanted to say, I was by definition on the water. Water, that mysterious liquid that covers three-fourths of the planet's surface, is just like music. As Aldous Huxley once said, "After silence, that which comes nearest to expressing the inexpressible is music."

There are some concepts so complex, so intricate, so multi-layered that without assistance, these concepts are impossible to convey. The hushed stillness at daybreak over a mist-shrouded pond, the fury of a storm-wracked sea, the unchanging current of a river create pictures that describe the essence of what we call peace, rage, and the eternal flow of time. Paradoxically, water also symbolizes how little I know. My inability to see below the water's surface illustrates answers to questions I'll never get to the bottom of.

I can't see across Lake Superior. Its horizons seem to stretch to infinity. Its vastness puts my life into perspective. The lake is scary. I'd last only a few minutes submerged beneath its waves. It teaches me the serious consequences of my actions. If I make a mistake, punishment can be swift and severe.

After a few years of fishing at Isle Royale, I was inspired to write. It dawned on me that if fishing could be used to describe topics like peace, or time, or life then perhaps learning how to write was—ahem—like shooting fish in a barrel.

I'm certainly not the first person to grasp the intimate relationship between communication and fishing. Mark Twain, Hemingway, Whitman, Thoreau, and Melville fished. What other activity can you be writing about and not really be writing about it at all? In *The Old Man and the Sea*, I became absorbed into Ernest Hemingway's tale of the hunt, capture, and loss of the giant marlin to sharks. But when I turn the last page, I've found that along with a great fishing story, I've gained a great respect for Diego. Hemingway enabled me to see into the old fisherman's heart, to empathize with his simple desires toward the end of his life.

Mark Twain's books certainly convey an adolescent's zeal for independence. Huck Finn's float down the Mississippi and his conversations with Big Jim covered topics that at the time were considered taboo, yet desperately needed discussion. Racial equality, unnecessary social constraints, and fairness in general, were ideas so aptly and colloquially expressed that schoolteachers, despite complaints about his slang, still insisted he be read. Few authors have inspired more boys to read.

In "Walden," Thoreau talks of politics, organic gardening, and admonishes people to return to nature and a simpler way of life. (After all, those were the crazy, hectic 1850s).

I have also discovered that fishing helps me get centered, to get back to the basics, to find that creative flow. In short, going fishing allows me to think more clearly. The mind-cleansing after-effects of a fishing trip can last for several days. How going fishing accomplishes this re-charging is a mystery. I feel fortunate and grateful to my dad, who introduced me to the experience.

However, in fairness to those who don't like to fish, I should point out that for all of fishing's mind-clearing properties, its capability to picture my innermost thoughts, or describe the indescribable it can also be as uncomfortable a way to spend time as I could ever wish for. The discomforts say something important too.

Trying to untie a snarled line in a bouncing canoe frazzles me. Sitting in a boat for hours on end with cold hands, a runny nose and without one nibble, pushes my limited patience beyond the breaking point. I throw a tantrum when I lose a large fish just as I'm about to land him. As my dinner disappears, my bellows of anguish echo across the lake. These frustrations—all caused by fishing—demonstrate as clearly as anything can my lack of fortitude, my nonexistent self-discipline, and my self-absorption.

The real reasons I fish, of course, are not due to the metaphors it supplies. I actually go fishing to catch fish, to get outdoors and enjoy the day or see a new lake or stream. I also go fishing to be with my sons or spend time with friends.

Fishing with friends can bring out a level of conversation almost unattainable elsewhere. Even if we're just talking about yesterday's ball game or most recent car problems, people seem to open up when on the water. Some of my most interesting and revealing conversations with family and friends have been in a boat on a lake. Discussions can range far and wide, covering inane matters like the best type of wax-worms to catch bluegills, to intimate revelations about past girlfriends, or our convoluted ideas about the nature of the universe. Any and all topics are fair game. What happens in the boat stays in the boat.

One must be careful, however, during these conversations. For reasons that are unclear, more *fish stories* are shared here than is normal elsewhere. The whole idea of telling a whopper comes directly from fishermen. My personal opinion is that conversatios expand due to the limitless vistas over vast stretches of water. My grasp of the truth easily slips across the line from fact into fiction as details shrink and eventually disappear altogether over the horizon.

This tendency to stretch the truth, which I share with my fellow anglers, is expected and permissible—another unexpected bonus. In fact, a fisherman who won't lie isn't considered normal or even moral.

There are drawbacks to fishing with other people. Some enjoy fishing in what's called a fishing party. It's a social affair and at times just an excuse to go drinking. I enjoy fishing with friends and a beer or two tastes good, but not to the point where I am in a haze. Besides the more obvious safety concerns, there is something lost when I fish intoxicated. I've also noticed that the same guys fishing and drinking are also hunting and drinking, golfing and drinking, or playing softball and drinking.

I don't fish for pay, but I do like to fish hard. However, I have seen people take it to a level that's excessive. They become men obsessed. Their minds become absorbed with the lust for the kill, the catch, The Trophy!

I would like to catch a trophy lake trout one day, but hanging fish on my walls doesn't really get me going. I do admit to a love for being on the water and part of that appeal is chasing big Lakers. But someone stop me when I no longer notice the sky's reflection mirrored back to me in countless glimmers or when I no longer stop to admire a bird on the wing.

Some people actually fish for a living—commercial fishermen, charter boats, and guides. I consider them fortunate and it's exceedingly strange I should feel this way since commercial fishing is the single most dangerous profession, having higher workman's compensation insurance rates than any other job—even tree workers, my trade. It's also higher than for policemen, firemen, or pilots. There's no argument from me that commercial fishing is dangerous. It's grueling work by all accounts. It's physically as well as mentally demanding. Still ... to be on the water day in and day out, there is an undeniable attraction.

One of its attractions, I believe, is that the Almighty is so close at hand. When on the water, His workmanship spreads before me as far as I can see. The feeling is very similar to the sensation that comes from being on a mountaintop. As a sports fisherman, I only catch glimpses of all of this. I am out of my element when on the water, and I confess that it can make me uncomfortable seeing His nature reflected so clearly. His omnipresence resembles the lake that surrounds me in every direction. The deep represents His unfathomable nature. Lest I forget, the lake teaches me that He is dangerous to disregard.

Uncomfortable as that makes me, I am drawn to the water just as I am drawn to Him. The pull is unmistakable. I think it might explain why crowds gather at the beach when a storm comes up, or explain why I pause to watch a river flow by, or stand transfixed on shore gazing at the ocean.

I remember taking my boys, who are just a year apart, out to the middle of Elk Lake to explain to them the facts of life. This is certainly a subject most of us find hard to verbalize. After I used my best teaching methods, which I will not elaborate on here, they looked at me a little puzzled when I was finished explaining things. Seeing their expressions, I told them that if they had any questions, they should feel free to talk to their mother, and that there were some points she might be better able to cover. They slowly nodded their heads all right with that look on their faces that meant not in a million years. Come to think of it, I never asked my mother any questions regarding the subject either, and after the age of thirteen avoided her regarding the subject of sex at all costs.

On the water seemed a good place to discuss this delicate topic with my boys. Water flows and so does life and fish are right in the middle of it. What better activity than fishing to get to the center of what's going on?
So ... I fish.

I fish in rough waters and quiet coves, on warm sunny days, and through a hole in the ice. I don't intentionally go fishing to ponder life or think about this world. I certainly don't go fishing with the purpose of better expressing myself. But intentional or not, it is an amazing and mysterious side effect.

I just like to fish. And, trying to describe why is just like trying to explain why I like the color green or a particular song. I just do.

Fortunately, there's fishing to describe it all.

# FISH TALES

LAKE SUPERIOR BULGED AND BUBBLED. WATER SWIRLED BESIDE ME. WE COULD feel the turmoil through the thin sheet of aluminum that was all that separated us from the lake. The hull creaked and banged as the bottom of the Smoker Craft tin-canned in the surges. Sprigs of cedar and birch rose to the surface, turned over, and then quickly disappeared, sucked underwater.

Ken and I were canoeing along the south shore of Isle Royale. Where we rounded Saginaw Point, an area of open lake the size of a large pond looked to tremble. It reminded me of a saucepan on a mild boil. Superior can be subtle when she wants to be. From a distance, the water at the point had, at first, looked like an oil slick. But it was no spill. The underwater currents that flow unseen beneath the waves were making one of their rare appearances. This wasn't like watching the power of the surf smash against one of the headlands of Isle Royale or the sensation we got when waves pitched the canoe like a toy boat. At Saginaw Point, I felt Lake Superior on the move.

We were in the process of paddling to our next campsite, the West Caribou Island campground, a sixteen-mile, open-lake journey. Skies were cloudy but they held little threat of rain—a high sky, Dad would call it. After leaving Malone Bay and paddling tight to the south shore for seven hours, we'd finally reached Saginaw Point and were making the turn. West Caribou Island came into view. The campground lay on the far side of the small island, three miles distance yet.

We'd faced nothing larger than one-to-two footers since leaving Malone Bay in the morning. The water between the waves was covered with tightly packed riffles. But at Saginaw Point the riffles were wiped smooth. We didn't see the surging water at the point until we were almost sitting on top of it.

"Ken, look at that."

"Yeah, the riptide along the coast plows into the water of the bay."

"Could be lake currents," I said, as we swiveled our heads left and right to watch.

Ken said, "Might be a reef too deep to see. Maybe the water takes a big uplift. There's got to be baitfish in here and where there's baitfish there's lake trout."

We'd seen this kind of roiled-up water before on the north side of Isle Royale. We'd even seen converging currents form large whirlpools. The one off Captain Kidd Island is thirty-feet in diameter. The whirlpool revolves very slowly at the surface. It reminds me of an old record player where the motor can't get up to speed. Toward the center of the eddy, it gains momentum before turning into an underwater funnel that looks like a submerged tornado. The funnel of air twists and contorts, spiraling forty feet down. In the clear water, we could see where the whirlpool scoured the lake bottom clean.

We'd also seen another whirlpool form where Lane Cove meets Robinson Bay. It is less dependable. Most of the time, the water looked normal enough. But there were other days, when just the right set-up of wind and lake conditions caused the eddy to take shape. We had never been able to figure out what those right conditions were. Lane Cove is close to Belle Isle and whenever the whirlpool appeared, we would fish its edges, often catching lake trout.

"To your left," Ken said, "about ten o'clock, did you see that fish rise? Looked like a steelhead. We've got to come back here after we unload the canoe."

"Didn't see it."

Fish rising or not, I wasn't crazy about the idea of returning. We'd be canoeing for eight hours by the time we reached the far side of West Caribou Island. The thought of unloading the canoe and then turning right around to troll for a few more hours didn't sound good to me. What I really wanted was to peel my butt off the canoe seat and unfold my legs.

We kept paddling and were soon past the lake convection. The more normal rhythmic waves and riplets reformed once we passed the apex at Saginaw Point. I could hear the mild clang of the buoys at Middle Passage, a welcome sound. During storms, the buoys make a sharp ring that carries an unmistakable warning. This stretch of water is similar to the crossing out front of McCargoe Cove. The island falls away to our left and exposes us to a large section of open lake. If the winds were to pick up from the north or northwest, the offshore wind would be trouble.

We both dug in. Our destination was in sight and with a clear goal straight ahead, and knowing we should hustle, we found a burst of energy. At such times, we tried to create a wake with the canoe. We don't ordinarily paddle in unison. It's too mentally absorbing to have to focus on keeping time. I'd rather pay attention to the scenery. However, there are moments when a little speed breaks the monotony, if you can describe any movement in a canoe as speedy. Our paddles ripped through the water together and the canoe lurched forward with each synchronized stroke. The blades struck the water with a crisp smack. Whitewater formed at our prow, and a wake that was a whole three inches tall curled behind us. After a thousand yards, our burst of energy spent, we relaxed and fell back into our disconnected paddling.

"That felt great," I said.

"It's about time you went to work. You've been lollygagging and gawking around like usual."

"You've got me at a disadvantage. How do I know what you're doing back there?"

Ken laughed, as if he hadn't thought of that before. "At least you don't have to stare at my backside all day."

"I suppose."

"Vic," Ken said, "you couldn't see the bottom of the canoe back there. It shouldn't be buckling in rough water. We need to have that welder reinforce those struts again before our next trip."

"I couldn't see it, but I heard it. If we quit hitting rocks, it might help."

"We? You sit up front. You're the scout."

He could argue like this all day, so I let it drop.

"What do you suppose really caused those boils back there?" I asked.

"Either an underwater reef, like I said, or there are small tides on Lake Superior. They aren't much. The water only rises and falls a couple of inches. High or low air pressure systems moving across the lake can change surface height too. Think about it," Ken said. "Remember how the waterline changes on calm nights at Belle Isle when the moon comes up late."

"Yeah, I guess so. Didn't connect it with tides. Makes sense. Wouldn't take much change to move a lot of water."

"Plus," Ken added, "all those rivers flowing into the lake have to go somewhere."

We kept paddling, and I turned my attention to plotting a course.

At Middle Passage, a rock as big as an apartment building rises thirty feet out of the lake. It bisects the passage into Rock Harbor. We were going to pass the rock on the right. Nothing but seagulls and lichen live on the rugged stone. Its sides fall steeply into the water. I wondered how many people had passed the landmark over the centuries, grateful like me to leave the open lake and find shelter in the protected waters behind it.

Middle Passage is one of only two locations where the water is deep enough for large boats to enter Rock Harbor. Rock Harbor is a naturally formed bay that runs parallel to the main island and is nine miles long and less than a mile wide. The outer islands run along the south side and form a long chain that protects it from the big lake. Four major campgrounds are on the main island side of Rock Harbor. Two small campgrounds are located on outer islands.

Mott Island is one of these island chain-links, and at Mott Island, the Park Service keeps its equipment, houses its staff, and warehouses supplies. Isolated from the main island, they can shield the public from the infrastructure necessary to maintain Isle Royale as a wilderness National Park. Here the rangers, the maintenance staff, and volunteers enjoy enough privacy to let their hair down. Mott Island has electricity, running water, and *hot* water. Ken and I have seen Carl, the ranger is stationed way out on Amygdaloid Island, clear on the other side of Isle Royale, cruise by on Friday evenings to find some company. His boat ride to headquarters must take at least an hour. Ken has mentioned more than once, "There goes Carl heading to *town*."

Rock Harbor reminds me of a southern Michigan inland lake where cottages and docks line the shore. It's not that congested, but with the six campgrounds, the park headquarters, the lodge, marina and the passenger ferry's dock, the harbor does see more activity than anywhere else except for Washington Harbor, which serves the western end of Isle Royale. Boats cruise up and down the bay and backpackers dot the waterside trails. Compared to the rest of the park, it feels busy. Ken and I spend most of our time on the north shore where we seldom see anybody. Returning to Rock Harbor in order to be within easy reach of catching the *Isle Royale Queen* to go home, and after spending several days removed from people, Rock Harbor feels like coming back to civilization—Isle Royale style.

After we paddled through Middle Passage, straight ahead across the Harbor, Daisy Farm Campground came into view. With its thirty lean-to shelters arranged in an arc, Daisy Farm reminds me of an old-western movie version of an Indian village. It's a busy campground, within a day's walk of the ferry dock. We avoid Daisy Farm.

On the left side of Middle Passage, and tucked inside the bay, is Edison Fishery. Here, Mr. Edison, his wife, and sons lived and worked one of the last commercial fisheries. The family left in the seventies, replaced by park staff who now give talks about what an "olde-time" fisherman's life was like on Isle Royale. Both Ken and I find it difficult to see real fishermen turned into museum pieces, which I'm sure is unfair of us. From what I'm told, staff do a commendable job depicting the commercial fishing era. But in spite of being only a short paddle away, we've never stopped—even to say hi. This is because we're so bent on keeping everybody at arm's length whenever we're on the island. It's particularly eccentric of us since they hold information about fishing that, normally, we'd be willing to pay dearly for.

After passing through Middle Passage, we turned right. Once inside Rock Harbor, the one-foot waves on the open lake smoothed to just rippled water, and as we rounded West Caribou Island, the dock for the campground came in sight. There were no boats, canoes, or kayaks at the dock.

"Looks like no one's home," Ken said.

"Good," I replied.

We paddled toward shore. I kept a lookout for submerged rocks and deadheads. "Looks clean," I yelled. "Stay slightly left. There's a sand bar to the right."

I stopped paddling and Ken steered us in the last few feet. I jumped out as the canoe beached in a couple of inches of water, the bow instantly rose when my weight was removed. I yanked the Smoker Craft ashore. Ken stepped out and helped me pull up the rest of the fully loaded canoe.

We don't normally fish while we travel, but we'd been fortunate today. The winds had been so light we decided we could get away with dragging lures behind the canoe. Within two hours of leaving last night's camp at Malone Bay, we had caught dinner. Trailing behind the beached canoe on a stringer was a nice catch of steelhead and lake trout.

The reputation for the great taste of pan-fried fish, cooked moments after leaving their icy domain, is well earned. We'd paddled hard all day, taking just one break. The fish, now lying belly-up in the shallows, barely resembled the underwater missiles they are. Ken's reel screamed when the steelhead hit. If he hadn't had his drag set loose, it would have snapped his line.

After unpacking, we headed down to the lake to clean fish. We turn this chore into a two-man job. Ken does the filleting. I wash the meat off in the lake and package it. When finished, one of us carries the entrails out the required one hundred yards past the drop-off and dumps them.

To keep fish cold, we sometimes wrap the baggie of fillets in a wet towel soaked in the frigid waters of Lake Superior and set it in a shady spot inside the shelter. If it's too warm inside the shelter or if we are going to try to store fish for more than a day, we sink the bag in deep water attached to a long string tied off at the dock. Today we set the bag in the water right at shore under a stone. It was too warm inside, but we were going to eat soon.

We finished all of our chores, and Ken got out the flask of Jack Daniels and his jar of *jalapeno* peppers from the pack for our version of happy hour. The peppers and Jack are like liquid heat. After spending a long day on the cool waters of Lake Superior, they take the chill out of the bones. To top it off, Ken pulled out a couple of cigars.

We'd paddled over some spectacular water. We'd watched lake currents, eagles, ospreys, flocks of ducks and geese, and admired the long, blue vista of Lake Superior. It all added up to a day well spent. We sat in the late-afternoon sun, a few flies hovering nearby gauging by the quiet buzz. The harbor looked bright and the water was very quiet compared to the big lake. I glanced over at Ken, who was sitting on a seat cushion on the shelter steps with his back propped against the wall, nodding off. I could feel myself getting drowsy. The picnic table was in full sun. Walking over, I lay down atop the table, placing a cushion behind my head. A little nap wouldn't hurt.

*Man, listen to the gulls on the bay,* I thought. *Sounds like they're excited... I wonder what they're all worked up about. Maybe I should check it ....*

The planks from the picnic table pressed against my shoulder blades. Dazed, and comfortably warm for once, I struggled to shake off sleep. Rolling off the table, I groaned, and stood up. I looked over at Ken. He was still asleep.

"I need to splash some water on my face."

When I reached the end of the dock, I stretched and yawned. The bay shimmered in the sun. Shielding my eyes with my hand, the glare caused me to squint. Two hundred yards away, Cemetery Island squinted back. The small island was used as a burial plot for families who lived on Isle Royale decades ago and for the fishermen, loggers, and miners who'd come to an untimely end. Lowering my gaze, I stared down into the deep water beside the dock. I sat down, and on a whim, leaned over and stuck my whole head into the lake to wake up. Opening my eyes underwater, I tried to peer through the liquid—to no avail. Even in that crystal water, everything turned blurry.

While my face was submerged, I bubbled. "What a great loss that I can't see underwater. How do loons or fish manage to see so well?" It's hard to hold a conversation underwater, even with yourself. Sitting up, cold water running down my neck and shoulders, I shivered.

Seagulls were fighting in the bay. Their squawking carried across the water and drowned out the closer peeps and whistles of the birds in the nearby trees. The gull's fracas seemed a bit strange. What could they be battling over way out there? Answering my own question, our bag of fillets sprang to mind. I looked over at the spot where we'd stashed them in the lake. I couldn't see the bag.

"Oh, please tell me we didn't lose them."

I yelled back up toward camp. "Ken, did you move the fish?"

It was a long shot, but I hoped he'd moved them to a safer spot while I slept. "Hey, Ken! Did you move the fish?"

Striding up to our shelter, I found Ken, who was struggling to wake up. "What are you shouting about?"

"Where are the fish? I can't find the bag of fillets. Did you move it?"

"No."

For the next five minutes, we turned over stones along shore looking for our wayward fillets. Then, Ken said, "Over there, isn't that a plastic bag?"

Fifty feet down the beach, a piece of plastic about the size of our baggie lay on the bottom in the shallows, all ripped up. He lifted it out of the water. The shreds of plastic dripped in his hand. As we stared at it, in the background, like a camera zoomed in for close-ups then redialed for distance, the gulls came into focus. The seagulls had quit fighting. I could have sworn they had a full and satisfied expression in their normally blank faces.

"Well, this sucks."

I had eaten only a few sticks of venison jerky, a tiny chunk of Colby cheese, and a Kit-Kat bar since breakfast. It was time to make dinner, and my stomach rumbled as if to emphasize the point.

We eat a hot breakfast every morning that consists of bacon and oatmeal and/or pancakes, washed down with coffee. However, we had decided long ago that stopping to cook lunch would slow us down too much. Daylight was precious, and to waste it on tending to either a fire or a backpack stove was time ill spent. We brought venison jerky or salami sticks for quick shore lunches.

During our journey to West Caribou Island, we had pulled over for our midday meal where Chippewa Harbor empties into Lake Superior. The sun beat on the rocks, the wind was only five knots, and the lake could only muster ripples in the mild breeze. No ships were in sight. It felt like we were the only people on Lake Superior. After eating lunch, we each had picked out table-top rocks to lay on and bask in the noontime sun. We looked like walruses sunning on a warm Pacific beach.

Wadding the shredded plastic up and shoving it into his pocket, Ken asked, "Well, you want to go fishing now?"

I couldn't very well say no.

We unpacked our fishing rods and our tackle, and prepared the canoe for fishing instead of traveling. I pushed off, and grimaced when I sat down on the seat.

It was one of those times when paddling the few hundred yards over to Edison's Fishery to beg for a couple of fish would have been smart. It was getting late. We had only two more hours of daylight left and if we didn't catch anything, it would be freeze-dried spaghetti tonight. Comparing fresh fish—lake trout no less—to freeze-dried meals is like comparing your finest steak to hamburger helper.

We didn't get one strike. The wind picked up and even Ken wasn't keen on the idea of paddling across the bay to return to the broils at Saginaw Point. Instead, we fished the narrows of Middle Passage, thinking the drop-offs and currents at the entry would hold fish. We'd fished here before on previous trips with some success. Today we caught nothing. We tried all of our favorite lures, tried several different fishing techniques, and said various incantations. I even inverted my hat into a rally cap. As the classic angler's lament goes, "All we did was wash lures."

We fished until dark, pulled lines, and headed back to camp. When we reached shore, I jumped out, and said to Ken, "I'll heat some water."

"Alright, see if you can drag that crap that you call dinner out of the bottom of your pack."

"You know, last year, I never had to break out these meals. I think this spaghetti is a couple of years old."

"You better check the expiration date."

I pulled out the bag and could barely read the smudged expiration date. "It's still nine years away! What the hell do they put in this stuff?"

"You're about to find out."

The seagulls had dealt us a major blow.

We always brought a couple of pre-packaged meals, just in case fishing went bad. Good years are when we never need to open a can of stew or a freeze-dried meal. However, there's nothing like living outdoors with metabolisms on hyperdrive, to make even cardboard taste good. At dinner that night, I mentioned to Ken, who I couldn't help notice was rather enjoying his spaghetti, "We should try to go see Mark Rude sometime."

"Who's he?

"Last year, when I was here alone, three guys pulled up in a fishing boat to tie up for the night. Said they come to Isle Royale every fall to fish. They say they always try to make a point of visiting Mark. He lives in Fisherman's Home Cove—said he's been there for years."

"I've never heard of it."

"It's east of Siskiwit Point, not far from McCormick Reefs. They say they struggle to get their big Lund into the tiny cove. He's a character—sort of salty."

"Imagine so, living way out there."

"One of them said something I won't forget. I asked them how fishing was, like I normally do, hoping for a tip or two. Their boat had a Loran, thermometers on the cannonballs, GPS, and navigational charts—fully decked out. You'd have loved it. I thought maybe I'd finally met someone who's figured out how to catch fish here."

"The oldest of the three answered without skipping a beat, and I might add, as if he knew exactly what I was really doing, 'No one knows this lake *well*. I've been fishing here for forty years and my dad fished it before me. But if I had to pick one person to talk to, I'd pick Mark Rude. He catches fish, even in August, when the lakers go deep.'"

Ken said, "It'd be a hell of a trip in a canoe. That's really exposed. There's nowhere to escape if things go wrong."

"The weather would have to be perfect." I agreed.

We dropped the subject of visiting Mr. Rude. There was no time this trip to go see him and probably no time any other trip as well. Mark lived so far down the island that we'd have to make the whole week's vacation centered around visiting him. Still it's good to know someone is left at Isle Royale who knows more about fish than just research data.

There was a time when a hundred families made their living fishing around Isle Royale. Now there's barely one. When Ken first came to Isle Royale in 1970, the Johnsons ran a few nets out of Crystal Cove on the north shore. They stopped shortly thereafter. The owners of the *Voyager* and *Wenona*, the passenger ferries that run out of Minnesota, used to fish after the Park closed in mid-October for a couple of cold months. Brian, my brother-in-law, worked for them for a couple of autumns after the park closed. They too retired their fishing skiffs. These men are the last to possess first-hand knowledge of the habits of lake trout, whitefish and herring, as well as Ken's bait-fish.

It's not the Park Service's fault no one commercial fishes the island any longer. And, for once, it's not the fisherman's fault either. They didn't over-fish the lake. What killed their way of life was the Soo Locks. When ocean freighters were allowed access to Lake Superior, the sea lamprey appeared soon afterwards. Within a single generation of fishermen, the lampreys literally sucked the life out of the game fish and caused lake trout numbers to crash all around Lake Superior. Merle Johnson in Crystal Cove is reported to say that at one point, he remembered seeing the bottom of the reefs completely covered with bodies of lake trout. Fish populations plummeted to a point where the whitefish and lake trout came close to extinction.

Sea lampreys were brought under control by the combined efforts of the Great Lake states, and the U.S. and Canadian fish and wildlife agencies back in the sixties. Once the lampreys were subdued, lake trout, whitefish, herring, and a few introduced species, like salmon and smelt, rebounded. Due to fifty years of treating for the lampreys, fish numbers have returned to pre-canal days.

Like salmon, sea lampreys run up rivers to spawn. Biologists found a chemical called TFM (3-trifluormethyl-4-nitrophenol) that when released in adjacent streams and at just the right time of the year kills the newly emerging fingerlings. The terrible story of the near demise of the fisheries in the Great Lakes is common knowledge, taught in ecology classes in grade schools.

The Clean Water Act helped turn the tide for reducing pollution. The pollution is not completely eliminated, of course, but the Act certainly made a significant difference. However, invasive species like the sea lamprey, zebra mussels, and the spiny water flea remain a serious threat. They are transported inside ballast tanks of ocean freighters then discharged into the lakes. These critters have been getting shipped here ever since the locks opened. It hardly seems possible, but legislation has only recently been submitted to regulate the dumping of ballast water into the Great Lakes. This new regulation is being fought in court by the shipping industry. At present, international freighters regulate themselves, which, as anyone might guess, is not working.

We're lucky. Researchers are often unable to move fast enough to find as effective a remedy as TFM. As an arborist, it's been my experience that science doesn't always thwart these catastrophes. The tragic loss of the American elm and the American chestnut due to introduced diseases, the loss of the grayling in Great Lakes streams due to loss of habitat, and the eradication of the passenger pigeon are all classic examples of scientists unable to respond in time. More often than not, species go extinct. The current ballast tank situation has been compared to playing Russian roulette with the largest fresh-water reservoir in the world.

Despite increases in fish populations around Isle Royale, commercial fishing never returned. Now a National Park, Isle Royale is unlikely to see commercial fishing return anytime soon. Those who know where to fish, how deep, and at what time of the year are gone. With them went generations of accrued expertise. For people like Ken and me, who fish for food and for recreation, and have an interest in the marine life, the old fishermen's knowledge is missed.

After dinner at night, Lake Superior and fish are common topics of conversation. In the process of fishing for several hours each day, we spend a great deal of time on the water. We're interested in aspects of the lake that recreational paddlers are unlikely to think about. In a sense, it's no different than talking shop back home.

Ken shared with me a well-written article in *Trout Magazine* he'd read several years ago. According to the article, there are four different native species of lake trout in Lake Superior. I've read elsewhere other biologists think there are only three. Reports from old commercial fishermen speak of many more. Of the four species the author reported, he held there are the coasters that tend to hug the shore and remain in shallow waters. They have a more slender shape than their relatives. The lake trout coaster is not to be confused with the brook trout found in Lake Superior, which is also called a coaster.

There is a lake trout with a massive head and a narrow body. The first time we caught one, we both remarked how it could have been a cross between a northern pike and lake trout, it looked so barracuda-like. A third laker is the Cisco, a football-shaped lake trout that prefers the deeper water. There's more body fat and oil in these fish, which protects them from the cold and tremendous water pressure found at the great depths they prefer. These were prized by fishermen who lived in an era when extra fat and oil were a bonus. The fourth species is similar to the coaster in appearance, but lives in the open lake.

Lake Superior is the only Great Lake that sustains a naturally reproducing stock of lake trout. The other four Great Lakes must be planted every year, and despite decades of attempts to restore them and for reasons that are still unclear, lake trout have not reproduced well enough to maintain a viable population in the other four lakes.

Both Ken and I tend to be critical of research. One of the shortcomings, in my opinion, is that it tends to take a narrow focus on issues. This is, in large part, because it must. Variables must be removed in order to acquire accurate information, and especially from something as multifaceted as a Great Lake. When those variables are removed, much is lost in the process.

In their defense, biologists know this is true and say as much. Marine biologists can tell me what water temperatures lake trout prefer. But they can't tell me with any consistency (and I've asked), where those water temperatures will be located on any given day come late September. They can print growth charts, tell what age a lake trout starts to spawn, and even provide statistics on survivability. However, they can't tell me, with anything resembling accuracy, where someone like myself might find a twenty-pound laker. Nor can they tell me at what depth I might find whitefish, and they certainly couldn't tell me *how* to catch them without using nets, which is what scientists use to count fish. They use chemicals to stun the fish, causing them to float to the surface for easy collection. They also rely on counts provided by Native Americans who gill net in designated places elsewhere around Lake Superior. Researchers also use sportsmen's tallies.

My selfish beef with the researchers is that the information they are trying to gain isn't what I want to know. They want to maintain a healthy, freshwater ecosystem—me too—but would it hurt if I were to catch just two lake trout tonight?

After dinner, Ken and I pulled out our books. We both like to read and when we saw campers bring books with them on the *Isle Royale Queen* to fill the uneventful hours during the journey over the lake, we made mental notes to bring one or two with us for future trips. Although a book is a heavy item to haul around in a backpack, both of us enjoy getting nose deep in some story after dark. Reading by flashlight or candles makes me think back to an era before electricity. If someone could look into our open-air, lean-to shelter, they would see a scene reminiscent of a hundred years ago, when men slept in rustic fish camps, jawing over the day's work, reading or writing letters, or playing cards. There's something special about reading at night over a candle with only the sound of the surf and the wind through the trees for background noise. Even inside the shelters, we feel gusts. Sometimes I have to set a small stone on the page to hold it in place.

Living outdoors brings stories to life. Settings become more vivid. When the protagonist says he's cold and lonely, I feel his torso shake, and with a subconscious reflex, I shiver too. There are books that should not be read while all alone in the wild. As much as I love Tolkien, when I'm miles deep in the woods, orcs and wargs and necromancers are not visions I like to take to bed with me. The old fireside ghost stories told to Girl and Boy Scouts before they turn in leave a traumatic impression. At fifty-years-old, they still do.

We tend to bring books about the outdoors or perhaps something about spiritual growth. Ken loves John McPhee and his attention to detail and his extensively researched subjects. I tend toward Bill Bryson or John Gierach and their humorous, everyman approach.

Edward Abbey, Thomas McGuane, Annie Dillard, Barry Lopez, and many other great outdoor authors all bring a view of the natural world I appreciate. They also somehow manage not to use the same descriptive metaphor twice. I've yet to catch Mc-

Guane resorting to a cliché, even when he talks of a fish strike or the bend in a river for the thousandth time.

Both of us ate up Jerry Dennis' books. He's a Michigan outdoor author with several collections of essays. *On the Water*, *The River Home*, and *From a Wooden Canoe* are on our bookshelves at home, dog-eared and soiled from camp life.

Reading at night doesn't last long. Keeping our eyes open after a day spent on the water—nap or no nap—is no easy task. We rise at dawn, and the day's activities are regulated by weather and daylight and the life cycles of fish. After staying only a night or two within earshot of the lake, we fall into a more natural rhythm. The wash of the surf ticks like a bedside clock. The fourth dimension takes tangible shape, and for once, it's a clock that doesn't cause me to rush.

The surf on Lake Superior has a different pitch than the sound of lapping waves on an inland lake. The surf leaves an impression of depth. The breakers resonate with the beat of a large drum. Fish swim behind those breakers. What deception will I use tomorrow to snag my next day's meal? To be able to cast a net *right there*, and know exactly where to set a net as Christ did—wouldn't that be something? I can understand why the fishermen were quick converts.

No one would inform me what works, except Dad. Now I teach my sons. Maybe that's the way learning how to fish is supposed to work. I've yet to read in a college catalog, "Fishing 101, basics of lure selection, casting techniques, and netting will be discussed, 3 credits, spring semesters." I haven't even seen it offered in the marine biologist's curriculum.

At Isle Royale, the people with first-hand experience on the matter are gone or not talking, and it's dangerous to rely strictly on studies. I could mistakenly believe I'm an expert on Lake Superior from studying the literature, and it's doubly easy without someone around who knows better to remind me of my ignorance. There are a few stragglers around Isle Royale like Mr. Rude. But, I can't help but wonder, if I did make it all the way down to Fisherman's Home Cove, could I trust him?

Fishermen lie. This is unfortunate, or fortunate, depending on your perspective. I've asked commercial fishermen on the Great Lakes elsewhere, "Where can I catch a few fish?" To my inquiry, I have received anything from a tight-lipped, stony silence to "Eh? Why we catch all of our fish in the lips."

Ken and I have been lucky. Isle Royale is one of the finest fisheries in the world. Over the years we've seen all four types of Lake Trout. Ken is the more pure fisherman of the two of us, and every time he catches me writing about the fishing here, he cringes. He chastises me for putting anything down on paper, convinced that even the slightest hint about how great the fishing is at Isle Royale will bring droves of anglers. When he sees me writing in my journal, he'll say, "Don't mention where we've been or what we use. You should keep two books, like businesses do, one for a log that records actual locations, weather reports, time of day for strikes, etc. The other journal should be for your damn reflections, where anything about how we fish is falsified and twisted beyond recognition."

"Why don't I just say all fishermen are liars?"

"Better yet, why don't you use that paper to start campfires."

"Who's ever going to read this?"

"You never know."

# NAKED IN THE STREAM

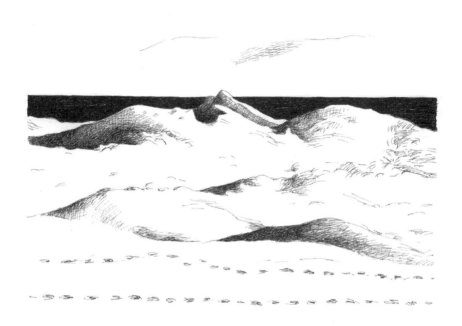

CHUNKS OF ICE BOBBED IN THE RIVER, TUMBLING DOWNSTREAM IN THE SWIFT current. I watched the ice float past and then disappear over the lip of the waterfall. Sitting down in the snow, I took off my boots, stripped from the waist down, and jammed the clothes into the backpack. I tied my boots together and hung them around my neck. Taking a deep breath, I stepped into the stream.

It's strange how disconnected one's thinking is. Despite the cold water that gripped my ankles, a part of my brain processed all of these instructions. This so-called rational portion of my mind worked as if divorced from any feeling.

*"Set foot into river. Ignore cold. Retain balance. Set other bare foot into river. First foot is numb. Second foot is numb."*

Then, as if an afterthought, *"That happened fast."*

My other self—the self-preservation self, the more emotional, supposedly irrational half—was swearing, yelling, and demanding immediate attention to the indisputable fact that I was about to commit suicide. Slipping and falling would be nothing short of fatal. In this water, I'd go hypothermic in seconds. I probably wouldn't even feel the plummet over the falls. This subjective portion of my personality cursed the world—sometimes audibly. I swore at the sharp stones and slippery rocks under my bare feet. I screamed at the trees. I hurled obscenities at the cold. I hated the crush of sound, knowing that if I fell—when I fell—no one would hear my last scream.

Taking a cautious step deeper into the river, the water rose to my knees. I cursed myself. Who in their right mind would want to wade across ice-choked streams, half-naked?

"Evidently you do," the objective half replied. "You thought this would be exciting. You wanted to do something different for spring break. It was *you* who chose to go north instead of south with the rest of your friends. You have nobody to blame but yourself."

This more mature, and accurate assessment, only caused the subjective part to go into another tirade. Taking one more step, the water level rose to my crotch, choking off the tantrum. My two personalities briefly merged and cried in unison, "Pay attention, you fool!"

Unable to hold it together, the rational part re-split. "Don't you think it's amazing how easy it is to find oneself in predicaments like this?"

I heard myself answer aloud, "No shit, Sherlock."

Late one winter's night at Michigan Tech, Ken and I, along with some other college friends were eating popcorn in his dorm room. Winters are long at Michigan Tech. The University is located in the heart of the Keweenaw Peninsula, which protrudes north for seventy miles into Lake Superior. The northernmost of the Great Lakes surrounds the school on three sides, and acts like an icebox. Average annual snowfall is over two hundred inches, and as a result, the University faces some unique challenges for drawing students.

Lack of warm sunshine isn't the only handicap. There's little nightlife. Michigan Tech is adjacent to the city of Houghton, a small town of about 5,000 people, and except for a handful of bars and restaurants, the town closes at six. Adjacent to the now abandoned copper mines, the city was built on the side of a steep hill, which makes any escape from Michigan Tech in the wintertime difficult. The roadways do a very authentic imitation of bobsled runs.

This had to be where the term "winter-beaters" was first coined. The locals laugh among themselves when they see a shiny, brand new sedan come to town without four-wheel drive, saying from their favorite breakfast joint to one another over their morning coffees, "Looks like Toivo's Body Shop's is gonna have a new customer."

With that said, the university does have its pluses. It offers excellent academic programs, specializing in engineering and forestry. Michigan Tech, or Tech as we usually called it, is about as far north in the state as it can be placed. Since Ken and I are both from southern Michigan, Houghton was as far away from home as we could get and still pay the much reduced in-state tuition rates. And what it lacked in fine arts, music, Starbucks, malls and clubs, it made up for in unpopulated northern forests, unpolluted lakes and streams, and—Lake Superior.

On that February evening, a group of us sat in Ken and Randy's dorm room, munching popcorn, complaining about the weather. Randy was Ken's roommate. We all met in their room at a predetermined time each night, supposedly as a study break. Everyone was looking forward to the upcoming spring break, and each of us in turn was discussing his plans.

The usual warm locations were discussed. Some guys were already locked into Florida, looking forward to seeing girls in something besides snowpants. At that time, Michigan Tech had a male-to-female ratio of ten-to-one. Our friends going south had already made motel reservations and were carpooling. Those of us who couldn't afford Florida were heading home to work to financially squeak through until the end of the school year. I normally worked. I was only a junior, but Ken and Randy were graduating in June, so this was to be their last spring break. Ken, I noticed, was unusually quiet.

After everyone else filtered back to their rooms, I hung around a while longer, dragging my feet about going back to memorizing botanical names of obscure trees. I strongly suspected that, since my professors were also stuck up here for the winter, they wanted me as miserable as they were. As I was about to walk out of the room, Ken said, "Hold on a second."

Turning at the door, I said, "What? You want to take a sauna later?"

The dormitory has a Finnish sauna downstairs and we sometimes used it to boil our winterized, claustrophobic brains into a mental haze. Long winters can create some ingenious thrills. For extra effect, we would get the sauna as hot as we could stand it, and then dump pails of ice-cold water over our heads. You'd feel like someone hit you with a sledge hammer. The thud of pain was quickly followed by a tingling sensation, and then a warm glow that lasted for several minutes.

"Maybe," Ken said. "Actually, I have an idea I want to show you."

I walked back in.

He pulled out a map of the Keweenaw Peninsula from a desk drawer, and unrolled it on top of the bed. "Check this out. I was thinking of hiking around the point."

"What do you mean?"

"Well, look at this." He pointed to the far end of the Keweenaw. "It's totally uninhabited."

I looked closer at the map and he was right. The peninsula protrudes north and then curls east making the Keweenaw Peninsula look like the crook of a finger. As a result, the tip of the peninsula actually points east instead of north. Other than a seven-mile long two-track that led from Lac LaBelle to the Montreal River Falls along the south shore, and another road marked seasonal that led from Copper Harbor to the point along the north shore—not connecting each other—nothing else was on the map. Both roads are unplowed in the winter. Not only was there no road rounding the point, there were no towns, nor any other man-made sites evident. The tip of the Keweenaw is as far north in Michigan as you can go, not counting Isle Royale. It is one of those rare, large, undeveloped tracts of land—land with miles of waterfront no less—which tempts some people to wonder what's out there.

Ken is definitely that sort of person.

I am too.

"Hmmm... that's interesting," I said.

Ken walked over to the door and locked it. He then pulled out of his desk drawer a different sheet of paper. Treating it like a treasure map, he gently unfolded a detailed topographical map of the very tip of Keweenaw Point.

"Where did you get that?" I asked.

"Ordered it."

"You've been holding out on me."

He looked at me with a conspirator's glance, and then slowly looked down at the heavily contoured end of the peninsula. We poured over the map, looking for names indicating abandoned mines, towns, anything. There was nothing but green-tinted paper filled with tightly packed contour lines.

"Cool. What are you thinking?"

Ken paused for effect and slowly said as if long rehearsed, "For my last spring break at Tech, what do you say we hike all the way around the Keweenaw Point?"

I swallowed hard.

When I didn't answer, Ken added, "As best I can tell, it's thirty miles … measured in a straight line. Given all of the nooks and bays, I'm sure it's much longer."

I still didn't respond.

Searching my face, Ken said slower, "It'll be difficult. So, only you and me, what do you say?"

I stood up from bending over the map, blinked, and like a deer caught in the headlights, I said with no hesitation, "Let's go."

Spring break was the third week of March, and the month of March in the Keweenaw is still wintertime. This, of course, is the reason several of our friends were heading south. Even southern Michigan feels warm by comparison. After returning to my room trying to focus on my tree-book with visions of an expedition swirling in my head, it slowly dawned on me that in reality this was a winter trip, not a spring hike. We were going to need snowshoes. We were going to need winter sleeping bags and I didn't even own a scarf.

As the necessities for such a trek began to seep through my adventure-crazed brain, all kinds of questions assaulted me. How much food do we need? How would we get out there and how would we get back to school? (Neither of us owned a car.) With no bridges, how would we cross rivers? What if there's a blizzard? What if it drops below zero? My book fell into my lap. "Hell, what will I tell my parents?"

The next night we talked and, after the popcorn break and everyone but Ken and I and Randy had left, I went over a long list of concerns. I gained volume and pitch with each issue raised. With a twisted smile on his face, I noticed Ken was making a poor attempt at suppressing his laughter. Realizing I was having no effect, I finally stopped and asked with more than a little frustration, "Are you listening to me?"

"I'm listening. You aren't seeing the half of it yet."

"What are you talking about?"

Ken allowed me a couple of seconds to cool down, then said, "What you probably didn't notice last night is that we have to figure out how to get past the waterfalls. I've been out to the falls. I went fishing with Don Stone out there this fall. We tried casting spoons where the Montreal River dumps into Lake Superior. It's a wide stream, twenty-five feet across at least."

"No, I didn't see any waterfalls or a river."

"In March, who knows how much snowmelt is rushing through."

Randy, who'd been studying over at his desk in the corner, shook his head at us and said, "You guys are nuts."

Ken didn't pay him any attention. "The whole journey, I predict, will take five days."

I said, "So ... *if* we can get across the river, you're figuring on five days?"

"Yeah, but I suggest we pack enough food for six, just in case. We should be able to walk along the shoreline most of the way. As far as I can tell, the Montreal River is the only river we have to cross."

I was suspicious. "It would be nice to talk to someone who's been out there before."

"Yes, it would. But I can't find anybody. I've tried. Hard to believe we're the first ones to attempt this, but if anyone else has ever done it, I've never heard of it. Nor has anyone I talked to."

"Who'd you talk to?"

"The old-timers up at church and a few locals they suggested."

I scratched my chin, not very satisfied with what I was hearing, and said, "Well, we certainly have some planning to do."

"Let's get together this weekend," Ken said. "Keep this to yourself. If word gets out, we'll have a bunch of guys wanting to go along."

"I doubt it," Randy said without looking up from his work.

"This is going to be tough," Ken said. Looking over at Randy, Ken said to him, "Please keep quiet. I'd rather not have to tell anyone they can't come."

He just nodded and smirked.

"All right," I said. "I understand. Better to let them set their spring break plans in stone before we break the news."

Over the next month, and after we'd argued through a list of what we mutually agreed were drop-dead, absolutely-must-bring-with-us necessities, Ken and I scrounged together our gear. This was as difficult a task as the trek itself. As college students, neither of us had money nor did we own cars. We didn't have winter backpacking gear or appropriate winter clothing for such a hike. We had done a couple of overnight winter camping trips while at Tech, but nothing like this.

What we did possess, however, was what most college students possess. While away at college we'd acquired a talent for talking others into loaning us what we wanted. As quietly as possible, we proceeded to impose, beg, borrow, and on rare occasions, buy supplies.

Many years later, when sitting in camp on Isle Royale talking over our shared history, Ken and I have discussed this critical portion of our college education. Looking back, "the hike" as we came to call it, was the pinnacle of our street-smart classes at Tech—our final exam if you will. Acquiring our supplies, making logistical arrangements, talking our parents into letting us go, ("After all I'm not asking to go to Ft. Lauderdale," is how I think I phrased it to them), and convincing girlfriends to arrange for rides was all the direct result of the real education we'd gained. By our senior year, these skills had been honed to a con-artist's sharpness.

We brought one of our more reclusive friends into the conspiracy so we could store our gear in his room without anyone noticing—at a technological school, not a difficult person to find. The week before spring break, we carried it all down to Ken and Randy's room to start the packing. An imposing pile of clothes and supplies were stacked at one end of their tiny dorm room. How were we going to carry all of it on our backs through waist deep snow, snowshoeing thirty miles?

Ken looked confident. "Don't worry. I've been to Isle Royale a couple of times. It can't be too different. Anyway, we'll be wearing most of the clothes, and all of the packaging for the food will be thrown away."

"Why?" I asked. I'd never camped for more than one night or been to the island yet.

"We need to repack all of the food into baggies, squeezing the air out to conserve space. Everything needs to form-fit into the packs. No air pockets, no wasted space. You'll be surprised how everything presses into a compact kit."

"Hope so," I said, scanning the mound of jackets, long underwear, tent, and food.

My expression must not have been very encouraging. Ken quickly added. "In a way, we're lucky. There are lots of trees where we're going. We can burn wood to cook our meals. Don't need to carry any fuel or a stove. We also don't have to carry water. We can drink lake water or melt snow."

"Have you thought anymore about the waterfalls?" I asked.

"I think the best we can do is bring a hatchet. We can cut down a tree that leans over the river at a narrow spot, somewhere upstream. Then, all we have to do is crawl across to the other side."

"That might work," I said. *Things are looking up,* I thought. "One last hurdle and I think we're there. How are we going to get a ride?"

Ken looked at me hard and said, "You know who we need to ask."

Ken asked his girlfriend, Patty, to pick us up in Copper Harbor on Friday afternoon at the trek's projected finish. Patty got permission to borrow her parents' car. However, she could not give us a ride Monday morning to the trek's start at Bete Gries. She wasn't on spring break the same week we were. She couldn't convince her parents to let her out of school. We asked her to keep pressing her parents, but she was still in high school, learning.

We decided I would ask my girlfriend's mother to drive us the forty-five miles from our dorm to Bete Gries. I'd been dating her daughter for a couple years but still took some nerve for me to make the request. Jo, who would later be my mother-in-law, had no good reason for hauling Ken and me out to the far reaches of Keweenaw County, but she agreed. We hadn't lost all sense of propriety and did offer to pay for gas. But not knowing the family real well at the time, I wondered at her generosity. I remember suspecting the real reason she said she'd drop us off in the middle of nowhere, in the dead of winter was not altogether due to my powers of persuasion.

The day of departure finally arrived. We managed to cram all of our gear into two backpacks, strapping the snowshoes on top. We threw the packs into the trunk. Jo looked very happy. Turned out she was just grateful to get out of the house and get a reprieve from cabin fever. After an hour on the road, we pulled up to the snowplows' turn-around. We didn't see another car for the last six miles of the ride. She seemed to know where we needed to go. She pulled over along the side of the road. Judging from the break in the tree branches over the snow bank, we were at the start of the unplowed two-track. The roadside snow banks stood eight feet tall.

I asked Jo to take a photograph of us standing together in the snow with our packs and snowshoes on. I'd borrowed a cheap Instamatic, and she snapped two pictures. Handing me the camera, she wished us luck, got in the car and drove away. The silence after her car was out of hearing range was a little unnerving.

Ken turned toward me and stuck out his hand. "Here's to a successful journey."

I pulled my mitt off and we shook hands. "Keweenaw Point or bust," I said.

We strapped on the old, borrowed Iverson snowshoes to our feet, hoisted our packs, and clambered over the snow bank.

Trudging through deep snow, we went slow. We had discussed bringing sleds or a toboggan to haul our gear. Unfortunately, we couldn't find anyone to lend us one. After hiking only a mile, and despite the cold, we were already sweating. We were in danger of becoming soaking wet. Whenever we paused to catch our breath, the cold wicked through our soggy shirts, making us shiver.

"Let me try hiking without the snowshoes," Ken said. "The snow is fairly packed down."

He sat down, unstrapped his snowshoes, got up, and gingerly took a few steps. He only sank three or four inches. "Hey, this ain't bad. I'm going to try it without them for awhile."

"I don't know. If you fall through, you could twist an ankle or worse."

"I won't go far. I'll just try it and see."

He moved so much faster that within five minutes, he'd hiked out of sight around a bend in the road. I kept trudging along in my snowshoes, following his tracks until I came upon evidence of a large spill in the snow. He must have broken through the hard-pack. I could see handprints where he pulled himself out of the drift. Even so, his tracks picked up from there, and he still wasn't in sight. A few minutes later he hiked back for me, walking almost as if he was on a dirt trail.

He yelled as he walked up, "Come on, it's a lot easier."

I unbuckled my snowshoes and stepped out of them. Walking as if on thin ice, I took a few cautious steps, and the snow crunched ominously underneath my feet, as if I could go through at any second. But after going about a hundred feet, I gained enough confidence to forget—for the most part—the three feet of fluff beneath me.

Ken said, "If you feel like you're going to fall through, stick your arms out.

"Why's that?"

"It keeps you from falling through as far."

"What are you saying? Should I get the rope out and tie it to each other like Alpine climbers?"

"No, that's not necessary."

I had good reason to be concerned about walking on top of the snow. When we broke through the hard-pack, which happened enough to keep me on edge, we really could break a leg. At minimum, it meant squirming out of waist-deep powder. And, in order to climb out of the sugar snow, we had to wriggle out of our packs, set them on top of the firmer snow, pull ourselves up, hoist the packs back on, and tiptoe past the soft section. Fortunately, we broke through so seldom that the speed we gained without snowshoes far outweighed the grief of falling through. After the first mile, we never wore them again. However, I didn't ever quite get over the sense that at any moment I could go for a spill.

It was a good thing Ken had hiked the road in the fall. Other roads crisscrossed ours. Even with Ken's recent experience, he struggled at times to remember the correct turns. Everything looked different in the winter, he complained. But after deciding a course, we'd go a little farther, and he'd say, "Yeah, I remember that rock" or "that twisted tree." Had he not remembered which way to go, we'd soon have been lost in a maze of logging roads. There are no maps that show all of the meandering forest trails. Once the loggers are finished with them, some of these temporary two-tracks disappear after only a couple of years.

Snow fell in small pellet-like flakes, falling in sparse patterns between the trees. The sun broke through the cloud cover, but only for brief moments at a time. When it did, the snow appeared to fall from thin air. It was cold out, but not unbearable. The cold actually helped. It kept us from overheating. I used my head like a heat vent. By taking my hat off and then putting it on again, I could release or store heat. I could tell I was getting tanned. The skin on my cheeks and nose felt tight. My lips were chapping.

There was little conversation. We both fell into that self-absorbed state of mind that long-distance runners regress into during marathons. It's difficult to talk when panting for air and focused on each and every step. Breathing deeply from our labors, the cold, clean air gave us an energy boost. It reminded me of getting a second wind. The fresh air provided a kick that acted like a sugar rush, only better.

Our road ended at an abandoned house called Smith's Fisheries. It was marked on the map. An old fisherman once lived there, plying his trade from a boathouse on the beach. He winched his boat up a ramp to get his skiff out of harm's way during storms. The old cable was still anchored to a rusty spool. When the lamprey invaded Lake Superior and decimated trout and whitefish numbers, he left his fishing business and never returned. We walked by the boarded-up main house and down to the lakefront. This was the first time all day we'd seen Lake Superior. Our two-track had passed through thick woods and avoided the water's edge.

Now standing at the shore looking back toward Bete Grise and Lac Labelle, the direction we'd come, I whistled in surprise. "Glad we used the road. There's no way we'd have been able to follow the coast."

"Look at those cliffs," Ken said. "They drop at least a hundred feet straight into the water. There is no beach."

We stared at the coastline, letting this unexpected news sink in. We'd taken the road instead of the "beach" because we believed the road would be shorter, not because we thought we couldn't walk the shoreline. More interested in the blank green spaces, we had sort of skimmed over the topo details on our map.

I said, "Now what?"

Ken paused as if in thought and then said, "Let's follow the path to the falls and see what it looks like past the river. The trail to the river is about a mile long. By then it'll be time to make camp. I doubt we have time to cross the river today."

"All right," I said.

We hiked the last mile to the falls. The thirty-minute walk to the river mouth reinforced the fact there would be no sandy beaches. The path meandered back to the lakefront in a few spots, and where it did, we looked up and down the coast. A tangle of wiry cedar, birch, and poplar formed a thick mesh above the rocky waterline. The ice-glazed, steep slope to the lake looked impossible to hike.

With this sobering realization, and at the end of a hard day, neither of us felt like discussing it further. We trooped the last thousand yards to the mouth of the Montreal River. It was just as Ken had described it. A twenty-foot waterfall emptied into the lake. The dark water roiled at the base of the falls until the stream regained momentum and continued out into Superior. The current was still visible several hundred feet from shore, where the band of iron-tinged river water mingled with the clearer waters of Lake Superior. It was a spectacular setting, and seen from the comfort of an easy chair, drink in hand, next to a fire, I'm sure the view would be inspiring. However, at the end of a long march with nagging doubts, it was too raw a vista to enjoy. We decided to head upstream to look for a quieter, less stimulating view, under some trees with a little protection from the wind.

Setting Lake Superior and the waterfall to our backs, we hiked inland. Around the first bend in the river, we found a sheltered nook under some cedars with a flat smooth space that looked as if it had been used before for a camp. It was getting colder, the sun sinking behind the tall hills. Mount Houghton and Mount Bohemia and a row of snow-covered ridges cut off the view to the north. The hills loomed over our heads. Snow-filled clouds streamed over their tops.

"We better get some wood," I said.

"Okay. I'm going to tamp the snow down to set up the tent."

There were plenty of deadfalls sticking out of the snow. I collected several armloads of wood, and soon had enough for the night, as well as for cooking tomorrow's breakfast. As I dumped the last armload on the ground, Ken was inside the tent setting the last pole in place. The tent rustled and moved as if possessed.

"Fill the canteen at the river," Ken yelled from inside. "We'll need the water for cooking noodles for the spaghetti."

"Are you sure this river is clean? The water looks funny."

"Yes. It's all the iron and minerals up here. You'll taste the iron, but there's certainly nothing wrong with the water."

"Camp looks good," I said. "With all the snow packed down, it's easy to walk. You'd think we did this winter camping all the time."

When I returned from the river, Ken had the fire going and was digging for the spaghetti mix and noodles in the pack. The sun had set behind the ridge. Stars began to show between the clouds. The wind dropped off at dusk, and when we quit moving about, a silence blanketed the land. Neither of us was accustomed to so much quiet.

The fire helped. Once it was large enough to throw some light, the crackle from the resin-filled cedar was almost as welcome as the heat. Even so, we sensed the area's vast quiet. The trees marched into the distance behind us, tall hills brushed against the low, fast-moving clouds, and Lake Superior lurked as a backdrop. As we sat around the fire, the trees that ringed camp seemed to lean in to listen as we reminisced about the past semester. We talked about life after college, and wondered about our friends who were now at the southern edge of the country on a wholly different sort of peninsula. We talked as if we were still back in Ken and Randy's dorm room eating popcorn.

"I still can't believe you got Jo to drive us out here," Ken said. After a moment he added, "Are you getting serious there? And don't tell me you don't know what I mean."

He caught me off guard, and I said, "I don't know. We still have a year of school left. We haven't really talked about it." I paused, thinking, and then said, "I was hoping to do some traveling after school—hit the road, see the world—that sort of thing. Do something before I work for the rest of my life. However, if I wanted to get married …."

Ken smiled. The fire lit our faces in that strange yellow glow that campfires throw. He set more wood on. "Hey, what are you doing?" I asked. "You planning on staying up late?"

"Why, you got classes tomorrow?" he mocked. "There's plenty of wood, plus, there's zero fire danger in all of this snow. We don't have to stay up and watch the fire until it burns out."

"I guess. What about you and Patty? You're the one that's graduating, not me. Is she still planning on going downstate with you in June?"

Ken grew quiet. This is probably what he really wanted to talk about. He cleared his throat and said, "Her sister, Lois, lives in Grand Rapids. She can stay with her. I don't know if Patty really knows what she wants. She's just getting out of high school. You remember what it was like then."

"Why isn't she going to college?"

"No money—you know—Dad's a small town Baptist minister with four kids. Besides, I think she just wants to get away from here. She's lived in Calumet her whole life."

"I'd stay here if I was her. I don't think she's going to like the city."

"We'll see how it goes," Ken said, and then fell silent.

The fire popped and sprayed glowing bits of wood. One landed on my wool pants I'd borrowed from my grandfather. They were red plaid, and too big and baggy for me. I had to hold them up with suspenders, which he'd also leant me. I quickly knocked the ember off before it could burn a hole.

"I think I've got a job lined up," Ken said, changing the subject. "I didn't tell you yet, but Williams and Works said they'd hire me as a surveyor. Wish I could hack around like you're talking about, but I've got loans to pay back."

"Too bad, it'd be cool if you could go with me."

The past summer I'd worked in an auto plant moving car bumpers from one rack to another all night long, seven nights a week. I'd made great money. But the experience caused me to make a pact with myself to never work indoors again.

My back was cold. One side of me was freezing, the other too hot. I kept rotating like a roasting marshmallow. Now that it was completely dark, temperatures were dropping fast. We could hear the ice on the lake crackle and then boom from the expansion rifts when it split apart. The booms rifled like gunshots across Keweenaw Bay. The constant, dull rumble of the waterfall throbbed in the background. To our city-trained ears it sounded like traffic on a distant highway. The sound of the freezing ice and the falls against the backdrop of all of that silence had a disquieting way of reminding us about tomorrow.

Despite feeling tired, the thought of crawling into my ice-cold sleeping bag made me reluctant to turn-in. Whenever I looked over at the tent lying half-buried in snow, it reminded me I'd be sleeping inside the equivalent of a freezer. *How did our ancestors ever survive,* I wondered.

Ken was starting to nod off.

I finally said, "Let's get some shuteye."

The next morning, we each lay deep inside our sleeping bags, the only bare skin showing a tiny six-inch-diameter ring of eyes and nose. My body ached. We were young and in good shape. But neither of us were used to yesterday's sort of effort. I never did get totally warm during the night, and lying in my bag, the thought of four more days of this didn't motivate me to leap to action. Our breathing had created a fog inside the tent. A layer of hoarfrost coated the interior tent walls and the outer skin of our sleeping bags. I lay there watching my breath steam in bursts of hot air.

"Man, it's cold." I said. My voice sounded muffled from inside the bag.

"Get up," Ken said.

"After you."

We lay there a few minutes longer, and then groaned in unison and unzipped our bags. We quickly grabbed our clothes and boots, which were frozen stiff from yesterday's sweat. To get into our shirts, pants and socks, we had to take them outside and shake them to get the fabric to relax. Even so, my shirt still scratched when it went on.

"I've got to get moving," I said, stamping my feet. "I'll go get some more water. You light the fire." Ken didn't answer, but didn't need to.

I walked down to the river, and when I reached the water, the distinctive, deep, chirrup of chickadees sang from within thick, snow-clad evergreens. The wind sifted through the snow on the needles, and the sound of the river washing over stone made me feel like I was part of the landscape this morning and not an interloper. *Maybe I had to prove I could survive a night*, I thought.

Pausing to admire the winter setting, the river reminded me of an old painting on the wall of a small, local restaurant: The kind of picture with a log cabin on the crook of a trout stream, with warm lights shining through small-paned windows. The picture I looked at this morning had no dust on it. Despite the cold and a desire to hustle back to the fire, I stood at the riverbank for a moment and sniffed the wind. The cold air hurt my chest when I breathed in too deeply. I knelt down and splashed water on my face. If I hadn't been fully awake before, the shock resolved that. Refilling the canteen, I walked back to camp. Ken was just setting a match to the kindling. I crawled back into the tent and rolled up my sleeping bag. Ken had already done his.

From inside, I said, "I'll tend to the fire if you want to take down your tent."

"All right."

During breakfast, which was only oatmeal, we finally dared to broach the subject of the river crossing. "Well, what do you think?" I asked, not mentioning it by name.

Ken hesitated and then said, "I didn't see any trees between here and the falls we could use. We're going to have to hike farther upstream and see if the river narrows. I've been all the way to the upper falls. That's at least two, maybe even three miles. But I was moving slowly, fishing. It's a long walk. There's a lot of twists and turns in the river and downed trees."

"Maybe a tree's already fallen over the river."

We packed up our gear and set out. It was still early and the sun hadn't crested the treetops. Overhead, between trees, I saw clear skies. It held promise for a good day of hiking. The lake breeze returned, but wasn't strong.

We walked down to the Montreal. The stream slid softly through its watercourse, appearing to steam in the frigid, early morning air. The lower tree limbs that hung over the river looked flash-frozen, the bottom branches covered in a thick coat of ice where rising vapor froze to them. We turned, and started to hike upstream. Moving against the flow, it gave us the impression we were traveling twice as fast.

The river never narrowed to less than thirty feet. I could easily throw a rock to the other side—underhanded if I tried. It might as well have been a thousand. Each time we went around a bend, we looked ahead for a convenient tree. After an hour's hike, and then another hour, and then a third, we stopped to regroup.

"This doesn't look good," I said. "There were a couple of old birch trees we could drop *into* the river, but nothing that'll reach across."

Ken said, "We can keep going, but it's not narrowing at all. We might have to go past the upper falls. We could lose two whole days."

"I don't want to turn around now," I said.

"There is another way."

"Yes ...?"

"We could ford the river."

"Get real! Do you know how cold that water is? We don't dare get wet."

"I know, I know ... we'd have to strip, carry everything on our shoulders."

"No way."

Ken paused, and then quietly said, "You have any better ideas?"

Only the sound of our labored breathing followed his question. I was thinking hard, staring at the water in silence.

Ken finally said. "Let's head back toward the falls, see if we can spot a shallow section. If it's not too deep, we can do it."

I still didn't move. I continued to gaze into the river, hypnotized by the sliding water. The river blurred, and I shuddered, aware for the first time of the sound of the rafts of floating ice where it crunched against the rocky river bottom in the shallower water. Without much conviction, I said, "We'll see."

We turned around and headed back downstream. Backtracking down our trail, we used our footprints as a path. Walking was easier on the already tramped down snow. The tobacco-tinted water and rippled current made it difficult to see how deep the river was. Sunlight flashed on the surface causing us to squint. Now that we were studying the river more closely, where we could see the bottom, we noticed how jagged and uneven the riverbed appeared.

"We should have brought tennis shoes," I said.

Ken just nodded.

After four hours of slowly moving downstream, carefully searching for shallow water, the sun was starting to creep toward the western ridge tops. We'd debated over a couple of promising looking sections, but ruled them out. When we'd almost reached last night's camp, the river fanned out before it made its final run to the lake. We could see small pebbles protruding through the surface in the middle—a hopeful sign.

"This might work," Ken said. "I don't see any black water. If we move a little upstream after wading two-thirds of the way across, we'll avoid that deep-looking hole at the far bank."

I didn't say anything. I was studying the river. It still seemed a dubious plan, and I hadn't really bought into it. I kept thinking, *first law of winter survival is stay dry.*

Ken said, "It's getting late. If we don't go soon, we'll have to wait until tomorrow. I don't want to stay on this side another day if I can help it."

"I don't know," I said.

In reply, Ken unhooked the hatchet from his pack and walked into the trees examining branches. He broke off a straight piece of maple, and with the hatchet, chopped it to size for a walking stick. I sighed and searched for a solid branch. A cedar limb caught my eye, and I cut it off, peeling twigs from it.

"Now what?"

"Get your rope out and we'll tie it to each other. I'll go first."

I eyed the rope. "You know this is just a clothesline. It's meant for drying wet clothes over the fire, not this."

Ken sat down in the snow and started to untie his boots. He slipped out of his pants, long underwear, and boxers, leaving his socks on for a little padding for his feet. "I packed extra socks," he said. He then shoved his clothes into his backpack and slung his tied-together boots around his neck. He tied one end of the clothesline around his waist. "You ready?" he asked me.

I nodded, looking him in the eye to see if I could read any hesitation. Ken blinked, looked away, and then gingerly stepped down the bank to the river. With the over-stuffed pack mounted on top of his shoulders, he looked like a buffalo with skinny legs and thick forward shoulders. He paused at the water's edge, looking left and right as if preparing to cross a street. The waterfall, only a hundred yards downstream, droned away and threw clouds of mist into the air.

Ken turned to the river and stepped in. He grimaced. He slowly set his other foot into the river and a gasp escaped his mouth.

"How bad is it?"

Through clenched teeth, Ken hissed, "Don't let the rope drag in the river."

"But, how bad ..."

"Just watch the damn rope!"

I wrapped the clothesline halfway around a tree trunk and pulled out the slack. I realized he was worried the rope might catch on floating ice and pull him down.

As Ken started to wade across the river, I let the line play through my hands, keeping tension as he went. Only eight feet from shore, there was a drop-off. Ken tried sliding down the underwater slope, but stumbled and lurched forward into the trough. He caught his balance with his walking stick at the bottom. The current washed against his legs, splashing his shirttail, which had come untucked from under his pack belt.

Just six feet farther, the river grew noticeably shallower. If he could just get through the channel, he could walk most of the rest of the way across the river in ankle-deep water. But the current was strong. He only inched along, slowly shuffling through the trough, not daring to lift his feet for fear of being swept away. Slushy ice drifted past him. He used his free hand to shove them aside. The mats of ice twirled away and then glided downstream. Ken struggled with balance in the fast water. But after a couple of tense moments where he seemed to bounce across the channel, he started to move a little quicker. The water level fell to his knees and then to his shins. He was through the channel.

"Watch that line! I'm having a hell of a time with my balance." Ken shouted at me as if in a lot of pain.

"I don't want to pull you over," I shouted.

He said no more, and I cinched the line as tight as I dared. This was no place to get sensitive. He wasn't yelling at me and I knew it.

Ken started across the mid-section of the river, but the riverbed was so broken and uneven that even in ankle-deep water he struggled to find good footing. After taking only two steps, he sprang up, pack and all, acting like he stepped on a tack. He almost slipped and fell, but finally settled onto smoother rocks. He stood still, hesitating to move.

"Are you all right?"

Ken straightened up his pack, which shifted when he jumped. Looking back at me, he said, "Got to try something different."

He started sliding each foot forward and leaned more heavily on his walking stick. Probing the riverbed with his toes, he looked like he was walking over broken glass. He carefully searched for smooth spots to place his weight on.

The water level never rose above his knees across the middle of the stream until ten feet from the other side. Then he stopped. He must have seen something that I couldn't from my position. He turned and started walking downstream. I only had another twenty feet of rope left and I gave it a light jerk. He halted and looked over at me.

Holding up what was left of the clothesline, I shouted at the top of my voice to be heard over the swirl of water. "Hey! No more line."

Ken didn't even nod, quickly turning his attention back to the river. Moving another four feet downstream, he halted again. He then turned toward the far side, and stepped down. The river rose to just above his hips, and for an instant, I thought he was going to fall. He teetered for a second, but remained upright.

The current crested in a wave against his torso. Ken looked unsure of himself, and evidently deciding his position in the deep water too precarious to inch through. He set his walking stick toward the far side, leaned forward, and vaulted toward the riverbank. The current swept him a yard downstream, and appeared to deposit him in knee-deep water. Another step, he was ankle deep, and then he was across.

Splashing up the far bank, he turned and raised both arms. He was shouting, but I couldn't hear what. I exhaled, not realizing how tense I'd been.

We stared at each other across forty feet of river. Ken pulled his clothes out of his pack, dried his legs off with a spare shirt, and got dressed. While he did, I took off my boots, slid out of my pants, underwear, and left my socks on for some padding. I then tied the clothesline around my waist. I looked over at Ken to see if he was ready. He was doing jumping jacks on top of the riverbank trying to warm up. When he was done, he pulled in slack line until I felt a tug. He gave a gentle pull as if to say "anytime now."

There wasn't much else I could do. *Give grace to fools*, I prayed, and stepped into the river.

To say I was shocked does no justice to it. Despite knowing it was ice water, in spite of seeing how much Ken suffered, and even after steeling myself for what I thought was the worst, no amount of coaching, no amount of mental preparation, no amount of liquor could have prepared me. The instant I set my foot into the river it lost all feeling. When I placed my other foot in the river, the same sensation occurred in exactly the same split-second.

I understood the significance. I recognized the danger, but at first it didn't register. The Montreal rolled across my feet, and I watched a chunk of ice bump against my ankles. No way were those my legs.

I couldn't will myself to move. I felt nothing. It was as if my feet weren't even there. Then, while I was standing there immobilized, my emotions caught up with the situation. My mind started to race. Several disasters went through my head all at once—all of them ended with me drifting facedown with the ice floes somewhere in Lake Superior. I wanted to untie the clothesline and run clear back to Bete Gris. I wanted to scream at everything and everybody. This was totally insane. What was I thinking?

But then an amazing thing happened. The panic faded. My mind cleared, and a small but very logical voice took over. Various episodes of drowning still played through my head. However, my feet were still attached. They were only very cold. My thoughts could go wherever they wanted just so long as my reeling brain left me in control.

I picked up a foot and set it down, testing it. The foot moved up and then down. I glanced across the river at Ken and smiled. I must have looked daft because he started shouting at me. I couldn't hear what he was saying.

I swallowed hard, and then waded out to the edge of the drop-off. As I approached the channel, my shins and then knees lost feeling. I hesitated. My legs started to feel like they were burning, but the sensation disappeared after a few seconds. The greater difficulty, the one that Ken had somehow overcome, now became apparent. Like he had complained, my balance was shot. Without the walking stick, I could not have managed. At least my hands retained feeling. Taking three deep breaths to steady my nerves, instead of trying to slide down the drop-off like Ken did, I jumped into the trough. The water rose to my waist. I battled another surge of panic. The cold penetrated through me. The numbness stopped at my legs.

I gripped the cedar limb. I needed to hurry to avoid hypothermia, but didn't dare move too fast. I inched through the trough just as Ken had. From the top of the riverbank, where I'd watched him ford the channel, I could see to the river bottom from my elevated angle. But with my face now only three feet above the surface, the river reflected the bright sky like a mirror. I couldn't even see my knees. I only knew I'd waded across the channel when I stubbed my toes against the incline to the middle-shallows. The sensation registered only as an impediment to movement.

I climbed up the underwater slope and then started across the middle of the river through the shallower water. The rocks were sharp and jagged, but I didn't feel any corresponding stab of pain. I kept slipping and struggled more than expected. Watching Ken cross this section, I hadn't completely understood his clumsy pace in only knee-deep water. I understood now.

Following his lead, I carefully placed my weight over each foothold and tested it. If it held, I'd found solid footing. If my knee buckled, I needed to shift, placing more weight on the walking stick. My legs behaved no differently from the pole in my hand.

It seemed to take forever, but finally reaching the edge of the far deep channel, I looked up at Ken, only twelve feet away. He was pulling in line from the top of the riverbank. He looked intense, following my every move.

He said, "Go downstream. The channel is narrower there."

"I d-don't think I c-can. Your l-legs longer than mine."

"Go downstream."

I shook my head and said, "I'm t-trying up-p…stream. It's f-farther from the … falls."

I talked through chattering teeth and my hands were shaking. I had just enough wits left to recognize the hypothermia. Ken's expression darkened to concern. My last sentence about the falls sounded, even to my ears, like gibberish.

Ken and I are the same height, but his legs are four inches longer than mine. Downstream, the river had risen to his waist. I'd never make it. We slowly made our way upstream linked together by twelve feet of clothesline looped over the churning river. He paralleled me as I plodded upstream. After going about twenty-five feet, I spotted a small sandbar that protruded from the other side. I studied the bar to see if it looked solid enough. It still left a four-foot-wide jump across the channel. If the sandbar gave way, and I slid backwards… I wasn't sure I had the coordination any more to scramble out, backpack intact.

"I'm-m … goin … to g-go for it … I c-can't stand … ere … ny … l-long … ger."

I tensed to jump. The heavy pack felt like a building on top of my shoulders, my legs more like anchors than springs.

"When … I … jump-p-p, yank me … p-pull me … me up!"

Ken stepped down the riverbank to the edge of the water, "Whenever you're ready."

I leaned backwards and then leaned forward hard, using the momentum to help me try to leap. "Now!" I shouted.

I jumped, landing far short of the bar, slipping into deep water. Reeling backward, I looked up into Ken's face and screamed, "PULL!"

Ken jerked so hard that I pitched forward, sprawling. The pack slid over the top of my head.

I fell so far forward that I landed on all fours into twelve inches of water. Ken reached down, grabbed me by the armpits, and hauled me up. We scrambled ashore, Ken half-carrying me and the pack up the riverbank.

I felt released. Raising my arms and shouting, I turned around and shook my fist at the river. The Montreal flowed unchanged. The rumble from the falls droned unabated.

I dropped my pack, and Ken and I started to jump up and down, whooping and screaming, slapping each other on the back. My legs trembled. Catching my breath, I leaned back—faced skyward, and howled.

"Hey, you're bleeding," Ken said.

I bent forward, setting my hands on my knees, panting hard, and staring down at the ground. Where we'd been prancing around, celebrating, the snow was all pink. "What the hell?"

"You're bleeding," Ken said again.

Sitting down on top of a pack, I examined my feet. Sure enough, my right foot was lacerated across the inside of the arch. Blood seeped into the white snow.

"I never felt it … I don't feel it now."

"Jeeze, shut-up," Ken said. "Where'd we pack the bandages?"

"I think they're in the bottom of your pack." I pulled my sock off and used it to wipe blood away for a closer look.

"You should have stitches," Ken said.

"I don't think so. It doesn't look too deep. You find them yet?"

Ripping through his backpack, scattering supplies, Ken said, "Here it is. Oh wait, nope ... ahh ... here they are." He walked over with the first-aid kit and a bag of gauze.

The feeling was beginning to return, and it wasn't entirely welcome. "I can't seem to get my hands to quit shaking. You mind bandaging this for me?"

Ken put a couple of squares of gauze over the cut. The bleeding had slowed to barely a trickle. He then wrapped it with what looked like fifty feet of medical tape.

"Not so tight. You'll cut off circulation."

"Relax," Ken said, cutting off the last piece of tape with his teeth. "Now that's a first-rate field dressing."

"Thanks—I think."

Standing up, I struggled to finish getting dressed. My hands still shook. Pulling my pants on, I couldn't grip the zipper or grasp the big black button at the top. Thankful I had worn suspenders, I slung them over each shoulder. It took a bit of concentration, but I managed to tie up my bootlaces in big square knots.

"Get moving," Ken said. "We need to get your blood pumping ... the sooner the better."

"I do feel kind of funny."

Ken repacked. We helped each other put our backpacks on. Before setting out, he said, "Check the area, I don't want to leave any gear behind."

We scanned the ground, picked up the baggie with the white gauze that blended into the snow, and we were finally on the move again. The day was almost spent, and we wanted to put some distance between the river and us. If we measured today's progress, we'd traveled a total of a hundred feet toward the point. Taking one last glance at the far side of the river, we started hiking down to the lake. When we reached the falls, we turned left.

Past the Montreal River, there are no more roads or trails. It's twelve miles from the river mouth to Keweenaw Point, and if we'd been looking to walk where no man had gone before, then the land gave every appearance that we found the right place. Tall hills run down the center of the Keweenaw Peninsula. The ridges descend a thousand feet to Lake Superior. On these wooded slopes, outcrops of stone stand out on the flanks of the Keweenaw like fortress bastions. The rugged hillsides make a person think twice before deciding to hike cross-country.

Where the bedrock of the peninsula finally meets Lake Superior, the lake washes the thin veneer of earth away. The constant wind and waves at the shore expose tilted slabs of dark, weathered stone. The rock descends another thousand feet, unseen, below the surface of the lake. If by some cataclysmic event Lake Superior was drained, the exposed lake bottom would form one of the deepest valleys in the Midwest.

It had already been a tough day, and picking our way over the maze of stonework along the shoreline was difficult. The old rock is slippery. We scrambled up and over boulders, jumped from one rock to another where they were close enough, and weaved our way through the labyrinth of stone and piled-up ice. With heavy packs on, it was awkward work. In some places, we had to tiptoe along the edge of thirty-foot drops, leaning backwards over the edge, gripping onto tree limbs as we carefully slid around tight spots.

After hiking only a half-mile down the shoreline, we were sweating, and had thoroughly warmed back up. "How's your foot?" Ken asked when we pulled up on top of one of the few tabletop rocks that allowed enough room for both of us to stand side by side.

"Not too bad. It's throbbing a little," I said, studying our next move. "At least we're warm now."

"That's a good sign. Let's go." Neither of us was in any mood to talk, bent on getting as far away from the river as possible. We continued, scrambling over ice and rock, threading a course above Lake Superior. It was becoming evident that we couldn't manage this obstacle course for much longer today.

"Hey Ken," I finally said, "Let's try it inland. Just keep the lake within sight."

Ken headed up the slope and into the trees, smashing his way through the tangled growth at the edge. The woods are thick. The short, stunted conifers grabbed at our clothes and packs. The inland terrain was more rough and broken than the shoreline.

Rocks the size of garages, lay piled in a hundred different angles. In between the stone, the land was thick with spruce, fir, juniper, and a sort of twisted shrub with red berries that I didn't recognize. They caused us to weave a terribly meandering course around the obstacles. Downfalls constantly blocked the way. We didn't think it was possible, but the going was worse than the lakefront. After thirty minutes of trying to negotiate the terrain, we walked back out to the lake.

Breaking through the trees, we stopped to catch our breath. The wiry branches had scratched our faces and hands. My down jacket was ripped, and feathers spilled from the nylon shell. Breathing hard and losing steam fast, we scrutinized the shoreline below us.

I followed the band of pack ice down on the lake front that hugged the shore. Just around the bend toward the point was a tiny cove we hadn't noticed before. The cove was no more than two hundred feet wide and cut fifty feet deep into the peninsula. A smooth section of ice lay between the two arms of the cove.

"That's a place to camp if I ever saw one," I said. "Come on, we're almost there, and … Ken?"

"Yeah?"

"Let's test the ice."

"I was just thinking that too." Looking over at me, he said, "It's a bit risky. This ain't Lake Michigan. The water's deep next to shore."

How deep was a mystery. The pack-ice was piled up against the rocks as if compressed against the shore with a giant's hand. For a hundred feet into the lake, the ice formed a ruffled, white roadway that traveled up and down the coast. Where ice met the open water, the ice rose and fell in sync with Superior's rollers.

"Wait a second," Ken said. Picking up a rock the size of a bowling ball, he heaved it onto the ice below. It hit with a solid thud.

"That sounded good," I said.

We clambered down the bank, stepping off the rocks onto a cake of ice. "Careful," I said, "you could fall through a snow-covered crevasse, like you read about on glaciers. Use that walking stick."

Ken poked at the ice ahead of him. Everything seemed firm, and he found no disguised holes or cracks. We began to cautiously work our way down the shoreline, keeping tight to shore.

"So far so good," Ken said. "If this holds, we may have stumbled upon something."

"This is like walking on crooked pavement. Just a little slipperier," I said.

"I'm not going much farther today. I want to allow enough daylight to collect lots of wood. Tonight … I'm making a *big* bonfire."

We hiked into the cove, and risking the shortcut across the smoother ice between its arms, we ventured out, looking like blind men with white canes. "Don't walk so close to me," Ken said. "Spread out."

At about a third of the way across the cove, the ice began to creak. "I wish we'd brought a couple of extra rocks," I said.

"Wish you'd thought of it sooner."

The ice groaned a couple of times as we slowly crossed the cove, but gave no other sign of breaking. We were gaining confidence with each step, and Ken was only testing the ice with his walking stick every six or seven steps. Finally making it to the far side, we climbed onto the thicker ice right next to shore.

Ken then climbed up to the top of the rocks. We went into the trees and after going only thirty feet, discovered a clearing.

"This'll work," I said, "Close to the water, lots of wood."

Dropping our packs, we turned around and walked back to the lake. Looking toward Lac LaBelle—roughly our journey's beginning and now ten miles away, we could see how far we'd come. Our little cove's point allowed for a panoramic view down the entire length of the Keweenaw Bay. The Montreal waterfall was clearly visible, just a mile down the shore. I could easily make out the brown path of water that flowed into the lake.

Across Keweenaw Bay, thirty miles distant, we could see the tops of the Huron Mountains on the mainland. Between them and us, lay open water splotched with sheets of drift ice. It was a scene straight from the Arctic. Sunlight slanted horizontally over the bay. The edges of the ice floes and the crests of the waves were tinged red.

"Well, we didn't get far today, did we," Ken said.

I answered, "No, we didn't. Let's hope we make better progress tomorrow. If we don't show up in Copper Harbor at noon on Friday, Patty will get worried."

After a pause, Ken said, "I'm gonna start gathering wood. If you're up for it, why don't you see if you can find a way to draw water from the lake. Tie the rope to the canteen and throw it into the lake, so you won't have to get too close to the edge."

"Yeah? … All right, I guess. Why don't we melt snow?"

"It's pretty tough to melt snow over a wood fire. Too much ash and soot gets in it. It takes forever, too." Walking into the woods, Ken added, "Don't lose that canteen. It's all we have to hold water."

I went back into the clearing, grabbed the canteen, found the rope, and headed back out onto the ice.

In front of our new camp, the pack ice extended for fifty feet into the lake. Studying it from the trees, I picked out a thicker looking section and climbed down the rocks. Slowly working my way out onto the pack ice and toward the edge, I poked at dark patches of ice with my walking stick. The dark spots looked as if they might be soft, but were really black ice swept clean by the winds. I remembered to bring some stones this time and kept throwing one out ahead of me every five or six feet. With each toss, it thumped hard on the surface as if hitting concrete. When I got within twenty feet of the edge, I stopped.

Due to the inward curl of Keewanaw Bay, I could see where the open lake met the ice farther down the shoreline. The waves undercut the ice pack, and had I not stopped short of the edge, I could have easily stepped onto the thin overhang.

I inched a few feet closer. When I got within ten feet, I lay face down, spread eagle to better distribute my weight. Crawling within five feet of the water, I halted and played out line. I tightened the knot on the canteen and slung it into the lake. It splashed, and I held my breath in order to hear the gurgling stop when it filled with water. When it did, I pulled the line in, but the canteen caught on the lip of the ice. "Aaagh … come on, baby," I pleaded. Lowering it back into the lake, I tried again, slowly pulling in line, hoping to ease it over the edge. When the canteen peeked over the top, I quickly hauled it in—only three-quarters full.

"That's gonna have to do," I said, and screwed on the cap.

I lay there for a moment, resting. The wind had died. The gentle swish of the waves beat a steady three-second rhythm, matching my heartbeat, which I could feel thumping against the ice.

The lake had worn the edge of the ice pack smooth. The polished ice reminded me of the mysterious, marbled dark glass of a crystal ball. Splayed on the ice, I turned my head left to look toward Keweenaw Point and hopefully tomorrow night's campsite. I then turned to look down the shoreline in the other direction, the way we'd come. The inward curl of the bay allowed me to see all the way to the beacon at the channel into Lac Labelle. All together we'd come almost ten miles.

With my nose just above Lake Superior, the ice field looked like toy Alaskan mountains, with broad white plains. Rising onto my elbows to raise the perspective, I peered straight ahead, cupping my chin in my hands. Positioned only twelve inches high, the waves looked like rolling hills of water.

*Many animals only stand this tall,* I thought. *Must be strange to always view the world this close to the ground.*

Squirming backward, away from the edge, I stood up and retraced my tracks back to shore. When I got back to camp, Ken had already collected a big pile of wood and sticks.

As he headed into the trees for more, I said to him, "You weren't kidding."

That night we ate Dinty Moore Stew. The old standby dinner-in-a-can, never tasted better; the hot broth, or gravy, or whatever it really is, burned going down. Heat seemed to flow through my limbs. My foot throbbed a little, but didn't hurt. After we finished eating, we threw more wood onto the cooking-fire until the flames were shooting six feet high. The heat caused our damp clothes to steam, and we kept backing away from the fire. It occurred to us that a smaller campfire would do just as good a job, but we didn't care. Let it burn. It was the first time in two days I felt relaxed.

Ken made popcorn after dinner, which proved to be a tricky affair over a bonfire. He tried lying on his belly to pop the corn, but it was too hot. He got up, scratched his chin for a second, gave me an "I know what to do" look, and then grabbed a long stick out of the wood pile. He pushed some hot coals away from the main blaze, creating a satellite campfire.

The saucepan steamed as the corn popped and the smell visibly drifting in the frigid air. With no thermometer, we had no idea how cold it really was. If the butter was any indication, then it was well below freezing. We'd pilfered at least fifty of those tiny pats of butter from the dorm cafeteria. They were frozen so hard that the hot popcorn never did thaw them. The corn was all covered in yellow blobs.

I cleaned up dishes afterward, using snow to scrub the hardened gravy off the plates and spoons. Then I threw some clean snow into the saucepan. Heating it to a boil, I poured the scalding water over every pot, plate, and utensil.

"Don't get carried away," Ken said. "We're just going to get them dirty tomorrow morning." He pushed the coals back into the bonfire and threw on another armload of wood.

Standing as close as I dared, I stretched my dripping hands toward the fire to dry. We just stood there and watched the fire, not saying too much. We celebrated in our quiet way. Ken had brought a pint of Southern Comfort. We had agreed to a shot each night for "heat." For making it across the river, we splurged and had two. When I walked away from the firelight to take care of business and looked up, the clear winter sky was so speckled with stars, the black of space so—black, between the whirling heavens and having a slight buzz from the whiskey. I felt dizzy. I grabbed a tree to steady myself, and then headed back to the fire.

"Hey Ken," I said after a long stretch of silence. "Did I ever tell you about the one and only time I went to Lac Labelle—on a date?"

"I don't think so," he said. He poked at the fire. The pine, spruce, and cedar snapped and popped.

"I was on this double date—sort of—Dave and Samantha, plus me and Kathy. We drove up the east shore of the peninsula in Dave's car. I was just a freshman. The girls were locals and they said to Dave, 'Let's go up to Lac LaBelle via Lake Linden. You guys'll like it. There's nothing up there but summer cottages and nobody will be there this time of year. The highway hugs the shoreline. You can see down the whole bay.'

"So off we went. We drove up the coast, almost all the way to where Jo dropped you and me off at Bete Gris. It was late April— I think. I know the ice was beginning to break up. And ... Ken ... I'm telling you, it was the most beautiful thing I ever saw."

"Really, that's high praise."

"I've never told anyone about it before. It was one of those clear, starry nights and a full moon was rising straight out of the lake. God, it was huge, and it was mirrored perfectly off the ice, making it seem twice as big. A sheet of yellow light stretched across the bay like a road. I really thought I could walk all the way to the moon on it.

"On the other side of the road, opposite the lake, the whole sky was lit up behind Mount Houghton and Mount Bohemia. The hills were silhouetted against all of this glowing, pulsating light, like there was some sort of distant battle going on. The Northern Lights were out, and as we drove up the coast, they grew and began to shoot over the mountains. Red and green streaks zoomed across the sky, causing the trees beside the road to glow in different colors, shifting, fading in and out, and then flashing bright. Then, all of a sudden, the whole sky blazed. The Northern Lights swept over the ridge top and streamed overhead in every color you can imagine, shimmering, throbbing. With the snow-covered ground, the land took on all the same hues as the sky, doing this sort of visual echo."

Ken said, "I saw 'em like that once on Isle Royale. You could almost read by them."

"Even as cold as it was outside, we had our heads out the car windows, straining to see. The girls were screaming at Dave, 'Stop the car! Stop the car!'

"No one else was on the road, and he finally pulled over into this little roadside park. We all piled out and looked up. The Northern Lights stretched from horizon to horizon. We kept yelling at one another, 'Did you see that one?' or 'Look, look, over there!' There was so much going on, we couldn't see it all. We decided to lie down in the middle of the road, right on the centerline.

"We must have laid there for one-half hour, just gawking, oohing and aaahing. Dave had this tape of Cat Stevens playing with the windows rolled down. When the last song finished, we all fell quiet. In the silence, which we hadn't noticed before, we could just barely hear this gentle, tinkling sound. It sounded like a trillion glass chimes ringing in the distance or like someone softly shaking all the chandeliers in the world."

"What would do that?"

"I didn't know, but Samantha said, 'Come on, you guys, I think I know what this is,' and she got up and ran into the woods.

"Dave and I sat up and looked at each other, wondering what we were getting into, and then followed her. She led us through a belt of trees between the road and the lake and down a path to the beach. A few spots south of Lac LaBelle, there were actually sections of shoreline with real sand and no rocks. Anyway, when we caught up to her, she had run clear out onto the lake, jumping from one ice floe to another until she was standing on a ten-foot circle of ice, about thirty feet from shore.

" 'Come on, come on,' she shouted at us. 'It's alright.' "

"So we carefully stepped from one floe to another until we were standing on our own individual iceberg. When we'd each centered ourselves on our own circles of ice, Samantha said, 'Sssshhh … now everybody be quiet, listen.' "

"We all shut up, standing maybe twenty feet from one another, slowly rising and falling with the waves. The bay was breaking up into all of these floating lily pads of ice. In between each one, the lake ice had crumbled into this sort of crystalline broth. It was melting into tiny crystal ice shards, and as far as we could see, the ice was turning into a white, polka dot mush. The gentle rise and fall of the rollers caused the water to swish through the shards making them ring like chimes. Man, I'm telling you, it was like Lake Superior was singing or something, doing this tribute to the dying winter. "

"Ken it was so awesome. I've never seen nor heard anything like it again, swear to God—the full moon, moonlight dancing off that ice, the Northern Lights, the endless quiet in the background, the lake …

"It was so beautiful, so … rare, like we were *allowed* to share in this intimate moment between Superior and God. The girls just got down on their knees on their little chunks of ice and bawled their eyes out."

"And you?"

"I'll … I'll never forget it."

Ken and I grew quiet. The fire crackled and we stared into the flames, listening to the wood burn. Smoke drifted skyward. Leaning back against our packs, looking up, we watched the smoke climb until it disappeared into the night sky.

"You used to have a thing for Samantha," Ken said.

"Yeah, you know that. She was out of my league."

"Well, I don't know about that, but she'd have ignored you for sure if she saw how little it was at the river today."

"Whaa … you ass!" I heaved a wad of snow at him. We laughed, falling quiet again, slipping into our own memories of the past few years at Tech.

After a long pause, I said, "Thanks."

"For what?"

"You know, at the river."

"Wish I had a camera, your expression, sliding backward into that channel."

"I think I have whiplash. My neck still hurts from when you yanked me out."

"I'm getting tired. Listening to you go on and on ... That's as much as I've heard you say all week."

"I suppose."

He went into the trees to deal with his own business. When he came back, I said, "I can't believe you're graduating. It's sure going to feel strange next year without you, Randy, Doane, lots of guys."

"Yeah, I can't believe I made it. It was touch and go for awhile."

"I remember."

Ken yawned.

"Do you suppose we'll ever do anything like this again?"

At dawn, Ken said from within his sleeping bag, and to my utter delight, "I'll get the fire going."

*Let me know when breakfast's ready*, I thought. I lay deep inside my sleeping bag. The fog was even thicker in the tent this morning. On clear nights, there's no cloud cover to retain what little warmth the sun provides during the day. It evaporates as so much steam, and temperature differences at daybreak on clear nights versus cloudy ones can be considerable.

"It's going to be a nice day," Ken said from outside. I could hear him breaking sticks into kindling. "Come on sack-monster, I need more water for the oatmeal." For emphasis, a snowball thudded against the tent wall.

I closed my eyes and groaned. Summoning my strength, I unzipped my bag, letting all of my precious, stored body heat whoosh away. I grabbed my clothes out of the bottom of my sleeping bag, where I'd stowed them for extra insulation and to keep them warm—we were learning.

Ken tossed me the empty canteen as I stepped out of the tent. Catching it, I stretched, and headed for the lake. When I got back, Ken boiled the water over the fire, saying, "The coals were still hot from last night. I didn't even need to relight the wood." We ate oatmeal *again*, and since neither of us drank coffee yet, we washed it down with lake water. After cleaning up, we immediately packed. We both felt like we needed to put some serious miles behind us today. "Let's make tracks," is how Ken said it. The goal was to be standing at Keweenaw Point by nightfall. If we made it all the way to the point, we then felt confident about reaching Copper Harbor by the pick-up time in two more days. As soon as we finished breaking down camp, we set out.

Sliding down the bank onto the icepack, Ken noticed my footprints out to the edge of the ice for water. "I never asked you how that went."

"Not too bad," I said. "Your idea of throwing the canteen into the lake with the rope was smart. The waves undercut the ice. Don't get any closer than five feet, if *you* go for water."

It was early and the sun, measured with my arm extended, was just two finger widths above the horizon. A fiery ball appeared to rise from the depths of Lake Superior, much like my moon from three years ago. The sun glared so intensely off the water I could only glance at it. Pinpoints of reflected light struck the curl of waves in horizontal rows. The ice floes glowed in Keweenaw Bay with a more subdued light. Even they hurt my eyes if I looked east for too long. Turning away from the sunrise, I gazed up the shoreline toward the point. The fringe of pack ice resembled a white-hemmed skirt. I frowned. Our course lay on that flimsy hem.

We experimented with what pack ice was best for hiking. There was a hundred foot wide smooth section that lay in between the ice piled up against the rocks at shore and the mounds of ice that built up at the water's edge. Between these parallel rows of heaped bergs was a very enticing, expressway-wide, white sheet. It appeared to run all the way to the point. However, like a terribly maintained highway, it frequently buckled and cracked, fissures crisscrossed it, and bergs the size of cars thrust through it as if a rockslide had scattered boulders across the road. We feared that sections had separated and then recently refrozen, the thinner ice camouflaged by snow.

There was good reason to be suspicious. Sporadic patches of open water, looking like puddles from afar, dotted the sheet ice. We gave any open water wide berth. Both of us carried a couple of fist-sized stones, despite the weight. Testing the edge of one of the open leads, I lobbed a stone at the rim of an opening. When it ripped through the ice like a pane of glass, Ken swore.

Staring at the hole, I said, "This must have been what it was like for polar explorers—trekking across the icecap, probing for skin ice, no one around for miles and miles."

"Let's stay closer to shore," Ken said. "We've been lucky."

"Yeah, no kidding, if not for the ice, we'd be crawling and hacking our way through the trees, probably why we never heard of anyone else ever doing this before. Look at those woods up there." I waved at the trees above the shoreline. "No way we'd make any time through that mess. Plus … look at the coast. It's more jagged than a saw blade. It makes me sweat just thinking about trying to follow it. Like I said before, there's no beach."

"True … *but* what I meant was this smooth ice is hard to read."

"Oh, right …"

"You're right about the coastline, though," Ken said. "I should have thought of that, should have figured this side would be just as ragged as the other side of the peninsula."

"I think the west side's worse. When my parents hauled me up to Tech as a freshman, I remember us taking M-26 between Eagle River and Copper Harbor. The highway hugs the west shore. They'd never been this far north and wanted to say we made it all the way to Copper Harbor. We couldn't get over how rocky the country is, nothing like southern Michigan. At every little turn-out along the lake, I begged them to let me out of the car to explore. They stopped, too. I climbed the rocks, checked out the lake, dodged surf. We made a whole day of it. It was like we were pretending I was twelve again."

"Yeah, my parents and I did the same thing when I was a freshman," Ken said. He started to angle closer to land and when we reached the piles of ice at shore, we climbed on top and proceeded to use it as our new pathway. It was slower going but safer.

Walking along in silence, we finally started to click off some miles. Normal conversation is difficult enough when backpacking on groomed trails. Winter backpacking, over a challenging terrain, worried about soft ice, made it close to impossible to carry on any dialogue. Ken poked at slushy spots and would grunt if we needed to veer aside. I'd respond with no more than a "See it."

The day's hike soon reminded me of a paddle down a twisty river, where you're always hoping to see the take-out around the next bend. Several cuts, small coves, and bays caused us to hike a meandering trail that undulated with every little cut into the land. As we hiked, we couldn't actually see Keweenaw Point. Every time we rounded a promontory, we could see only to the next outcrop of land. We wondered if we'd even know when we rounded the point, unable to tell the difference.

But despite the scramble over and around chunks of pack ice that stood taller than we did, we were making progress. Just as importantly, there was no mistaking the way.

Toward mid-afternoon, rounding another outcrop, we hoped once again to see the end of the peninsula. To our surprise, we discovered a large sweeping cove with a real beach. We both stopped, staring at such a startling change in the terrain. With some imagination, you could almost picture palm trees with a thick jungle marching up the slope. The cove curved inward in a gentle curl. The winds had blown the snow off the beach to reveal black sand. And, on the far side of the cove, eight deer were feeding on cedar trees that grew down almost to the lake. The black sand must have radiated heat from soaking in the sunlight. It was easy to understand how it attracted deer. I wondered if they had ever seen a human before.

Ken whispered, "Do you see them?"

"Yes," I said, following his gaze across the ice to the far side of the cove.

We watched them for only a couple of minutes and then continued. The deer caught our movement, even from a thousand feet away, and bounded into the cedar swamp.

Being outdoors for two solid days and nights, I was growing accustomed to winter conditions. I hardly noticed the cold anymore, and encouraged by our success thus far, my focus shifted from mere survival to noticing the surroundings. When I did, a view that few people ever see overwhelmed my normally insular awareness.

Perfect weather helped. Winds remained calm and the sun, high overhead in its March acclivity, beamed warmth. By noon, we'd taken off our outer jackets and strapped them to our packs. As the afternoon wore away, the gloves came off, and then hats. By three or four o'clock, we were down to just a shirt and light parka with the hood thrown back. It's hard to describe just how good the sun feels beating down on your face in March after suffering through four or five months of cold, grey winter weather at Tech. Every so often, one of us would tip his face skyward as we hiked, savoring the sunshine.

The trauma of yesterday's river crossing was fading. It had taken almost three whole days, but it finally dawned on me that at this moment I wouldn't exchange this empty, northern coastline for the warmest crowded beach in Florida. Toward dusk, rounding what must have been the hundredth spit of land, thinking this has got to be it, we finally turned the corner. The peninsula made a hard left, and we found ourselves at the broad, snub-nosed end of Keweenaw Point.

We kept going, backpacking another half-mile up the coast. It was our version of a victory lap. Except for a few subtle changes, a similar looking lakefront stretched before us. This was the first time since the river that we'd seen any sign of human activity. If there were any paths, beer cans, or old campsites, a blanket of snow obscured any trace of them. But a couple of old signs were nailed to trees. The signs were so weathered that whatever message they'd conveyed had faded. Some trees also had dots of paint on them, their meaning also open for conjecture.

"Someone's been here before," I said.

"A two-track from Copper Harbor ends somewhere around here," Ken said. "I've never been on it, but I hear four-wheel drive vehicles can make it all the way to the point, but not until the road dries out in the summer."

"That'd be a long bumpy ride," I said.

As if on signal, we both stopped walking at the same instant. Turning toward the lake, we gazed at the water for a long time, listening to the wash of surf. Ken cleared his throat, reached over, gripped my shoulder and said, "We did it."

I didn't know what to say, and so reached over and gripped his forearm in return.

In some regards, it was similar to Arctic explorers who reach the pole and say the land or ice looks just like the last hundred miles, and finally *decide* this spot looks as good as any other. We ought to celebrate.

Trouble was, I was so exhausted I wasn't capable of celebrating properly. Something inside of me told me that this was one of those times that wouldn't be fully appreciated until later, maybe not even until years later. I'd read about climbers who once they'd reach the top of a long-sought pinnacle, feel so worn out, so exhausted, so numb, that they'd only spend a couple of brief moments at the peak. They snap a quick picture and immediately start their descent, their minds too dulled from the constant Herculean effort. Perhaps it's unfair to compare reaching Keweenaw Point with climbing a mountain, but at that instant, all I really wanted was a little food and then some sleep.

Ken and I gazed across the straits to Manitou Island. In a sense, I wasn't really at the end of the peninsula. We hadn't made it to the farthest point. Staring across the water, I sighed. *Oh well,* I thought, *after all, the world is round. You could go on forever if you didn't pick some finish line. This will have to do.*

"What are you sighing about?" Ken asked.

I realized he'd been watching me, as if trying to read my thoughts.

Hitting close to the mark, he said, "Come on, let's find a place to set up camp before you decide to swim to the island."

We searched around for a flat, smooth stretch of ground, well back from the lake, behind some trees to get out of the wind. It took some hunting. At the end of the Keweenaw Peninsula, vegetation is sparser and more stunted. The tree line is set back three hundred feet from shore. The rocky toe of the peninsula is worn smooth from wind and waves that erode the stone from three separate directions. The land slopes into the lake at a gradual angle, as if the Keweenaw was testing the water before jumping in.

Tucked inside a ring of boulders and trees, a full four hundred feet from shore, we finally found a flat pocket of land that offered enough shelter. We circled it as we checked the ring out, and then walked back and forth across the open space in the middle, probing for hidden rocks and sticks. Finding none, we threw down our packs and continued to stomp the snow down for firmer footing.

We immediately went about our chores. This evening, however, instead of heading back for water, I helped Ken scrounge for wood. The stunted, dwarf spruce, birch, and poplar offered little deadwood. It took us until dark to find three armloads of firewood. After scouring the area in ever-widening circles, he said, "That should do. We'll have to keep the fire small tonight."

I nodded. "I'm going for water now."

Walking without the backpack gave extra spring to my legs, and I would have almost bounced over the ground if I hadn't been so tired. At shore, I stepped out onto a large rock that protruded into the water. No ice hugged the lakefront at the tip of the peninsula. The three-sided exposure prevented the ice from piling against the land. The surf barely rose and fell in the evening calm. I dipped the canteen into the lake. *Good thing it's not windy,* I thought. *If the lake were rough, I'd take a bath.*

By the time I got back to camp, the tent was up, and Ken had started the fire. The noodles for the spaghetti were in the saucepan awaiting my return. Ken is camp cook, a task he prefers. He'd learned to cook as a kid after his mom died from cancer, something he rarely talked about. His dad, Bob, had remarried shortly afterward, which Ken had told me was an arrangement Ken's mother had discussed with Bob during her last few weeks in the hospital. Harriet, Ken's stepmother, was his mother's best friend. From what little I'd been told, Ken and his sister, Kathy, both rebelled. I'm sure it was ugly at times and difficult for everybody. It wasn't hard to understand why Ken learned to take care of himself so well.

Ken and Randy once hitchhiked from Tech to Notre Dame and then back again, over a thousand mile round-trip. He went to a concert without telling anyone where they were going. I remember his girlfriend, Patty, calling me, all worried and concerned. I'd told her it was probably nothing. He was just off on some jaunt or discovered an opportunity to do something exciting and seized it. Patty chastised him when he returned, a scolding he later told me he enjoyed, happy to have her care that much.

We were beyond exhaustion, only stopping for the three short breaks all day in our urgency to reach the point and get back on schedule. After dinner, we scrubbed the plates and the pot with a little snow, called it good, and rolled into the tent, minus the popcorn. We were asleep in no time.

Morning came late. I awoke from a great sleep, about as comfortable as if I'd been in my bunk back at the dorm. Judging from his smooth breathing, Ken was still asleep. A line of sunlight crept down the tent wall as the sun rose. *Only three nights, and living outdoors feels like it's the most natural thing in the world,* I thought, finding pride in the fact. *It's always the same. The first night is miserable. The second night is a little better, but by the third night, I sleep like a baby.* I had expected it to take longer for a winter campout.

I settled deeper into my bag, enjoying the moment. I knew as soon as Ken woke he'd want to get moving. As I lay snug in my cocoon, the peace and quiet was too good to be true. Then as if on cue, I heard this rumble outside that rapidly grew in volume.

Whatever it was, it sounded like it was approaching fast and going to roll right over the top of us.

"What's that?" Ken asked, waking with a start.

"I don't know. Sounds like a low-flying plane."

I got up, unzipped the tent door, poked my head outside, and peered around. Two snowmobiles thundered to a stop a full one hundred feet away, sounding more like ten feet away.

"Snowmobilers," I turned and said to Ken. "We better get up."

"What are they doing out here?" Ken asked.

We quickly dressed, pulled our boots on and crawled outside. Our movement caught their attention. One person motioned to the two people riding together on the other snowmobile, and then pointed toward us. They all took off their helmets, dismounted, and walked over. Three men each looking about a generation apart in age shuffled over, a little stiffly, as if they'd been riding for awhile.

"You guys trapping?" the oldest man, who looked to be in his sixties, asked when he got close enough to be heard. Evidently, the snowshoes sticking upright in the snow, the fire pit, and the weathered appearance to our camp, not to mention our just waking up, made him think we were based out here. Involuntarily, I smiled at the notion of appearing like trappers.

Ken said, "No, just out for a hike."

"Hiking?"

The three of them shuffled their feet in the snow and glanced at one another, as if thinking 'hiking, sure.' The same guy who asked if we were trappers cleared his throat, swallowed and said, "My name's Ken. This is my son Robert, and his young son Daniel. We're out for a *spin* this morning." He said the word spin as if expecting us to laugh like fellow conspirators.

"I'm Ken, too, and this is Vic," Ken said with a deadpan face, finishing the introductions. We didn't shake hands.

Neither Ken said any more. Some snow swirled between us in a sudden gust of wind, and after what felt like a full minute of silence, snowmobiler Ken said, "Past two days been beautiful, eh?" obviously hoping we'd crack first.

"Yep," Ken said. I nodded in agreement.

This was followed by another long pause. A fresh gust shook talc-like snow out of the pine branches, the whisper sounded loud in the quiet.

Gramp finally said, "Ahem ... well ... we just wanted to take a look at the lake, good luck to you." His face was visibly strained at not getting any further information. They walked back to their machines, turning occasionally to see if we'd do something strange. At their snowmobiles, they held a conversation between themselves that we couldn't hear, and must have agreed we were up to no good—poachers maybe—but that it was safe to leave their snowmobiles unattended.

They walked out to the lake, threw a couple of snowballs into the water, and skipped ice chips across the surface. Bored with that, I guess, they returned to their machines and mounted them. With a half-hearted wave, they fired up their snowmobiles and roared off. Ken and I continued to stare after them, not saying a word until their motors finally died away into the distance. The smell from the exhaust lingered in the air. It took a long time for the sound of the machines to disappear.

"How'd they ever get out here—snowmobiles or not? There's no groomed trails,"[1] I said.

"Don't think we'll ever know," Ken said. He turned and started to stack kindling to make breakfast. "Don't think I want to know either."

Having reached the point, and despite having our solitude bubble burst, we took an hour to poke around. It was the first time we focused on something besides "the mission." Lake Superior spread to the horizon in three directions, and in the winter light, the water was a cold, steel blue, flecked with white bergs.

Inland, rocks poked through the snow. The wiry trees were windswept, branches growing only in one direction. The ground gently sloped down to lake level. Where Lake Superior met the shore, the stone was scoured of lichen or moss. Wet and glistening, the rock looked newborn, emerging from the weathered, gray landscape.

Ken climbed out as far as he could onto some rocks that jutted into the lake. It appeared to extend the farthest east. It was *the Point*. "Hold still," I yelled at him. "I want a picture." For once, he stopped to allow himself to be photographed. Turning partway toward the east, he pointed at the lake, and took a stern pose. "Got

---

1    *In 1973, no groomed snowmobile trails reached all the way to Keweenaw Point. Several trails now run through the end of the peninsula and the area has become a snowmobile destination.*

it," I said. He then clambered back and I took his place. Ken took one shot, and we were done.

"We've been lucky," Ken said. "The weather's perfect."

"Yeah, not too warm," I said. "You know, I never thought I'd want it cold, but as long as it stays below freezing, you keep dry. It's just a matter of wearing the right clothes."

"I suppose. Still, we've been lucky. No blizzards, and without the ice shelf we'd have been screwed."

We fell quiet, listening to the lake wash against the ice and rocks. The angle of the waves caused the sound of the surf to grow and then fade as the breakers moved from left to right across the shoreline. Blowing snow drifted across the ground in the freshening breeze. We barely noticed it.

"Well, I suppose we better get going," I said.

"If we can reach Horseshoe Bay by dark, we'll be within easy reach of Copper Harbor tomorrow. Hope our ice-road holds."

The Keweenaw Peninsula curls like the crook of a finger. It starts north and then turns east. The tip bends so far east that the end of the northern-most portion of the Michigan mainland faces the morning sun. We hiked along the point for three miles before the land began to curve west and we finally were heading toward Copper Harbor.

The ice shelf didn't return, and we had to pick our way across the stone. Our rocky path slowed us down, but by now, we'd almost grown accustomed to rough terrain. Whenever we came across even twenty feet of flat, smooth ground, one of us would remark about it, as if it were a strange phenomenon. Winds had been increasing all morning. The surge from the building rollers pushed us higher and higher toward the tree line and its obstacle course of fallen timbers.

The northwest side of the Keweenaw is fully exposed to the prevailing winds, and despite the bitterly cold winters, Superior is so big and so deep it rarely freezes over. The windward side of the peninsula has a broad, bare shoreline of exposed bedrock, providing a jumbled, tilted avenue to hike. A few scrawny cedar and birch grow in small crannies among the boulders, well back from the waterline. The high-water mark on the stone, set far back from lake level, reveals just how terrible storms get. Even the normally prolific moss and lichen that seem to grow everywhere disappear where they come within Superior's reach.

At noon we stopped for lunch, which was nothing more than slices of stick salami, Colby cheese and water. We sat together, gazing out at the lake, chewing our food—slowly—trying to get what enjoyment we could out of the cold meal. Dark, snow-filled clouds scuttled overhead. With our panoramic view from the point, we saw snow squalls scattered across Lake Superior's broad surface. The snowfall screened sections of the horizon. We zipped our jackets and pulled our hats down tight.

Ken elbowed me and pointed. A wall of falling snow was racing up the coast. "Guess I shouldn't have talked about the weather," Ken said.

I stared at the snow, feeling like I was watching a tidal wave approach. Misreading my silence, Ken said louder, "The weather—guess I shouldn't have said anything."

I shouted back, "Yeah, it's your fault all right." When he too didn't respond, I said louder, "Nothing we can do about it."

The breakers now surged thirty feet up the rock. An occasional gust of wind would catch the spray and scatter it like buckshot. When we got up that morning to greet the snowmobilers, the weather had given no indication of being anything but another fine winter day. Now, only a few narrow shafts of sunlight beamed through holes in the gathering cloud cover. The beams slowly swung across the water like searchlights. A touch of color glowed where they struck the waves. Everywhere else, Superior had faded to black and white.

Finished with lunch, we continued to hike down the coastline. The wind had become so strong that Ken started to use large upright rocks and the occasional tree as temporary windscreens, taking advantage of every minor reprieve he could find. The wall of falling snow was approaching fast. When it was a hundred feet away, Ken yelled at the top of his voice, "Here we go!"

As if we were stepping through gray, sheer curtains, the snow squall swept over us. Snow swirled everywhere. The large flakes moved so fast they hissed. Back-currents of air caused as much snow to rise as fall. Visibility dropped to twenty feet.

We each held a forearm at our brow to shield our faces. Using the slope of the land and the sound of the breakers as a directional guide, we kept hiking, but it was slow going. My field of vision fell to a circle right at my feet. My sole focus became keeping Ken within sight. If I lost him, he could be fifty feet away and I'd never see him, nor would he hear my shouts.

The whiteout lasted twenty minutes. After it passed, we stopped to regroup. Another snow squall was quickly approaching and we only had a few minutes before it was on us.

"This is no good," I shouted, leaning toward Ken's ear.

"We're all right," Ken hollered back. "Stay close!"

By mid-afternoon, the clouds had completely filled in. Gusts of wind shrieked and whistled past our ears. The surf was starting to hit the rocks with a thud instead of a splash. Between whiteouts, it just snowed with less intensity. A few gusts of wind were so severe, they made us stop and turn our backs to them. I pulled out my ski mask and pulled it down all the way over my head. It was a cotton mask with only holes in it for my eyes and mouth. I must have looked goofy, but I felt warmer. My nose and cheeks had been losing feeling.

During one lull, when visibility cleared enough to be able to see for a couple of miles, we could just make out through the falling snow the beginnings of what looked like an escarpment. Standing maybe a hundred yards off-shore, a forty foot-wide, forty foot-tall hump of rock in the water ran parallel to the shore. From a mile away and slightly blurred by the falling snow, it resembled a long loaf of French bread. (All objects were beginning to resemble food.) As we got closer, we discovered that the "escarpment" was a wall of stone stretched down the coast for as far as we could see. We couldn't have asked for a better wind break.

Ken turned. "Horseshoe Bay, I think."

"Weird looking bay," I said.

We picked up our pace. When we reached the lee side, between the rock wall and the shore, the lake was frozen solid. In the calm behind the protection of the forty-foot tall stone was a perfectly smooth, hundred-yard wide, swath of black ice.

Walking down to the surface, we hesitated when we reached the ice. "Probe that with your stick," I yelled.

Ken had kept his walking stick. He jabbed at the ice. "Come on," he shouted over his shoulder.

It was like somebody had freed us from shackles. We could walk upright, nothing to climb over or walk around, and we could look up the coast without shielding our faces. A few times, we actually ran and slid across the ice, backpacks and all. Snow collected in a few drifts. But for the most part, the snow piled up at shore, the winds sweeping it into heaps around the boulders.

It was late afternoon, and there were at least two more hours of daylight left. But with little hope for a better campsite, Ken said, "We should stop here for the night. If this wind doesn't let up, we'll be hard pressed to find anything better."

Frowning, I scanned up and down the jagged coastline. "All right, stopping early sounds good at least."

"Don't get comfortable. Setting the tent up won't be easy." Ken said. "No way are we driving those flimsy aluminum tent stakes into this ice. We'll have to find some loose stones to use as anchors to tie down to."

"Let's find a spot with snow for a cushion." Nose to nose, we were shouting at each other in order to be heard. The din from the pounding surf had been steadily growing louder since midmorning. Even with the ridge of stone in the lake as a barrier, the noise was one long, steady clap of heavy water. The idea of trying to sleep with all of that noise wasn't promising.

We found a patch of snow-covered ice and took off our packs. Just to be safe, I jumped up and down on the ice to double-check it. Ken pulled the tent out of his pack.

"I guess we'll have to melt snow for water," I said. "There's no way I'm going near the lake. I'm going to go look for some rocks."

I searched among the ice-covered boulders at shore and dislodged a few softball-size rocks, carrying them back to camp. After I returned with my third load, I dropped them onto the ice. Ken looked up and said, "Man, don't set anything light down, not without putting something on top of it. I took off a glove to untie a strap, and it was gone in a flash. If it hadn't hit a drift I'd have never caught up to it."

Together, we spread out the tent floor on top of the snow, quickly setting one snowshoe on each corner, and then piled stones on top of the snowshoes, finally putting them to good use. Ken said, "Crawl inside and set the poles up, while I tie cords from the tent grommets to the rocks."

I found the opening, pulled the limp tent over my head, and wriggled inside. Sticking a hand out of the door, I yelled, "Give me the poles." Ken place two assembled poles in my hand. I found the stitched nooks at either end of the old pup tent's roof and pushed each one into place. The two peaks weren't tied down yet and the tent immediately flapped wildly, the nylon walls slapping me.

"Hold those poles up straight," Ken shouted.

From inside, I watched one corner expand and grow taut, and then as Ken pulled the other corner line tight, one side of the tent took shape. There was a long pause, and I heard muffled, angry remarks that I couldn't quite make out. "What are you doing out there?" I shouted.

"You didn't get enough rocks," Ken shouted back. "I have to use the two backpacks for the other side until we find more." After several more minutes of sitting there holding each pole upright, the other side of the roof slowly took shape over my head.

"You can let go now!" I heard from outside over the wind.

"That was wild," I said as I stuck my head through the opening. I slowly stood up, a little stiff after the day's hike. "It's really loud in there."

"Where's that clothesline?" Ken asked. "I have to cut more lines. This'll never last the night."

"In the bottom of the pack—of course."

"Where?"

"In the bottom of my pack! You should be able to get at it through the bottom zipper." The tent fluttered hard in the gale. He was right. It probably wouldn't even hold for another hour. Already, one of the lines had worked loose.

Ken said, "We need twice this many tie-offs. Plus, I want to put the tarp over the top of the tent to act as an additional windscreen. I'll throw our gear inside to help hold it down and unpack. Can you find some more rocks?"

"Yeah, it'll take me a while, though. You gotta dig them out of the snow."

While I walked toward shore, wind swirled at my back, sending sheets of snow out ahead of me across the ice. I could have glided to shore if I'd had a sail. Looking up at the steep slope of the Keweenaw as I walked, the lakefront looked all sugarcoated, the snow frozen to the rocks, stones and trees. It was still snowing. Thick flakes obscured the hilltops and higher ridges. I shivered involuntarily, thinking what tonight might have been like without the protection of the rock wall and our tent.

Reaching shore, I scrambled among the boulders and kicked at smaller stones to see if any knocked loose. It took a long time and six trips to find enough. It took almost another hour to set all the extra lines for the tent, plus cinch the tarp down over the top of it. Standing back, our camp looked like it was trapped inside a spider web. Even so, no matter how many adjustments we made, the tarp wouldn't stop rippling. Snow was already starting to pile up against the windward side of the tent.

"Come on," I said, "let's get inside. That's as good as we're gonna get it."

Ken wasn't satisfied, but shook his head in resignation. We finally crawled into the tent. Once we were inside, it was a relief to get in out of the wind. The noise, however, was louder. The nylon acted like a drum skin, amplifying sound.

"Let's get organized." Ken said, acting all business-like. "Wedge extra clothes and gear into the edges along the bottom. Boots, hats, and gloves go by the door. Map, book, and flashlights go in the middle within easy reach. See if you can set up your candle lantern. I'll go back out and grab the food from the packs, anything else?" We'd left the packs outside. They were too big to fit inside with us in the tent, too.

"No," I said.

With our shelter all set up , food was the next order of business. "It's going to be tough to find wood." I said. "And, it'll be almost impossible to start a fire in this wind."

"We don't need much, just enough wood to heat that last can of stew."

After everything was organized, we went to shore to look for wood. We each managed to scrounge an armload of sticks and brush from the few wiry trees above the rocks. Using the backpacks and our bodies for wind screens, we built our meager fire tucked leeward of the packs. We heated the stew to a mild boil and then ate. When we were finished, Ken set some snow in the saucepan. But before all of the snow could melt, our fire died, the wood spent.

"Your water's going to taste like stew tonight," he said. "I'm not wasting water on cleaning. Use some snow to scrape what you can off the pot."

We poured the brownish water into the canteen, kicked the fading coals across the snow to watch the embers quickly wink out. With one last look around us, we crawled inside the tent.

We settled on top of our sleeping bags and tried to ignore the sounds of the storm. Ken pulled out the playing cards and his cribbage board. When the second game was over, sitting there staring at each other, daylight fading, and with prospects for a very long, uncomfortable night ahead, it occurred to me that we might never have another opportunity to see Lake Superior so rough, not like this anyway. Sitting there hunched over in our small tent, idle hands doing their infamous evil work, I ventured as if it was the most brilliant of ideas, "Hey, Ken, let's climb up to the top of the escarpment. Let's check out the lake. I want to see the lake."

Ken had just pulled out a paperback, *The Tracker* by Tom Brown, and was pretending to read—an impossible task with the racket outside. I hadn't thought to bring a book. Ken didn't even look up.

"Come on," I said. "We may never see anything like this again."

He still didn't say anything. After a moment, he groaned, sat up, and grabbed his hat and gloves. Giving me a long look, he said, "All right, but let's make it quick. That wind up there will sap body heat in seconds." He paused and then said, "You're nuts, you know."

I smiled in response. We put on almost every piece of clothing we'd brought with us, crawled out of the tent, stood up and stretched. The storm was growing. In a few places, we could now see spray shoot over the forty-foot wall. The impact of the waves sounded like cannon fire.

We walked toward the rock wall, and when we reached it, we discovered that finding a place to climb up wasn't as easy as I thought it would be. We walked for a long way along the base of the wall before we found one spot that sloped upward at a more gradual angle.

"You first," Ken said.

It took some scrambling and some blind probing for finger holds, which heavy winter mitts made doubly difficult, but after getting past some awkward spots, I finally poked my head over the top. The blast of wind immediately sucked the air from my lungs.

Ducking down, I regained my breath. *What was I thinking?* I looked back down the wall at Ken and considered turning around. He was standing there, staring up at me. *I guess I can't stop now,* I thought. Taking a deep breath, I pulled my ski mask over my mouth and tipped my head sideways away from the wind. I slowly inched up and over the rim. The blast of wind was incredible. I stayed as low as I could and crawled on my belly across the crown of the rock, keeping my face down in order to breathe better. I crawled about halfway across the crown of the rock wall and stopped well back from the edge. Looking behind me, I saw Ken come over the top and crawl toward me. Gripping the stone, I carefully rose onto my knees, not daring to stand, and lifted my face to peek at the lake.

I froze.

An unbelievably huge roller heaved up right in front of me, only fifty feet away. It surged and then smashed against the rock. It hit with so much force the concussion of sound dazed me. Lake Superior was a war of water. Frothy, ice-filled waves surged and bucked everywhere at absurd angles. Water escaped hills of slush and squirted through the ice with the force of geysers. The liquid water exposed to the gale shot horizontally toward shore. The spray froze in mid-air, pelting the stone all around us.

The bounce of ice and water, the geysers, the rebound of waves off rock; they all pitched and lifted into spikes of slush and mounds of grey slurry that rose and disappeared, reabsorbed into Superior as quickly as they formed. Combined with the dim light, it made it impossible to find a horizon or even find a point that stood still to focus on. My sense of balance was stripped. Virtual hills of beer suds body-slammed against the wall, exploding. The wind shrieked with an unearthly resonance. I fell on my face and gripped the rock for all my worth, fearing I'd be ripped away, sucked into the watery melee. The same sense of fear I had felt when I first stepped into the Montreal River overwhelmed me. Only this time, no rational inner-voice with calculated instructions came to my rescue.

Ken hugged the ground beside me. He carefully and slowly reached over, grabbed my jacket and tugged. Placing his mouth next to my ear, he shouted at the top of his voice, "Let's get out of here!!"

We wriggled backward to the inside edge of the wall and half slid, half climbed down to the ice. At the base of the wall, we fell to our knees and gathered our shattered wits. It took several minutes before I regained any balance. I grabbed at the wall. The feel of the solid rock reassured me, and I asked, "Where's our tent?"

We lifted our heads, looked across a reassuringly flat, solid sheet of ice and saw camp. It was only a couple of hundred yards away. To me it looked like a picture of an Arctic explorer's camp straight out of *National Geographic*. The tent glowed in the dark from the light of the single candle lantern. Nothing could have looked more welcoming. Like an Eskimo's blubber oil lamp glowing through snow blocks, it was as warm and cozy a sight as any cabin. We ran across the ice and piled through the tent door.

Throwing myself on top of my sleeping bag, I said, "Don't ever let me do that again."

Ken nodded. We didn't say anything for a long time, allowing our reeling senses to quiet. He sat on his bag, cross-legged, head down. After our breathing returned to normal, Ken looked up and said, "Break out that salami and cheese. A little food will put some heat in us."

I grabbed the wrapped bundle of cold food and sliced off an extra share for both of us, throwing in a candy bar apiece. We slowly ate. It didn't take long before I felt a little heat grow in my belly, a heat that flowed to my limbs. "Strange how food warms you," I said. "Never noticed it before this trip." I was still shaking a little, but the everyday task of eating lent some semblance of normalcy.

It was early for turning in, but all I wanted to do was to go to sleep. Actually, I wanted to fall unconscious. I didn't want to hear, to feel, or think any longer. I wanted to reach over and switch off that constant blast of sound outside. Realizing I was losing it, I shook myself. *Snap out of it,* I thought.

"What are you doing? Ken asked.

"Nothing," I said. "I'm gonna *try* to get some sleep."

"That sounds good to me."

I undressed, if you can call wearing two pairs of socks, long underwear, three shirts, and a hat and gloves undressed. I was about to blow out the candle lantern, when Ken stopped me. "Leave it lit. I want to be able to see. If the ice starts to break up we might have to beat a hasty retreat."

We felt a breeze, even inside the tent, and despite the flame being encased in a glass tube and the lantern sheltered under the tent and the tarp, the candle flickered. The wavering flame was an unwelcome reminder of how tenuous our situation was.

And, so we went to bed.

The worst part of that long night wasn't the incessant pounding of massive waves against solid rock, or the deep cold, or the rattling tent, not even the thought of sleeping on a bed of ice. The worst part was this pervasive sense of tension, an excitement, a feeling that everyone was on the edge of their seats. I was as tired as I ever would be and equally wide-awake. Outdoors, just beyond our flimsy sheet of nylon, the weather vibrated with checks and balances stretched to the breaking point. The energy was such that no matter how tired I was, I couldn't relax. I couldn't shake the quickened tempo. It was like I'd been locked inside a big, raucous house party and they wouldn't let me leave. I wanted to say to the host, "Thanks, the party was great, but I'm tired. Can I go home now?"

The tent walls rustled and fluttered in the wind all night. The breakers continued to crash. Snow peppered the tent, as if someone was throwing intermittent fistfuls of sand at us. Eventually that sound stopped and the tent sagged. We realized the windward wall was covered with snow. Every time I started to get drowsy, some shriek of wind or sonic boom from a breaker or a crack-of-a-whip snap to the tarp, jerked me awake.

Sometime during the middle of the night, the floor shifted with a jolt. An expansion rift must have popped nearby. We both jumped. Ken was up on all fours, ready to spring outside. I was so exhausted I only lifted my head, snatched the flashlight and turned it on. I scanned the floor, waiting. When nothing else happened, Ken groaned and slowly crawled back into his sleeping bag. The ice had barely moved, but the shock eliminated what little comfort we'd taken in the notion of a bedrock of ice.

The tie-down lines for the tent held for a couple of hours. Then, one at a time, they worked loose and a piece of tarp would break free and flail away in the gale, risking ripping out the other lines. There was nothing to do but throw on our boots, go back outside and retie them. We ended up taking turns getting up in the night like a married couple taking shifts with a colicky baby. I'd crawl back into my sleeping bag shivering, fingers half-frozen from trying to work knots with bare hands, and all the stored body-heat escaped from my sleeping bag. I'd curl into a fetal position in my sleeping bag trying to warm up again. After what must have been the tenth trip outside, we let the tarp go. If it ripped away, so be it.

It was somewhere during that final night, that all desire for adventure drained away. The peninsula had cowed me.

Daylight barely seeped through the tent wall. It couldn't have come sooner. I wouldn't budge from my sleeping bag. I heard

Ken rustle and looked over at him. All I could see was his chook pulled down over the top of his ski mask. One open-eye stared through a slit. It had a dull, unaware look to it.

"Are you alive?" I mumbled.

The eye blinked twice and then rotated, scanning the tent as if unsure where it was. When his gaze fell back on me, the eye brightened, and Ken said, "Yeah, yeah … why don't you get up?"

"That was the worst night of my life," I said, not moving.

Then to my undying respect, Ken crawled out of his sleeping bag, got dressed, and said, "I gotta take a whiz."

I listened from inside to the sound of the wind, which was still at gale-strength, but seemed to have either slowed a touch or I'd grown numb to it. The booms from the rollers were still just as strong.

From outside, Ken shouted, "Vic, you have to see this. Get out here."

I yawned and said, "All right, all right," Like jumping into the deep end of a cold pool, I threw open my bag. I quickly put the rest of my clothes on. My shoulders and back were sore, my foot was throbbing again and my mouth was dry. Finished dressing, I crawled through the door and slowly stood up. "What? What are you shout …" I asked and then stopped short.

Ken pointed behind me. It had quit snowing and we could finally see farther than a couple of hundred feet. When I turned and looked, I whistled. The corridor of ice that I thought stretched for two miles between the rock wall and the shore was only a few hundred feet long. Rollers crashed and white foam hurtled up and down the lakefront just past the rock barrier and couldn't have been more than five hundred feet away.

"Oh, my God," I said.

"I couldn't agree more," Ken said. "We managed to find the only protected spot on the coast." He paused to let that sink in and then said, "Look at those waves."

Eastward, past the end of the rock wall, toward Copper Harbor, monster waves crashed up and down the shoreline, surging all the way to the tree line.

"Grab the map," Ken said. "We're going to have to figure out another way to get to Copper Harbor."

I pulled the map from an outer pocket of my pack, unfolded it, and tried to hold it still in the wind. Our topo map of Keweenaw Point had taken a beating since we'd first looked at it back in Ken's dorm room. Details had worn away where the fold lines crisscrossed the paper. Spilled spaghetti sauce covered Mount Houghton, and smudges of an unknown origin blurred several other locations.

Pointing to about where he thought we were, Ken said. "Best I can tell, we're behind that squiggle that stands slightly off from the coast, right about there. That means we're eight miles from Copper Harbor. I'm thinking, we might be able to pick up the seasonal road that runs from Copper Harbor to Keweenaw Point. If we hike straight inland, we'll cross its path. The road can't be more than a mile from here."

"Where are we meeting Patty?" I asked.

"I told her to meet us at Fort Wilkins State Park. Told her we'd try to be there by noon. She doesn't get out of school until two, but she said she'd try to leave early."

I yawned and said, "All right." Looking over Ken's shoulder and down the coast, I couldn't help but think, *so close.*

"Let's pack up and get out of here," Ken said. "We can eat later."

We grabbed the backpacks, which we'd stacked outside on the lee side of the tent. Shoving them inside, we proceeded to pack. When we were done filling the packs, I went outside and grabbed the packs as Ken handed them out to me.

"Help me take down the tarp and tent," I said after Ken crawled out.

We cut all the lines attached to the stones to avoid untying fifty knots. We then stowed the tarp and the tent, not bothering to roll them up. It was the last time, we hoped. In seconds the wind erased the snowdrift that had piled up against the tent during the night. All that remained of camp were the rocks with bits of line flapping in the wind. "What do we do about all these stones?" I asked.

"What about them? They'll sink come Spring."

"Sorry, of course. Must not be thinking too clearly yet."

Ken gave me that "Are you ready look?"

We headed for shore. The snow had stopped falling. The sky was overcast with no breaks in the cloud cover. The air had that Lake Superior winter clarity to it. Everything stood out in sharp relief, especially after the fuzzy air of a blizzard yesterday.

Without any snow blowing across the surface of the black ice, I could study it more closely. The ice was laced with silver bubbles, pockets of air. Leaves, twigs, and mysterious bits of plant life were also frozen in place at various depths. The ice appeared  about two feet thick, the litter disappearing beyond that. Hairline cracks traced the surface. As hard as I tried to see bottom, I couldn't. I had the impression I was walking over the abyss.

When we reached shore, we proceeded to climb up the slippery rocks and boulders. The treeline started about fifty feet above the lake and a hundred feet in. Without looking back, we entered the woods and continued to climb. The snow lay deep underneath the trees. In pockets, where the snow had a chance to settle, the fluff was packed down from its own weight. In other places, like crannies between slabs of rock or in drifts where it collected—places we needed to hike—the snow was the consistency of powdered sugar. There was nothing to do but wade through it.

The steep hillside was cluttered with fallen trees, outcrops of rock, and with the added obstruction of thick undergrowth, no different from the other side of the peninsula. The deadfalls and boulders caused us to zig-zag up the hillside. It was slow going, but our packs were lighter now. Most of the food was gone.

Our goal was to reach Fort Wilkins by noon. First, we had to find the road. Once on it, our course should be clear. However, neither Ken nor I had ever been on the seasonal road before. Closed for the winter, it ought to look like a ten-foot-wide lane that snaked through the trees, running parallel to the lake. On the map, the road showed up as a faint, dotted line. The problem was that there were lots of meandering lanes through the trees. Some were natural, caused by straight-line winds or due to a chance, linear layout to the woods. It soon became apparent we could easily miss a snow-covered two-track.

"Keep going," Ken, said when I hesitated at a thick tangle of underbrush. The roar from the lake had subsided a little. Underneath the trees, we could communicate without shouting. His voice had a strange echo to it and I could hear our labored breathing. Under the confines of the snow-laden trees, it was like walking down a tunnel. Even something as soft as our breath reverberated, the soft snow giving it a more dampened quality.

I'd seen where the road was on the map, but couldn't help but ask, "How far do you think the road is?"

"It looked to be on top of the second ridge, judging by the contour lines."

"I can finally hear myself think," I said. "Glad to get away from the lake."

"Never thought I'd hear you say that," Ken said.

We reached the top of the first ridge after a short scramble up a fifteen-foot rock face. I was thirsty. Mouthfuls of snow helped a little, but they lowered body heat. I knew I'd had enough snow when I started to shiver. My lips were cracked and my cheeks raw. Rather than stop to eat, we ate salami sticks as we hiked. The spicy meat gave me kickbacks. But in spite of everything, I felt pretty good. Both Ken and I had reached that point where we understood every gain meant effort and every effort equaled pain. It's just how it works. "Keep moving" had become our expedition slogan. One more step and then another. Don't think too far ahead.

After the first ridge, we dropped into a narrow valley with a frozen wetland in the center. The advantage of winter hiking is that anything that's normally wet and soft is now firm. It felt eerie to just walk over the top of a swamp. In fact, it was actually easier going since it was flat with no trees or undergrowth. Half way across, we started to trot. We jogged more because we were sick of plodding along rather than because we were in a hurry.

Looking ahead to the other side of the swamp, the land continued to rise in a series of hills and ridges, each one a little higher than the last. Reaching the far side of the swamp, we started to climb again. After a half hour trudge up the slope, we were on top of the second ridge—the one, supposedly, with our two-track. This time we stopped to rest. Turning back to look at the lake for the first time all morning, we gingerly stepped out onto a rocky overhang we'd seen from the swamp. It offered a view of the area. Clouds streamed overhead. They felt a lot closer now. Looking down at the lake, from about four hundred feet above lake level and roughly a half-mile's distance, the water appeared as gray as the sky. However, the two grays did not melt together at the horizon. Instead, the horizon was a hard, jagged black line that seemed to vibrate. It was the undulating waves and whitecaps. Even from this distance, we could hear the waves curl and break on shore. The breakers appeared as white lines against the dark water. The wave tops grew vivid and bright, and then faded and disappeared when the wave crests tumbled.

Our rock wall was clearly visible straight below us, and I thought I could just make out the cluster of stones on the ice that had held down our tent. The sheet of ice and our old campsite looked so small against the backdrop of Superior. I shook my head. If the wind had changed directions in the night, God knows what we'd have done. We'd found shelter behind nothing more than a one-walled snow fort.

Ken said, "See that raised, thick line on the horizon, a little to the left?"

"Yeah, barely."

"That's got to be Isle Royale. Someday you and I should go there."

"How can we see that far? Isn't Isle Royale fifty miles from here?"

"You can see it from the higher elevations. I've seen it before from Brockway Mountain Drive. You need a clear day, though."

Despite being exposed to the stiff breeze on the outcrop, we didn't hurry away. Not speaking, we just sat there and rested, gazing at that black line on the horizon. As I finished my last Kit-Kat bar, and shoved the wrapper into my pocket, I glanced one last time at Isle Royale in the distance, wondering if it looked anything like what I'd just hiked around. I finally said, "We better get going. I'm starting to get cold."

"Keep your eyes peeled," Ken said as he hoisted his pack. "The road should be close."

Our concern for finding the road to Copper Harbor proved unfounded. We walked only a hundred feet through the trees, and there it was. A twenty-foot-wide, snow-covered road or two-track ran perpendicular to us in either direction. There were no snow-mobile tracks or footprints. How the snowmobilers reached the point, only two days ago, remained a mystery. The road weaved along the top of the ridge just as it had shown on the map.

We turned right and started to hike down the lane through the trees. When we went around the second bend and then the third, with the road continuing, I finally started to relax. After everything else we'd faced, I'd steeled myself, fully expecting the road to peter out. Accustomed to walking single file for the past five days, I was hiking behind Ken. Realizing we didn't need to follow each other any longer, I moved up beside him.

"Not bad," I said.

Ken smiled with a proud grin, not answering.

"Not bad at all," I said, again. "How much farther to Copper Harbor?"

"Maybe five miles. If all goes well, shouldn't take us more than a couple of hours."

I winced when my growing smile split open my chapped, bottom lip. "Hope Patty makes it," I said, using my sleeve to soak up the drop of blood.

"She'll be there."

Conditions on the road to Copper Harbor were similar to the conditions on the two-track from Bete Gris to the river. There was still three feet of snow on the ground. But by now, we'd developed a knack for finding firm snow to hike on. We were making good time, breathing easier, and it started to sink in that we were almost there. We had actually hiked all the way around Keweenaw Point. Barring some unimaginable setback, we'd be back at school in time to eat dinner in the dorm tonight.

I allowed myself to dwell on how great a hot shower would feel, not to mention eating something besides oatmeal or salami. I'd been reluctant to look too far forward. Now that I could let myself go, there was more than a warm bed and hot food to look forward to.

I could picture everyone in Ken and Randy's dorm room talking about their spring vacations, the Florida crew lying about their conquests, the others griping about having to work. Ken would take center stage, retelling our story—our quest. The news of our expedition had spread once our vacation plans leaked just prior to spring break. No one tells a story better than Ken. I could hear the guys, see them shaking their heads over the river crossing, shouting how we were both nuts—the ultimate compliment.

This would earn us *major* bragging rights. But, for some reason I didn't feel like boasting. We'd done it all right, but any person with an ounce of brains could justifiably say we'd been lucky.

*True, but you have to create your luck, too,* I thought.

"What's your spring quarter look like?" Ken asked.

His question snapped my train of thought, and it took me a second to grasp what he meant. "Uh, not too bad, sixteen credits."

We hadn't talked about school all week, and it felt strange to think about anything other than the task at hand.

"I'm really jammed up this term," he said. "Need to hit it when we get back. To graduate in June, it's gonna be rough."

"You mean rough, like this?"

Ken chuckled, "No, I suppose not. Not like this."

The mention of school reminded me why we'd made the trek. He'd be gone come June. I couldn't imagine Tech without him or Randy. A lot of guys I knew were leaving this year. Was it like high school? It had only been three years since I'd left for college and I hardly ever saw my old high school friends anymore.

Two hours later, we hiked around what must have been the thousandth bend in the seasonal road and came face to face with a tall snowbank. We climbed over it. On the other side lay the northern end of US 41.

We slid down the bank and stepped onto bare pavement. I stomped on it, as if it was something foreign. Ken pulled his mitt off, bent over and slapped the road with the palm of his hand with a loud smack. We threw off our packs, and as if testing a trampoline, we started to bounce up and down on the highway, slowly gaining momentum until soon we were flinging ourselves into the air. Ken threw his head back and gave a war whoop. The echo reverberated down the tree-lined, empty road.

We bent over and placed our hands on our knees to catch our breaths. I sighed. We stood there for a long while, looking down the highway. Finding my voice, all I could manage to say was, "Imagine that."

"What?" Ken asked.

"Imagine that, U.S. 41, it goes all the way to Miami. Did you know that? I didn't think of it until just now."

"No."

We stood there, still catching our breath, staring down the road, thinking about what lay ahead.

Ken finally said, "Let's go. Patty's waiting."

Ken and Vic
Spring Break 1973

# ACKNOWLEDGMENTS

Ken and I still try to go to Isle Royale each summer, and a couple of years ago I broke down and bought a new canoe. The Smoker Craft was starting to leak a little. She was also starting to make funny noises, or more accurately, complaints we'd never heard before. Ken started to accuse me of being too tight to spring for a new one. When he got rather persistent, I pried open my wallet and purchased a shiny, red 17-foot Nova Craft. She's a beauty— soft woven seats, sprucewood rails and struts. Even has an eagle embossed on the bow. We're breaking her in. The new canoe is a little longer and a *lot* lighter.

My brother-in-law, Brian, perhaps inspired by his Trans-Superior kayak crossing, eventually landed jobs at both poles. He worked one winter—their summer—in Antarctica cleaning up garbage for the U.S. Park Service. The science stations discard significant amounts of garbage. In the cold dry air, it takes centuries for refuse to decay. To try to keep the place pristine, someone has to remove it. After he returned, Brian told me how he couldn't get over how windy it was. He then moved to Alaska to work several jobs, including commercial fishing. He's now back in the Keweenaw.

Kurt and Ginger Loosenort, inspired by their off-shore wind experience, give presentations and workshops about faith for area churches. They've produced an excellent CD. (It's available for purchase at www.lifebuilderswm.com.)

It has occurred to me several times in writing *Naked in the Stream, Isle Royale Stories* that the book may motivate a person to go to Isle Royale—maybe lots of people. If I have encouraged someone to spend more time outdoors or to find their own corner of wilderness to explore or share this place with me then I'm flattered. Although, that last part makes me nervous.

It's surprising how many people are involved in writing a book. For such a solitary venture, it really does take the proverbial village to properly care for each chapter and verse, to raise each story to a readable art form, and to grind out the details. This book is no different. Without the help—technical and spiritual—of many friends and colleagues, *Naked in the Stream, Isle Royale Stories* would have remained a vacation journal, mere memories jotted down to record all of the remarkable sights, events, and experiences of thirty years spent at Isle Royale.

I would like to offer my gratitude to Sue Hines and the rest of my friends and workmates at West Michigan Tree Services. Sue, in particular, was the first person who patiently worked on my writing and who saw enough hope to badger me to keep at it. Unbeknown to her and to me, her patient labors were preparing me to write this book.

In the basement of an old, decrepit downtown office building in Grand Rapids, Michigan, there is a small band of writers who meet every Wednesday night to risk placing their scripts under the spotlight of professional scrutiny. The old building is the home of the Urban Institute for Contemporary Arts and is primarily intended for edgy visual artists—sculptors, painters, performance artists and the like. The writers group is mostly an afterthought. But this talented group of writers has helped produce several good books.

My thanks go out to Mr. Steve Beckwith and Mr. Albert Bell who facilitate the workshops. They make sure the writer's group is not a support group. They mean business when it comes to writing and they pull no punches with their critiques.

To Steve's ability to grasp the big picture—what readers will read, to Albert's attention to detail, "do I have to explain again where to use lay, laid, and lain?" I'd like to thank Jane for her sensitive attention to eradicating most of my more pompous, self-serving phrases, and to Greg, Paul, Pat, Nathan, Karen, Donna, Roger, Dawn, Dan and to the other writers who have come and gone—I can't wait to see your books.

To Susan Bays and to Gail Schneider at Arbutus Press, I am deeply grateful. Susan took the time to talk with me about publishing. Skeptical at first about doing a collection of stories, she offered to read a couple chapters. A kindred love for good literature, trees and for paddling has evolved into a great working relationship.

Jill Burkland from The Isle Royale and Keweenaw Parks Association was a tremendous help with technical edits. A big thanks to Dr. Rolf Peterson for allowing me to tell his story about wolves. Special thanks go to Joel Patenaude at *Silent Sports*

*Magazine* and to Bob Guiliani at *The Jack Pine Warbler* for publishing excerpts.

Finding such a talented accomplished artist like Joyce Koskenmaki who shares my enthusiasm for all things Isle Royale was a stroke of magnificent good fortune. After only one brief meeting, Joyce agreed to take a look at this project, and after finishing the manuscript thirty-six hours later, said, "I couldn't put it down. What do you want done?" How could I not like her? Right from the start, an amazing artistic collaboration was set in motion. Joyce's sketches for each story were a joy to watch unfold. I really can't imagine anybody else doing the art work.

To my wife, to my sons, to Ken, my mother, to Brian, to Kurt—to all of the people between the covers of this book: one of my great hopes in doing this was that I could adequately portray the character and the joy of life all of these wonderful people possess, and that my words would reflect the love and admiration I have for you.